PROCEDURES IN

Experimental
Metallurgy

PROCEDURES IN

Experimental Metallurgy

.

A. U. SEYBOLT, Ph.D.

Research Associate
Metallurgy Research Department
Research Laboratory
General Electric Company, Schenectady, New York

J. E. BURKE, Ph.D.

Manager, Metallurgy Section
Knolls Atomic Power Laboratory
Operated for the Atomic Energy Commission
by
General Electric Company, Schenectady, New York

JOHN WILEY & SONS, INC., NEW YORK
CHAPMAN & HALL, LIMITED, LONDON

Dedicated to

CYRIL STANLEY SMITH

PREFACE

In recent years, much of the progress made in understanding the behavior of metals and alloys has been due to increasing interest in this field on the part of physicists and physical chemists who have been attracted to it by the interesting and challenging opportunities for fundamental work. However, investigators new to the study of metals rarely have the familiarity with the tools and the methods of the metallurgist to make their experiments with minimum effort. It is a primary aim of this book to describe most of the important laboratory techniques which are now used in the preparation of metals and alloy specimens for further study. We believe that enough detail is given to allow anyone familiar generally with physical and chemical principles to carry out the unit operations described.

Investigational techniques such as microscopic examination, x-ray diffraction methods, thermal analysis, and mechanical testing are purposely omitted. There are satisfactory monographs on these subjects, and to treat them adequately would require a book much larger than this one.

While assisting the nonmetallurgist is an important aim, we have not forgotten our fellow metallurgists, and we hope that many of our confreres will find our book of assistance in planning experimental procedures. In particular, we kept in mind the needs of the younger research metallurgist. However, the older man who is perhaps directing a program of metals research needs to be familiar with many techniques and procedures in order to assist his men in their various tasks.

The preparation of metal samples up to the point of making observations on the properties of the metal is the guiding principle or theme of the book. Hence, we have included the steps from preparation or selection of the base metal to be used through principles of alloying, melting without contamination, casting, fabrication into rod, sheet, or wire, and heat treatment to obtain a desired structure.

The chapter arrangement had to be rather arbitrary, and good reasons can readily be found for using a different order of subject matter.

In general, we tried to make the chapter order the natural sequence of events that occur in the laboratory: melting, casting, fabrication, heat treatment. We felt, however, that since most of the operations just mentioned require the use of high temperature, the book should start with methods of obtaining high temperatures and, of course, methods of measuring and controlling high temperatures. The chapter on refractories follows because the metal must be melted, or heat treated in contact with some kind of refractory material. Also the question of using a suitable atmosphere for high temperature work must be considered early in any experimental program, and the type of atmosphere needed often dictates the kind of furnace used.

The chapters on powder metallurgy and preparation of single crystals could have appeared at almost any time in a logical sequence, but, as special techniques, these subjects were treated after the more fundamental topics had been covered.

A word of explanation for including the subject "powder metallurgy" may be in order, as, of course, there are many good books on this subject. In the first place, since certain kinds of samples are best prepared or can only be prepared by the methods of powder metallurgy, it appeared to us that omission of this subject would be unwarranted. Second, the point of view used in writing this chapter is quite different from that of any author known to us. We have attempted to make this chapter a concise, useful exposition of the methods of powder metallurgy as applied to the preparation of samples in the laboratory.

In summary, we have written this book because it is one we believe needed to be written, and one we wish had been available to us in the past.

A. U. SEYBOLT

J. E. BURKE

October, 1953

CONTENTS

CHAPTER ONE

Methods of Obtaining High Temperatures

An important part of the facilities for a metallurgical laboratory is the equipment for producing and controlling high temperatures. Although methods involving the combustion of fuels are important industrially because they are cheap, laboratory workers almost always use electrical heating because it is clean and easy to control. Furnaces heated with nickel-chromium alloy resistance elements are commonly used for temperatures up to about 1100°C, with some special alloys being useful up to 1200°C. For resistance heating up to 2000°C, platinum, molybdenum, silicon carbide, and graphite resistance elements must be used. Induction heating is most satisfactory for melting operations, since very precise temperature control is not required, and a variety of other methods are used for certain special applications.

TABLE 1

PROPERTIES OF HEATER ELEMENT ALLOYS

Metal	Composition, %	Maximum Temperature in Air, °C	Melting Point, °C
60 Ni, 15 Cr, 23 Fe	60 Ni; 16 Cr; 24 Fe	950	
80 Ni, 20 Cr	80 Ni; 20 Cr	1150	
Kanthal	25 Cr; 6.2 Al; 1.9 Co; bal. Fe	1250–1300	
Alloy 10	37 Cr; 7.5 Al; 55.5 Fe	1250–1300	
Platinum			1773
Molybdenum			2625
Tantalum			3000
Tungsten			3400

FURNACES FOR TEMPERATURES UP TO 1100°C

The most popular and versatile laboratory furnaces are those heated with an electrical resistance element made of the alloy containing 80% nickel and 20% chromium [1] supported on a suitable refractory. The most common shapes are the tube furnace (Figure 1), the pot or crucible furnace (Figure 2), and the muffle or box furnace (Figure 3). All these are available commercially in a wide range of sizes. Small tube and pot furnaces can be made easily in the laboratory, but muffle furnaces and the larger tube and pot furnaces are better purchased ready-made from a commercial supplier.

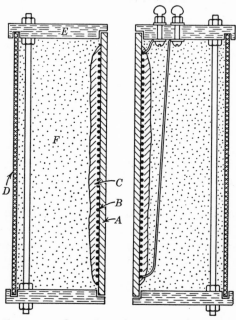

Figure 1. Tube Furnace Made in the Laboratory. Alundum core (A) is wound with wire (B), coated with alundum cement (C) and held in metal case (D), fitted with cement-asbestos board and plates (E). The insulation (F) is diatomaceous earth. It is sometimes more convenient to bring the lead wires through the end plates before fastening them to the binding posts.

The 80% nickel–20% chromium alloy is used because it is cheap, can be obtained in a large range of sizes, both as wire and ribbon, its electrical resistance is high and almost independent of temperature, and it has a long life if not overheated. For lower temperature applications it is commonly used in the form of wire wound directly upon a refractory tube, or coiled and inserted into grooves in a supporting refractory. At the upper limit of its temperature range scaling is rapid, and for maximum life a heavy section such as rod must be used. When this is done the resistance of the heating element is so low that a low-voltage, high-amperage transformer is required. At high temperatures the alloy is quite weak, and the refractory must be properly designed to support the heating element without stress.

The nickel-chromium alloy is useful more because of its oxidation resistance than because it has a high melting point. The oxidation

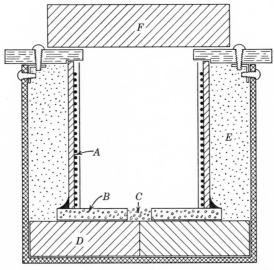

Figure 2. Pot Furnace Made from Replacement Winding. The replacement winding and supporting refractory (A) are sealed to an old grinding wheel (B). The hole can be filled with alundum cement (C). Insulating brick (D) is used for bottom insulation and diatomaceous earth (E) for the sides. The top can be finished with a hard cement or covered with cement asbestos board. An insulating brick (F) is used for a cover.

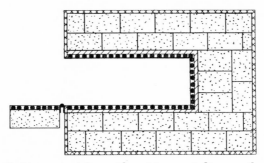

Figure 3. Muffle Furnace. A box with resistance windings on the inside. Many furnaces do not have windings in the door or the surface opposite the door.

resistance results from the development of an adherent protective oxide film that forms at high temperatures. For this reason the windings must be protected against materials that may flux and remove the oxide skin. Siliceous insulating materials such as diatomaceous earth, most heat-treating salts, and reducing or alternately reducing and oxidizing atmospheres are the most common sources of difficulty.

Construction of Furnaces in the Laboratory

One of the simplest and fastest ways to build a furnace in the laboratory is to use replacement windings and refractories for commercial furnaces. They can be purchased with coiled windings held on the inside of refractory supports and are often designed to operate directly on 110 volts. The construction of a pot furnace with these elements is illustrated in Figure 2. Tube furnaces of any desired lengths may be assembled in a similar fashion from such replacement elements.

More commonly, tube furnaces are made by winding an Alundum (bonded aluminum oxide) furnace core on the outside [2] with wire. These tubes may be obtained either smooth, or with a spiral molded in the outer surface to aid in spacing the wire. The spiral is helpful, but makes it impossible to use other than a uniform winding along the length of the tube. Frequently, it is desirable to space the turns of the winding somewhat more closely near the ends of the core, to compensate for end losses, so that a more uniform temperature is attained.

Difficulty is usually encountered in properly fastening the ends of the winding after the wire has been applied. Many furnace tubes are supplied with small holes through the ends, but these should not be used to fasten the windings since they usually break out of the holes, and if they do not they remain exposed inside the furnace tube. A simple way to fasten the end of the winding is to tie it in position with a short length of similar wire of smaller size. Another method is illustrated in Figure 4. A long lead about twice the desired final length is left, and the last turn of the winding is wound to cross the next to the last turn, and the free end is brought back and wound around these to fix them. Then by twisting the double lead wire the whole assembly can be tightened, and simultaneously a twisted lead of half resistance is provided.

Once the core is wound it should be coated with a layer of Alundum cement [2] to hold the windings in position and to prevent their reaction with the insulating material. This cement is a mixture of aluminum oxide grain, clay, and an organic binder to give it green strength. It hardens somewhat upon drying at room temperature, and becomes fully cured when the furnace is first heated to the curing temperature. Several grades are available, and the kind chosen depends upon the upper temperature to which the furnace is to be operated.

To finish the furnace, the ceramic tube and its winding must be supported in a suitable container, surrounded with insulation, and electrical contacts must be provided. Figure 1 shows a simple method. The tube is centered on cement-asbestos board end plates and surrounded with a metal shell. The ends are held in place with tie rods passing through the furnace, and the leads are brought out to binding posts. If the leads are doubled they will not heat up and need not be protected from the insulating material, which is usually diatomaceous earth. Many other methods can be used; for example, the core can

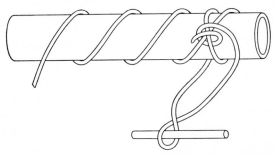

Figure 4.   Method of Fastening Wire on Furnace Core.   The stick is used to twist the lead wire to tighten the assembly.   This gives a low-resistance cool lead. Another method of fastening wires is described in the text.

be encased with soft insulating brick and the whole assembly wrapped in asbestos paper and painted with sodium silicate solution.

Calculation of Wire Size and Length.   If the maximum desired operating temperature inside the furnace and the necessary dimensions are known, it is necessary to select a suitable wire size, power input, and operating voltage.

It is customary to design furnaces with a wattage input sufficient to raise the temperature above the maximum desired operating temperature. Unless this is done, excessive time will be necessary to heat the furnace to high temperature after cooling, and it will be difficult to control accurately at the highest temperature.

The wattage necessary to heat a furnace depends upon the area of the hot surface, the thickness of insulation, the magnitude of end losses, and of course the temperature desired. A simple method of selecting a proper wattage is to match a furnace already constructed which is known to have desirable operating characteristics. If no such furnace is available, a good rule of thumb for computing wattage (W) is given by the expression

$$W = 100LD/T \tag{1}$$

where L is the length and D the bore of the furnace, and T is the thickness of the insulation in inches. This applies to a furnace internally wound to operate at about 1000 to 1100°C, with diatomaceous earth as insulation. For windings to be applied outside the supporting refractory, the power should be increased by 10 to 20%. Similarly for short furnaces (length less than ten times bore diameter) with large end losses the power should also be increased by 10 to 20%. For example, if it were desired to make an outside-wound 1-inch tube furnace 12 inches long with 2 inches of insulation around it, the power should be 650 to 700 watts.

Since furnaces of this type operating in this temperature range lose heat largely by conduction, the maximum temperature will be roughly proportional to the power input. The numerical factor 100 used in equation 1 is based on a maximum operating temperature of 1000°C. If another temperature is desired, the numerical factor should be about 10% of the maximum desired operating temperature.

If the wattage needed to operate the furnace at the desired temperature is given, it is easy to compute the total wire resistance for any given operating voltage, and to select a wire size that will give this resistance. Frequently, the wire size needed to give high enough resistance will be too small (see below); a larger wire can be used if it is coiled and wound on the support as a coil.

Temperature Uniformity. It is very difficult to construct a furnace that will have a large volume at a uniform temperature. A tube furnace with 1-inch bore and 12 inches long, with about 2 inches of insulation, will have only about 1 inch at the center where the temperature is uniform to ± 2°C. This results from loss of heat at the ends. If total power consumption is not important, the temperature can be made more uniform by decreasing the insulation thickness all along the length of the furnace; but, if the furnace is to be operated at temperature greater than about 500°C, it is difficult to reduce the insulation sufficiently and still reach the desired temperature.

Very frequently end losses are compensated for by spacing the turns of the winding somewhat more closely near the ends. For any desired temperature it is possible to correct precisely for this, but, since losses vary somewhat with temperature, gradients will still remain at other temperatures. The furnace may also be wound with independently controlled windings near the ends. By operating these at higher temperature, end losses may be compensated for and a uniform temperature zone attained. It might be pointed out that commercial tube furnaces can very frequently be easily reconnected so that the end elements can be operated at higher temperatures. In some cases it is also feasible to use heated plugs or doors at the ends of the furnace. Another method that may be used to smooth out the temperature gradient is to insert a metal tube or muffle of high thermal conductivity.

Wire is the customary winding material for furnaces. It is available in a variety of sizes, both straight and coiled. Coiled wire is frequently desirable for smaller furnaces since there may be insufficient space to wind a length long enough to obtain the necessary resistance. Wire sizes smaller than 20 gauge are undesirable since their life is too short except at very low operating temperatures. For large furnaces tape is occasionally substituted for wire. This has some advantage when it is desired to space the windings closer near the ends of the furnace, and it is easier to apply on a smooth tube.

FURNACES FOR TEMPERATURES ABOVE 1100°C

The instructions presented thus far apply primarily to the operation of furnaces to temperatures up to about 1100°C, using an 80% nickel, 20% chromium resistance element.

Alloys of iron, chromium, and aluminum (Kanthal [1d] and Alloy 10 [1e] are frequently used for temperatures up to about 1250°C. Both are quite brittle at room temperature, and, while light wires can be wound cold on a tubular support, the heavier sizes are better formed hot. They should be loosely supported on the refractory, and not wound tightly on a tube as is done with the 80 Ni–20 Cr alloy as the wire may break when it is stressed by the expansion of the refractory. For the same reason it is not desirable to hold the wires in position with a refractory cement as is done with the 80 Ni–20 Cr alloys. In commercially manufactured furnaces, alloys of this type are installed as very heavy windings, using a step-down transformer for power, to obtain longer life.

Platinum wire is frequently used to wind furnaces for use up to about 1500°C. Although the original cost of the winding is high, the scrap value is also high, and the over-all operating cost is not excessive. In fact, it is somewhat surprising that platinum does not find greater use as a resistance element for small laboratory furnaces. Precautions must be taken to protect the platinum from contamination in use. It is best used in an oxidizing atmosphere to protect it against contamination by the reduction products of the supporting refractory. Alundum (bonded aluminum oxide) is an excellent material on which to wind platinum resistors. If the platinum is operated at temperatures above 1500°C, volatilization of an oxide of platinum becomes bothersome.

Alloy resistance elements have a very small temperature coefficient of resistance so that the cold furnace can be started at the final operating voltage. On the other hand, because pure metals have a much higher temperature coefficient of resistance the room temperature resistance may be several times less than the high temprature resistance. To overcome this difficulty it is necessary to provide a transformer or rheostat so that the voltage can be increased as the furnace heats up. This large temperature coefficient of resistance aids to some extent in controlling the temperature. Line voltage fluctuations tend to be compensated for by the automatic resistance changes in the furnace.

In all furnaces, the windings operate at a temperature somewhat above that of the furnace cavity. This differential is least for an internally wound furnace, and greater for a winding outside the central refractory. Ordinarily the temperature differential is unimportant, but when it is desired to have the furnace operate at a temperature close to the upper permissible limit for the winding element the difference becomes important. One method that has been used to equalize these temperatures as much as possible is to surround the platinum-wound tube with a concentric tube wound with 80 Ni–20 Cr alloy.

In a similar temperature range (about 700 to 1500°C, maximum) bonded silicon carbide (Globar [3]) resistance elements are also frequently used. These are bars about 3/8 in. or more in diameter, and usually 2 to 4 feet long. Power is applied through metal clamps at the ends of the resistance elements. The ends are metallized so that little heating occurs at the point of contact. The furnace is usually constructed by mounting Globars on either side of the tube to be heated. This would not appear to give particularly good heat distribution; however, in practice this construction is found to be satisfactory. It is relatively easy to build tube furnaces of this kind in the laboratory, as indicated in Figure 5. Since the Globar elements are usually connected in parallel, it is important that their resistances are equal. Sets of bars which have been matched for resistance by the manufacturer can be purchased. The initial cost of Globar elements is less than that for platinum, but they are less useful for making small furnaces, and are not satisfactory for operation at temperatures much below 700°C.

The maximum temperature for Alundum refractories is about 1900°C, and this sets the upper temperature limit for wire-wound ceramic-supported resistance furnaces. Above 1500°C the only useful metallic resistors are molybdenum or tungsten, and they are frequently used for temperature above about 1100°C. Since molyb-

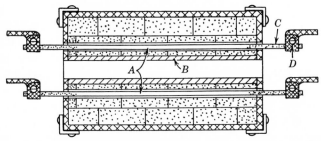

Figure 5. Globar Furnace. The Globar elements (A) are supported on either side of the furnace tube (B). The metallized ends (C) provide good contact for the current clamps (D), and permit the ends of the heaters to remain cool.

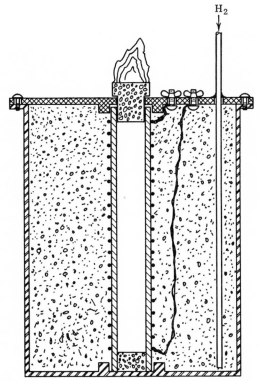

Figure 6. Molybdenum Furnace. The case is gas-tight. Hydrogen is admitted through a metal tube, diffuses through the refractory, and is burned at the mouth of the furnace.

denum is slightly cheaper and more ductile it is more commonly used, and is usually protected with hydrogen. Such furnaces are constructed in much the same way as lower temperature furnaces, except that provisions must be made for maintaining an inert atmosphere around the winding. This is easily done by inserting the furnace core wound with wire in a gas-tight case as illustrated in Figure 6. Aluminum oxide bubbles [2] make a good insulating material with which to surround the core. It is not customary to coat the windings.

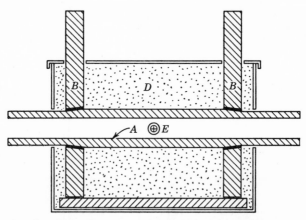

Figure 7. Graphite Tube Furnace. The furnace tube (A) is cemented to the terminal blocks (B) at the conical joints with 70% powdered graphite, 15% dextrine, and 15% water. Lampblack is used for insulation (D) and temperature readings are made through the sight tube (E).

A number of furnaces have been described that use graphite resistance heating elements. In a vacuum, graphite is useful up to about 2000°C, but at higher temperatures its volatility becomes troublesome. At this temperature it also reacts at appreciable rates with both hydrogen and nitrogen, although nitrogen has been satisfactorily used inside the graphite furnace described below, at temperatures of 3000°C. Atmospheres of helium, argon or carbon monoxide are to be preferred although the first two are more expensive and carbon monoxide presents something of a poison hazard.

A convenient graphite tube furnace which will operate for at least several hours at 3000°C has been described by Gartland [4] and is shown schematically in Figure 7. Essentially this furnace consists of a hollow graphite tube packed in lampblack in an air-tight container. The packing prevents oxidation of the outside of the resistance tube and provides the best possible insulation. Nitrogen gas (purified by passing over hot copper) is flowed through the center of the tube to prevent oxidation. Some reaction between the carbon and the nitrogen undoubtedly occurs, and better results might be obtained with a truly inert gas such as argon. The life of the tube at 3000°C, using nitrogen inside, is about 5 hours. The furnace tube is connected to the terminal blocks by smearing with a mixture of 65 to 70% powdered graphite, 15 to 17% dextrine, and 12 to 15% water. When the furnace is heated, this mixture graphitizes to give a contact with good electrical conductivity.

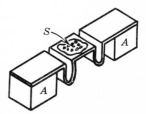

Figure 8. Tungsten Ribbon Heater. The tungsten ribbon bent in the form shown is clamped to the current terminals A–A. The specimen is placed either directly on the ribbon or on a thin quartz plate. The furnace must be used in a vacuum or an inert atmosphere.

The power requirements of such furnaces are great. The furnace described requires 1300 amperes at 15 volts (about 20 kw) to reach a temperature of 3000°C.

Very high temperatures can be attained by heating a tungsten ribbon on which small specimens are supported. This technique has been used, for example, by Cech [3] to heat specimens while they are being examined microscopically (Figure 8).

INDUCTION HEATING

Any material which will conduct electricity can be heated by inducing an electric current in it with a surrounding coil which carries an alternating current of suitable frequency. The temperature developed is a function of the energy dissipated in the charge and the energy lost by conduction and radiation. The method is used extensively in the laboratory to heat and particularly to melt metals, either by inducing the heating current directly in the metal itself, or into a heating cylinder or conducting crucible. It has the advantages that heating is rapid since only the charge or heater is heated, that very high temperatures may be attained, that the melt is stirred by the induced currents, and that it is particularly useful for heating charges contained inside vacuum or inert atmosphere systems. The chief disadvantages are that the equipment necessary for generating the high frequencies required is expensive and that it is difficult to control high temperatures very accurately for long periods of time. In spite of the disadvantages, the method is almost universally used for melting small amounts of metal in the laboratory, particularly those melting above 1000°C.

Induction heating is extensively used industrially for heating prior to hardening, for forging, brazing, soldering, and similar operations. Laboratory operations of this type are usually better done with resistance heating, and in this chapter we shall confine ourselves primarily to a discussion of induction heating for melting and for obtaining higher temperatures than are readily achieved by resistance heating.

FUNDAMENTALS OF INDUCTION HEATING

An electrical conductor can be heated by inducing a current in it, and, in common with any other kind of resistance heating, the heat input, W, is given by the relationship

$$W = I^2R \tag{2}$$

where I is the induced current and R is the ohmic resistance of that part of the conductor in which the current flows.

The high-frequency alternating current that produces the heating flows preferentially on the surface of the conductor. The depth of penetration is controlled by the specific resistance of the conductor and by the frequency of the current according to equation 3:

$$D = (\rho/4\pi^2f)^{\frac{1}{2}} \tag{3}$$

where D is the depth in centimeters at which the current density is $1/e$ or about 0.37 times the value at the surface, ρ is the specific resistance of the conductor in abohm centimeters (1 abohm = 10^{-9} ohm), and f is the frequency of the current in cycles per second. If the induction coil is a vertical solenoid and the conductor a vertical cylinder, the induced current will flow circumferentially. Thus the value of the resistance R in equation 2 will be directly proportional to the specific resistance of the conductor, and inversely proportional to the thickness D, and the width of the path. Thus, if the height of the conducting cylinder is h, and its diameter is d,

$$R = \pi\,d\rho/Dh \tag{4}$$

or, if the value of D is substituted from equation 3,

$$R = 2\pi^2\,d(\rho f)^{\frac{1}{2}}/h \tag{5}$$

Thus, other things being equal, the resistance of the conductor is proportional to the square root of its specific resistance and to the square root of the frequency.

Brewer [5] has computed that the current that flows in the conductor is given by

$$\frac{I^2}{I_0{}^2} = \frac{4\pi^4 d^4 n^2 \omega^2}{R^2 + \omega^2 L^2} \tag{6}$$

where I is the average value of the induced current, and I_0 the average value of the current flowing in the induction coil, n is the number of turns in the induction coil, and $\omega = 2\pi f$. The term L is the self-induction of the cylinder, given by

$$L = \pi^2 d^2 / h \tag{7}$$

when the current flows in the surface of the cylinder. Equation 6 holds only if R is small compared to ωL. If it is large, the value of I is one-fourth that given.

Brewer has further deduced that for a solid cylinder the optimum conditions for induction heating exist when the cylinder diameter is about four times the skin depth. Reasonably efficient heating can be obtained with diameters larger than $4D$, but, if the diameter gets much smaller than $2D$, difficulty will be encountered in reaching very high temperatures. In Table 2 values of D and $4D$ are presented for a

TABLE 2

VALUES OF D AND $4D$, IN CENTIMETERS, FOR VARIOUS MATERIALS AND FREQUENCIES

Conductor	Specific Resistance, abohm cm	Frequency, cycles per second							
		2000		10,000		30,000		300,000	
		D	$4D$	D	$4D$	D	$4D$	D	$4D$
Cu (20°C)	1.7×10^3	0.47	1.85	0.066	0.26	0.038	0.15	0.012	0.047
W (0°C)	5×10^3	0.80	3.2	0.112	0.45	0.065	0.26	0.021	0.082
W (2230°C)	74×10^3	3.08	12.3	0.43	1.73	0.250	1.0	0.08	0.32
Mo (0°C)	5×10^3	0.80	3.2	0.112	0.45	0.065	0.26	0.021	0.082
Mo (2000°C)	59×10^3	2.70	10.8	0.38	1.52	0.22	0.88	0.07	0.28
Ta (0°C)	12×10^3	1.23	4.95	0.173	0.70	0.100	0.40	0.032	0.127
Ta (2230°C)	94×10^3	3.48	13.9	0.49	1.95	0.282	1.13	0.09	0.36
Graphite (20°C)	80×10^3	10.0	40.0	1.42	5.70	0.82	3.28	0.26	1.04
Graphite (2200°C)	560×10^3	8.5	35.0	1.20	4.85	0.69	2.8	0.22	0.89

number of materials and frequencies. It can be seen that higher frequencies are needed for smaller specimens, and that the optimum size depends strongly on the resistivity of the material. In selecting conditions it must also be remembered that the resistivity also influences the amount of energy liberated. It happens that graphite is one of the easiest substances to heat by induction. Copper is too good a conductor to be heated efficiently, and for that reason is usually melted in a graphite crucible.

High-Frequency Generating Equipment

There are various kinds of equipment available for generating the high-frequency current necessary for induction heating. Their chief characteristics are presented in Table 3. Any of them can be used

TABLE 3

CHARACTERISTICS OF HIGH-FREQUENCY GENERATING EQUIPMENT

Equipment	Motor Generator	Spark Gap	Electronic
Frequency range, cycles/second	1000–10,000	20–100 kc	100–500 kc
Operating voltages	220–440	~10,000	~10,000
Power-output, kw	7½–500	3–40	1–50

satisfactorily for most operations in the laboratory if the setup is proper. Specific cases where one or another of the types would be superior are indicated in the previous and the following discussions.

Motor-Generator Sets. Motor-generator sets produce high-frequency current of definite frequency and of rather low voltage. A

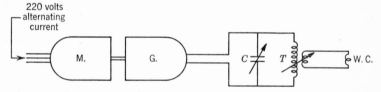

Figure 9. Schematic Diagram of Motor-Driven High-Frequency Current Generator. The motor generator M.G. is powered by line current, and the work coil and load W.C. are matched to the generator with the variable capacitance C and the variable or fixed transformer T.

schematic diagram of a typical unit is presented in Figure 9. Essentially it consists of a direct-coupled motor and generator; they may be either air cooled or water cooled. The water-cooled generators are quieter and much to be preferred. A tapped capacitor is provided to permit adjustment of the output power factor and, at least in some installations, a variable transformer to permit matching the impedance of the coil to that of the generator. For most laboratory melting operations it is possible to match the impedance by adjusting the number of turns in the multi-turn induction coil, as will be indicated later. It is usually convenient to have remote-control switches to add or to remove capacitors so that the power factor can be maintained at unity as the charge heats up.

Motor-generator sets are usually provided with meters to indicate the reciprocal of power factor (in kilovars), the output current and voltage. These are quite necessary because careful matching of the coil to the machine is necessary for efficient operation, since the machine operates on a single definite frequency.

If the impedance of the coil and charge does not match that of the machine, it will not be possible to operate it at both the full-rated voltage and amperage. If the voltage reading is too low with a given coil at zero kilovar reading, the coil has too few turns. The proper number of turns may be computed from the relationship

$$N = n(V_0/V) \tag{8}$$

where N is the proper number of turns, n is the number in the coil used, V_0 is the rated voltage of the machine, and V the voltage obtained at zero kilovars and full-rated current.

Similarly, if the amperage is too low, the coil has too many turns. The proper number may be computed from the relationship

$$N = n(I/I_0) \tag{9}$$

where I is the current obtained at zero kilovars and the full-rated voltage, and I_0 is the rated current of the machine. If an impedance matching transformer is available, these adjustments may be effected without changing the coil.

In many applications the induction furnace is operated very close to the machine. If remote operation is required, the shunting capacitor must be installed within 2 to 4 feet of the heating station for efficient heating. If this is done, suitable protection must be provided, because lethal amounts of electrical energy are stored in the capacitor during operation.

Spark-Gap Converters. A schematic drawing of a spark-gap high-frequency generator is presented in Figure 10. A condenser, charged from a high-voltage transformer supplied with 60-cycle alternating current, discharges through a spark gap to produce a high-frequency alternating current in the work coil. Two kinds of spark gaps are in common use. In one, the spark passes from a special electrode to a pool of mercury in a hydrogen atmosphere. Power is controlled by adjusting the level of the mercury and thus the spacing of the gap. The other type uses a large number of parallel sparks which pass across an air gap between carefully spaced parallel tungsten plates.

No provisions are made for tuning the mercury pool spark-gap equipment. The operating frequency changes with the size and number of turns in the coil, and with the electrical characteristics of the charge. This is a considerable advantage, because the machine automatically compensates for changes in conductivity of the charge during heating. Furthermore, coils of a large range of sizes may be used with the equipment. It might be pointed out that coils for these machines need a rather larger number of turns than coils for most other high-frequency generators, and to get the necessary number of turns with the desired height to diameter ratio it is usually necessary

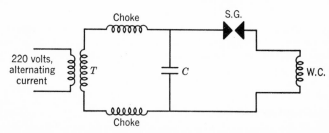

Figure 10. Schematic Diagram of Spark-Gap-Type Induction Heating Unit. *T* is a step-up transformer, *C* a capacitor, S.G. the spark gap, and W.C. the work coil.

to flatten the copper tubing slightly and to wind the coils with the turns very close together. Insulation with glass cloth and lacquer is usually satisfactory.

The converters just described usually supply frequencies between 20 and 40 kc. The parallel spark-gap instruments, on the other hand, have frequencies in the neighborhood of 100 kc. They also usually have an auxiliary adjustable tank coil in series with the work coil, so that some tuning is possible.

Electronic High-Frequency Generators. A schematic drawing of a vacuum-tube high-frequency oscillator is shown in Figure 11. It is essentially a high-powered radio transmitter. The frequencies available range from about 100 kc to a megacycle or even more. Coil matching is usually accomplished by adjusting the inductance of the tank coil. The impedance of the work coil may be matched to that of the generator either through a matching transformer or by adjusting the number of turns on the coil. The output frequency depends to some extent upon the characteristics of the external circuit so that this type of generator self-compensates to some extent for changes in load characteristics during heating.

Setups for Induction Furnaces.   A wide variety of setups are possible for induction heating.   A typical setup is shown in Figure 12,
and other examples may be found elsewhere in this book.   They all

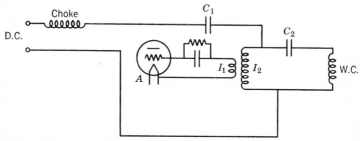

Figure 11.   Schematic Diagram of Electronic High-Frequency Generator.   High-
voltage direct current is supplied to the equipment. C_1 is a blocking condenser,
C_2 the tank condenser, A a triode vacuum tube, I_1 the grid coil, and I_2 the tank
coil.

consist of an inductor coil, a container for the material to be heated,
and some insulation or radiation shields between the coil and the
charge.

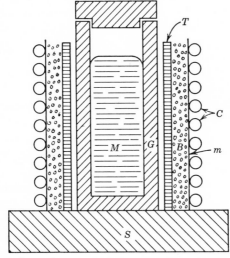

Figure 12.   Setup for Induction Melting.   Metal M is contained in graphite
crucible G, surrounded by a refractory tube T.   The induction coil C is lined with
a sheet of mica m and the annulus B filled with lampblack.   The support S may
be soapstone.

Induction Coils.   Multi-turn coils, having five to about thirty turns,
or even more, are used for most laboratory heating applications.   They

are invariably made of copper tubing of about ¼-inch diameter for smaller units, so that cooling water can be passed through the coil during operation. Usually round copper tubing is satisfactory, but with some kinds of high-frequency generating equipment coils having large inductance, and thus many turns, are needed. For this equipment it is customary to flatten the copper tubing so that a sufficient number of turns can be obtained in the desired height.

It is frequently possible to use temporary coils without support, but for permanent installations it is desirable to mount them on a cement-asbestos board, plastic or soapstone framework. If possible, conducting material should be avoided in the construction of these supports because of the possibility of its being heated by induced currents. If it is necessary to use a few bolts and nuts, they should be made of brass or copper, rather than iron, and they should be kept as far from the coil as possible.

Coil Leads. Leads from the generator to the coil should be as short as possible, and never over a few feet, although as pointed out above in the discussion of motor-generator equipment, operation remote from the generator is possible if the capacitors are moved up close to the coil. Power may be conducted to the coil through bus bars to which copper tubing has been soldered for water cooling. They may be fastened to the coil with lugs, and water cooling for the coil provided separately through hose leads. Finally, flexible leads may be used. They are usually copper bellows covered with heavy copper braid, and then with rubber tubing for insulation. Cooling water for both the leads and the coil may be passed through the flexible bellows, and water and power connections can be made with ordinary compression or flare fittings.

Power and Frequency of Equipment Required. If the generating equipment is operated with reasonable efficiency, it is usually possible to melt charges of about one pound in one hour for each kilowatt of output capacity of the equipment, but usually an attempt is made to melt the charge in a shorter time so that more power is needed.

As mentioned previously, almost any frequency can be used satisfactorily in the laboratory. In general, the higher frequencies are better for heating very small specimens, or materials with very high electrical conductivity. With lower frequencies these difficulties can be overcome by using conducting crucibles or auxiliary heaters. The lower frequencies are also slightly to be preferred since they cause more stirring of the melt. In addition the skin depth in which the current is carried is greater; thus conducting radiation shields can be used in place of other insulation to retain heat.

Heaters and Conducting Crucibles. For many melting applications it is desirable to use graphite crucibles, since, for most sizes of charge, graphite has a specific resistance which is more favorable for induction heating than the metal being melted. Molybdenum or tantalum is frequently used for this purpose also.

Brewer [5] has pointed out the interesting fact that when the diameter of the cylinder being heated is much less than 4D, hollowing it out will decrease the amount of heat generated; whereas, if *d* (the diameter of the conducting cylinder) is about equal to 4D, there is little change in heating. Where *d* is greater than 4D, hollowing the cylinder out may actually increase the amount of heating obtained in an important way. This is true because the current in the cylindrical shell is controlled by the inductance, as shown in equations 6 and 7, and the inductance is unchanged by hollowing the cylinder out. However, the ohmic resistance of the current path, *R*, is increased in an important way if the wall thickness is thin enough. Thus the amount of heat generated is increased. He points out that the optimum thickness for a hollow cylinder is given by

$$d_o - d_i = 2D^2/d_i \qquad (10)$$

where d_o and d_i are the outside and inside diameters of the cylinder, and *D* is the skin depth defined in equation 3. It should be noted that this thickness is much less than the optimum thickness for a solid cylinder.

Radiation Shields and Insulation. Insulation is necessary to prevent heat loss in induction heating as in other methods. Any of the standard methods may be used. For the very highest temperatures carbon black is the best insulation available. It has good insulating properties, and more important it does not decompose or become electrically conducting at higher temperatures. Carbon black, however, is very dirty and messy to use, and in vacuum systems outgases badly. Thus often other insulation, such as fused alumina or zirconia, is to be preferred.

With relatively low frequencies (up to 30,000 or 40,000 cycles, for instance) it is possible to use metallic radiation shields instead of insulation. Obviously they must be thinner than the optimum thickness defined by equation 10 if all the energy is not to be absorbed in the radiation shield. The thickness can be reduced in effect, however, by providing vertical slots so that there is no complete current path in a plane perpendicular to the coil axis. This can easily be done by forming the shielding foil into a spiral and not permitting successive turns to touch, as illustrated in Figure 13. As an example, Brewer has reported that a two-turn spiral of 0.003-inch molybdenum foil showed only a six-degree rise in temperature in 4 minutes, with a current frequency of 14 kc.

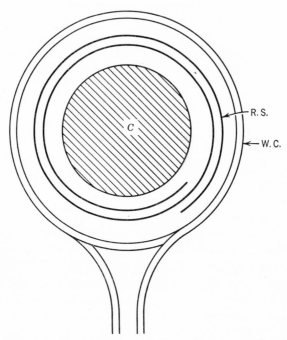

Figure 13. Arrangement of Radiation Shield. The thin metal radiation shield R.S. is placed between the induction coil W.C. and the conductor to be heated, C. By winding the shield in a spiral as shown, its resistance to a current in a circumferential direction is made high, so that little current is induced in it.

SPECIAL HEATING TECHNIQUES

For special purposes a number of other heating techniques are occasionally used in the laboratory. Arc melting is used commercially on a large scale for welding, and laboratory arc-melting equipment is described in the chapter on melting and casting.

Direct resistance heating by passing an electric current through the specimen is frequently convenient for small wires that are sometimes difficult to heat by other means. A convenient setup for doing this in a high-vacuum or an inert atmosphere is illustrated in Figure 8 of Chapter 12. The necessary high currents at low voltages can be obtained from rather inexpensive transformers.

Gas. The temperatures that can be obtained with a number of combustion mixtures are listed in Table 4. The temperature of a flame

TABLE 4

FLAME TEMPERATURES

Burner	Fuel	Oxygen Source	Maximum Temperature and Remarks, °C	
Bunsen	Coal gas	Air	1550	Above inner cone
Meker	Coal gas	Air	1700	Above small cones
	Natural gas	Oxygen	2600	
	Acetylene	Oxygen	2000–3000	Depending upon position in flame

depends upon the heat of combustion and upon the heat capacity of the gas mixture used. Thus oxygen-gas mixtures give much higher temperatures than air-gas mixtures because it is not necessary to heat up the large volumes of inert nitrogen. Similarly coal gas will not give as high temperatures as natural gas or propane because the heat evolved per unit volume of gas mixture is less. When this is the case, the temperature of the gas flame may be increased appreciably by bubbling the gas through a liquid hydrocarbon to enrich it before admitting it to the burner.

Gas burners must be designed for the fuel to be used. Although it is possible to make burners in the laboratory, it is almost always cheaper and more satisfactory to procure them ready-made from a commercial source. An attempt is made to design most burners to supply sufficient oxygen to burn all the combustible gas. On the other hand, the velocity of flame propagation must be balanced against the flow rate of the gas supplied. If the flame propagation velocity is greater than the velocity of the gas stream, the burner will tend to strike back. If the velocity is much less than the velocity of the gas stream, the flame will tend to float off the tip of the burner. In the Bunsen burner, striking back can be prevented by the installation of a screen as in the Meker burner. For gas mixtures with low velocities of flame propagation, pilot lights of several kinds are available to reignite the flame if it floats off.

Although the actual temperatures of flames may be very high, as indicated by Table 4, the temperatures to which reasonable volumes of material can be heated with them are rather lower. For example, a well-adjusted Bunsen burner will usually just melt a piece of copper wire, but will not heat a small crucible to much above 700°C. Chromel-alumel thermocouples can be readily welded with an oxygen-gas flame, but only the finest platinum wire can be melted in such a flame.

Occasionally, small gas-fired furnaces are used for laboratory melting. A furnace for this purpose that will attain a temperature of about 1200°C is described in the chapter on melting and casting (Chapter 7).

REFERENCES

1. The Chief American Manufacturers of base-metal resistance alloys are
   (a) Hoskins Manufacturing Co., Detroit, Mich.
   (b) Wilbur B. Driver Co., Newark, N. J.
   (c) Driver-Harris Co., Harrison, N. J.
   (d) C. O. Jelliff Manufacturing Corp., Southport, Conn.
   (e) Hevi-Duty Electric Co., Milwaukee, Wisc.
2. Manufactured by Norton Company, Worcester 6, Mass. Detailed information on shapes of tubes, cements, etc., may be found in their book, *The Construction of Laboratory Electric Furnaces.*
3. R. E. Cech, *Rev. Scientific Instruments*, **21**, 747 (1950).
4. J. W. Gartland, *Trans. Electrochem. Soc.*, **80**, 121 (1945).
5. L. Brewer, U.C.R.L. 653 (an U.S. Atomic Energy Commission declassified document).

CHAPTER TWO

Measurement of High Temperatures

The generally accepted absolute temperature scale was defined by Kelvin in terms of the efficiency of a reversible heat engine. Temperature measurements on this scale can be made with the ideal gas thermometer, and many determinations of temperatures up to about 1500°C have been made using the constant volume nitrogen thermometer, with corrections to make the nitrogen scale conform with that of the ideal gas thermometer. Although gas thermometry gives temperature readings on the Kelvin scale, it is experimentally difficult. Other instruments such as resistance thermometers, thermocouples, and radiation pyrometers permit much greater precision of measurement and are used for practical temperature measurement.

These instruments do not give absolute temperature readings and must be calibrated for use. To permit reproducible calibrations at different locations, the International Temperature Scale has been established. It is made to correspond as closely as is experimentally possible to the thermodynamic centigrade (Celsius)* scale, but it is defined in terms of certain reproducible temperatures. The fundamental fixed points are the freezing and boiling points of water: 0°C and 100°C, respectively. They establish the magnitude of the de-

TABLE 1

FUNDAMENTAL AND PRIMARY FIXED POINTS

International Temperature Scale, °C (1948)

Oxygen point (b.p.)	−182.970
Ice point (f.p.)	0.0
Steam point (b.p.)	100.0
Sulfur point (b.p.)	444.600
Silver point (m.p.)	960.8
Gold point (m.p.)	1063.0

* The 1948 International Congress named the centigrade scale on which the melting point of ice is 0° and the boiling point of water 100° the Celsius scale, and °C as the official symbol to indicate temperatures on this scale.

gree. International agreement has also been reached on the best experimental values for certain primary fixed points as shown in Table 1.

In addition to these values, a number of secondary fixed points, as listed in Table 2, are defined. Interpolations on this scale between

TABLE 2

SECONDARY FIXED POINTS

International Temperature Scale, °C (1948)

(The temperatures listed are the freezing points of the pure substances.)

Mercury	−38.87
Tin	231.9
Cadmium	320.9
Lead	327.3
Zinc	419.5
Antimony	630.5
Aluminum	660.1
Copper (reducing atmosphere)	1083
Nickel	1453
Cobalt	1492
Palladium	1552
Platinum	1769
Rhodium	1960
Iridium	2443
Tungsten	3380

the ice point and 660°C are officially made with a platinum resistance thermometer calibrated at the ice, steam, and sulfur points to determine the three constants in the equation

$$R_T = R_0(1 + AT + BT^2) \qquad (1)$$

where R_T is the resistance of the platinum thermometer at temperature T.

From 660°C to the gold point the interpolations are made with a platinum versus platinum-rhodium thermocouple calibrated at the antimony, silver, and gold points to evaluate the constants in the equation

$$\text{emf} = a + bT + cT^2 \qquad (2)$$

where emf is the electromotive force generated by the thermocouple. Above the gold point, the scale is extrapolated with optical pyrometry, using the Planck radiation law as described later.

THERMOCOUPLES

A schematic diagram showing the electrical circuit of a thermocouple is presented in Figures 1a and 1b. Two wires of dissimilar
metals are joined to make a complete electrical circuit, and the two
junctions are maintained at different temperatures. An emf is developed, the magnitude of which is controlled by the kinds of metals
in contact and the temperatures of the junctions. By determining
with a suitable instrument the relationship between the emf developed

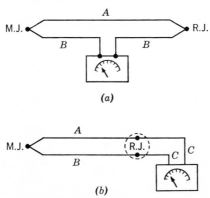

(a)

(b)

Figure 1. Equivalent Thermocouple Circuits. M.J. is the measuring junction,
R.J. the reference or cold junction, A and B are the thermocouple metals, and C is
any conductor. The circuit shown in (b) is most commonly used, with the reference junction frequently being at the meter terminals.

by the thermocouple and the temperature of one junction, maintaining the second junction at a reference temperature, the thermocouple
can be used as a temperature-measuring device.

The thermocouple is an almost ideal thermometric device. The emf
generated under a given set of conditions is highly reproducible, the
temperature-measuring junction may be made exceedingly small so
that the temperatures of small volumes may be measured, and finally
temperatures are indicated in terms of an electrical voltage; thus remote indication and control of temperature are easy.

Tables showing the emf produced by thermocouples as a function
of the temperature of the measuring junction are usually computed on
the assumption that the cold or reference junction is held at the ice
point. Methods of actually maintaining the reference junction at 0°C
or for correcting for deviations from this temperature are presented
later in this chapter.

Thermocouple Materials. In principle, any pair of different electrical conductors could be used for the construction of a thermocouple,
but practical consideration seriously limits the number of materials in
common use. A useful couple must be stable for reasonably long
times at the temperature of use, it must generate a high emf per degree,
and the emf must increase continuously with temperature. The commonly used thermocouple materials are listed in Table 3 with their

TABLE 3

COMMONLY USED THERMOCOUPLE MATERIALS

Name	Composition, %	Maximum Useful Temperature, °C
Platinum		1500
Platinum–13% rhodium		1500
Platinum–10% rhodium		1500
Chromel	90 Ni; 10 Cr	1100–1300
Alumel	94 Ni; 2 Al; 3 Mn; 1 Si	1100–1300
Constantan	60 Cu; 40 Ni	950
Iron		950
Copper		500

compositions and the range of temperatures over which they are used.
   Two types of noble metal thermocouples are in common use: platinum versus platinum–10% rhodium and platinum versus platinum–13%
rhodium. There is little to choose between these couples, although
the latter one generates a slightly higher emf per degree. The platinum or platinum-rhodium thermocouple was originally suggested by
Le Châtelier, and thermocouples that were nominally made of platinum versus platinum–10% rhodium were available from two different
manufacturers. These generated appreciably different emf's at the
same temperature so that automatic control instruments were calibrated for each kind. When it was subsequently discovered that the
thermocouple that generated the higher emf had been made with
impure platinum, the platinum versus platinum–13% rhodium thermocouple was introduced to permit the continued use of existing instruments. New instruments have been made to use the new thermocouple, and now both types are firmly established.
   The advantages of noble metal thermocouples are that they are
useful to high temperatures (about 1500°C), and with proper precautions are more reproducible than base-metal thermocouples. Their
disadvantages are that they are expensive, the thermal emf they
generate is low (about 0.01 mv per °C), and the relationship between

emf and temperature is not linear. In noble metal thermocouples pure platinum is the negative element.

The most generally useful laboratory thermocouple is Chromel-Alumel. It is inexpensive; it may be used to 1100°C continuously without serious deterioration and intermittently to about 1300°C. Its calibration curve is very nearly a straight line, and the emf per degree is large (about 0.04 mv per °C). In a reducing atmosphere its emf is subject to change, and under such conditions protection from the atmosphere must be provided. In this, and all other base-metal thermocouples, the convention is observed that the first-named member of the couple is the positive element.

For temperatures up to almost 1000°C the iron-Constantan thermocouple is frequently used, particularly because its thermoelectric power is large (about 0.055 mv per °C). For the upper part of its useful temperature range this thermocouple must be protected against oxidation. This protection may be accomplished by containing it in a protection tube filled with alumina mixed with about 3% by volume charcoal. At lower temperatures such protection is not necessary.

The copper-Constantan thermocouple is used principally for low-temperature work, up to about 500°C and particularly for the measurement of temperatures below 0°C.

Some other thermocouples, such as molybdenum-tungsten [1] and silicon carbide–graphite [2] have been used to a limited extent for the measurement of very high temperatures, but they can scarcely be considered to be standard materials.

Construction of Thermocouples. Thermocouples of all standard types may be purchased already made up and mounted from a large number of commercial sources. It is easy and customary to make them in the laboratory, however. Thermocouple wire of the above-mentioned common kinds can be purchased in spools in a wide range of wire sizes, and thermocouples made from these materials may usually be used without further calibration to measure temperatures to within about 5°C.

For low-temperature work it is possible to make a thermocouple by twisting the cleaned ends of the two wires together and silver-soldering them, although for precise work at these temperatures and for all work at higher temperatures it is necessary to weld the wires. Both noble and base metal thermocouples may be readily welded with the flame from an oxygen-gas torch. Usually the wire is twisted together a few turns to give mechanical strength, heated slightly, touched to a piece of borax or other flux, then welded. *No flux should be used with noble metal couples.* After welding, all flux must be very carefully removed from the junction or it will prevent the formation of the normal protective oxide film, and failure will occur in a short time.

Arc welding can be done by using a carbon electrode and 110 volts alternating current. The thermocouple and the carbon electrode are connected to opposite sides of the line with a series resistance such as a 100-watt lamp. The thermocouple junction is touched with the carbon and then drawn away.

Thermocouples are commonly finished by insulating the wires with porcelain beads or fine ceramic tubes, both of which may be procured in a number of sizes.

Thermocouple Protection. In the laboratory, thermocouples are frequently used bare. Under these conditions they respond rapidly and provide precise control of temperature. However, if the thermocouple is exposed to conditions that might cause its deterioration, and this includes most permanent installations, it is customary to use a closed-end tube made of Alundum, porcelain, or high chromium–nickel iron alloy to protect it. Other refractories or metals that will withstand the furnace conditions and that are sufficiently impervious to protect the couple are satisfactory.

Calibration of Thermocouples. The thermocouple wire supplied by reputable manufacturers agrees remarkably well with the published tables of emf versus temperature, and for a great deal of work it is satisfactory to make a thermocouple of this wire and use it to measure temperature without further calibration. There is little point in using very precisely calibrated thermocouples in conjunction with automatic control equipment because, in general, the difference between the true temperature and the temperature indicated by the controller, using standard tables, is less than the uncertainty in the temperature controlled. It is, however, necessary to check thermocouples in permanent installations from time to time to be sure that they are indicating approximately the right temperature, and for more accurate work it is occasionally necessary to have an accurate calibration.

Working thermocouples are almost always calibrated by comparing them with carefully calibrated standard thermocouples. These standard couples may be either noble or base metal although, for precise work, platinum–platinum rhodium couples are always used.

Before noble metal couples are calibrated they should be "annealed" at about but not above 1500°C for an hour or so. The purpose is not to recrystallize the wires but to distill out impurities that may have been picked up by the couple. This can be done most easily by attaching the thermocouple to binding posts and passing an electric current through it. The temperature can be measured with an optical pyrometer with sufficient accuracy, although it may be necessary to provide an extension tube for the front lens of the pyrometer to be able to focus the image of the thermocouple at a size large enough to permit satisfactory brightness comparisons. The couple is then calibrated by measuring the emf at three of the standard temperatures listed in Table 2. Materials having certified melting points for such calibrations may be procured from the National Bureau of Standards. From these three temperature measurements the constants in equation 3,

$$\text{emf} = a + bT + cT^2 \tag{3}$$

can be evaluated, and a complete curve of emf versus temperature can be constructed. Thermocouple calibrations are customarily plotted as difference curves, to show the difference in temperature to be added to or subtracted from the temperature indicated by the couple, using standard thermocouple calibration tables.

Such calibrations as this are rarely carried out in the laboratory. Calibrated couples can be obtained from the manufacturers of pyrometric equipment, and the Bureau of Standards will calibrate thermocouples sent to them. Since the operation is rather time consuming and requires some special equipment it is usually cheaper and more satisfactory to have such primary calibrations made in this way.

Given such a calibrated couple it is an easy matter to calibrate any number of working couples by comparing their emf's over a suitable range of temperatures. Some precautions must be taken to insure that both thermocouples are at the same temperature. A satisfactory method is to insert both couples, with their junctions close together, into a heavy pipe or copper block and heat them together in the same furnace.

In certain cases, particularly where calibrated thermocouples are not available, less complete calibration is useful. If a thermocouple is to be used only over a small range of temperatures, a satisfactory calibration can be obtained at only one point, for example, by determining a melting point at a temperature close to that which the thermocouple will be required to indicate. This is particularly useful for the base metal couples that have nearly a linear emf versus temperature curve. If only reproducibility is required, a number of couples may be intercompared by heating them together in a furnace, and those that differ from some selected couple by more than the desired amount may be rejected. One of the couples may then be reserved as a standard for subsequent comparisons.

Measurement of Thermocouple Voltages

Millivoltmeters. The millivoltmeter is the least expensive of the instruments available for the measurement of thermocouple voltages. It consists of a coil and pointer suspended between the poles of a magnet and arranged so that the deflection of the coil and pointer is proportional to the current passing through the coil. If the instrument is used to measure thermocouple voltages the resistance of the external circuit must be constant, because with a given emf this resistance will control the current passing through the coil and thus its deflection. For the greatest sensitivity it is desirable that the millivoltmeter have a low resistance to permit a high current to flow through the coil for a given emf. A low-resistance coil has, however, the great disadvantage that the length of the thermocouple must be very accurately controlled, since most thermocouple materials have high resistance, and small changes in length will change the resistance of the over-all circuit appreciably and lead to false readings. To overcome this difficulty, the better instruments for reading thermocouple voltages have coils with many turns, which give them a high sensitivity and permit the use of an internal resistance that is much higher than the resistance of the thermocouple. Under these conditions the accuracy of the temperature reading is not seriously affected by minor changes in thermocouple length. Millivoltmeters are frequently calibrated directly in terms of temperature for use with one particular kind of thermocouple.

A millivoltmeter designed for use with a thermocouple of high resistance can be used with one of lower resistance without recalibration by inserting a resistance in series with the thermocouple of such value that the total resistance of the external circuit is equal to the design value.

For some laboratory applications where only an approximate indication of temperature is needed, a small panel-type millivoltmeter or microammeter may be used. It is usually best to calibrate the thermocouple and meter together by measuring several known temperatures and constructing a calibration graph.

Temperature-Controlling Millivoltmeters. Several models of commercially available millivoltmeters are equipped to control temperature automatically. These are relatively inexpensive instruments and, unless great accuracy is required, are quite satisfactory. A temperature-controlling millivoltmeter must have a mechanism for comparing the desired temperature with the temperature indicated by the thermocouple, and for changing the power supply to the furnace as required by this comparison. This may be done most simply by providing adjustable contacts for the pointer of the meter which will turn the power on or off, but this method is rarely used. In a common type a chopper bar intermittently locks the indicating needle in position, and an auxiliary feeler determines whether the temperature is above or below the desired value. The feeler then throws a furnace power switch to the on or off position, depending upon whether the temperature is too low or too high. In another instrument the signaling of temperature relative to the control point is performed without mechanical contact. A pair of coils in the instrument is attached to the control point dial, so that its position is controlled by setting a pointer for the desired temperature. A vane attached to the instrument pointer passes between these coils, and, when the control point is approached, the inductance of the coil is changed by the entrance of the vane. By measuring the inductance of the coil with a suitable electronic circuit, the position of the pointer can be sensed and an appropriate signal sent to the control relay.

Potentiometers. The potentiometer is an instrument with which a voltage is measured by opposing it with a known, variable voltage of opposite sign. The null point is determined with a galvanometer. A voltage may be measured with great precision by using a carefully constructed instrument and a sensitive galvanometer. The potentiometer has the advantage that no current flows at the time the measurement is made so that readings are independent of the resistance of the external circuit except as it affects the sensitivity of the galvanometer.

A schematic diagram of a potentiometer is shown in Figure 2a. The voltage from the thermocouple, T.C., is balanced by suitably positioning the slide wire contact until the galvanometer G shows no deflection. In all instruments the slide wire R_1 is calibrated to read millivolts or temperature directly so that the voltage drop across the full length of the wire must be adjusted to a definite value. The adjustment can be made with the circuit shown in Figure 2b. By closing switch SC an auxiliary circuit is used in which the voltage drop produced by the dry cell B across resistance R_3 may be adjusted with rheostat R_2 until it is just equal to the voltage produced by the standard cell. This adjustment also adjusts the voltage drop across the slide wire R_1 to the desired calibration value.

A number of types of potentiometers are available, and the type chosen for any given measurement depends largely upon the precision required in the measurement. The most precise measurements are made with large potentiometers that are set up on a work bench and use external galvanometers, standard cells, and working cells. For measuring most thermocouple voltages in the laboratory, the so-called portable potentiometer is used. This instrument has a self-contained standard cell, dry cell, and rugged pivot-type galvanometer. It is normally supplied with two scale ranges, 16 and 60 mv, so that it can be used with either noble or base metal thermocouples. Readings on

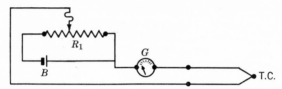

Figure 2a. Simple Potentiometer Circuit. Voltage from dry cell B is adjusted with slide wire resistance R_1 until galvanometer G shows it to be just equal to voltage from thermocouple T.C.

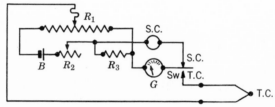

Figure 2b. Potentiometer Circuit. Switch Sw may be thrown so that voltage from dry cell B may be compared with either standard cell S.C. or thermocouple T.C. See text for details.

the high scale can be made to about 0.2 mv or about 3°C. These instruments are normally equipped with a manual cold-junction compensator as described later.

For more precise temperature measurement, portable precision potentiometers are available. These are self-contained as are the portable potentiometers, but they have a longer slide wire, or its equivalent, in a bank of resistors that can be selected with a switch, and they are normally equipped with a lamp and scale-type galvanometer. Depending upon the manufacturer, the portable precision potentiometers may or may not have provision for cold-junction compensation. With this instrument, voltages may be read to about 0.05 mv or about 1°C with a base metal thermocouple.

Automatic Potentiometers. A wide variety of methods have been devised for using potentiometers and thermocouples to control, indicate, and record temperatures automatically.

In one class an attempt is made to determine only whether the furnace temperature is greater or less than the desired value, and no attempt is made to measure the temperature continuously. These instruments operate satisfactorily for control purposes but of course cannot be used either to indicate directly or to record temperatures. Another class of instrument is the self-balancing potentiometer, which is kept continuously in balance with a suitable motorized system. It can be used to control the temperature, to indicate it on a dial, or to record it continuously on a chart.

The simple temperature-control potentiometers are operated by setting the slide wire so that an emf corresponding to the control temperature desired will be generated, and the galvanometer will indicate zero when the furnace is at the desired control temperature. In one instrument the position of the galvanometer needle is then detected with a chopper bar similar to that described above for a millivoltmeter. In another arrangement, the position is detected photoelectrically. A beam of light is reflected from a galvanometer mirror into a photocell, and the control relay is signaled to turn on or off, depending upon the position of the light beam with respect to the photocell.

In self-balancing potentiometers of the older type, the position of the galvanometer needle is detected, and, depending upon whether it is above or below the null point, a reversible motor repositions the slide wire to balance the potentiometer circuit. By gearing a carriage with a pointer to the slide wire, the pointer may be made to indicate the temperature on a dial or it may be used to drive a pen to trace the temperature on a chart. These instruments have the disadvantage that it takes several seconds, sometimes as many as 30, to obtain complete balance if the temperature is far removed from the last reading. Furthermore, the position of the galvanometer needle is observed only intermittently at periods of at least several seconds; therefore, it is impossible to follow rapidly changing temperatures.

Another type of automatic potentiometer dispenses entirely with the galvanometer. The output from the thermocouple is compared with the potentiometer voltage, and the out-of-balance voltage is fed through an interrupter that converts it to alternating current. This voltage is amplified electronically and is used to drive a two-phase motor, which repositions the slide wire and also drives the indicating arrow or the recording pen. The phase of the current used to drive the motor, and thus determine the direction of motor rotation, depends upon whether the temperature is above or below the balance point.

These instruments provide very rapid response, full-scale deflections being possible in times of 2 to 4 seconds. They have the additional advantage that they are somewhat more rugged than instruments requiring a galvanometer for detection of the null point.

In general, automatic potentiometers are equipped only to observe a single thermocouple. However, models of most kinds of instruments are available that will successively look at a series of thermocouples, sometimes as many as twelve. By using suitable electrical circuits, it is thus possible with a single instrument to control the temperature in several furnaces, or by using different inks to record the temperature in a number of furnaces. For the greatest accuracy of control,

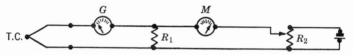

Figure 3. Schematic Circuit of Photoelectric Potentiometer. Resistance R_2 is adjusted until the voltage drop across R_1 equals that produced by thermocouple T.C., as shown by galvanometer G. Current flowing through R_1 is measured by milliammeter M so that voltage generated by the thermocouple can be computed.

it is not desirable to use a multiple-point controller because during an appreciable fraction of the time the temperature of the furnace is not observed at all. Thus, if the temperature is changing rapidly, serious overshooting may occur.

To obtain more expanded scales, some automatic potentiometers have a "suppressed zero." By suitably designing the electrical circuit, the potentiometer will control or record temperatures over a range of 1000°, for example, but the range extends from 200 to 1200°C. This device adds somewhat to the precision of control but, of course, slightly reduces the versatility of the instrument.

The recording photoelectric potentiometer uses the circuit shown schematically in Figure 3. The thermocouple output is opposed by a voltage drop across the resistor R_1, and the out-of-balance of the circuit is detected by the galvanometer G. The circuit can be balanced by adjusting rheostat R_2 and the current flowing through the resistor determined with a milliammeter M. From a knowledge of the value of resistance R_1, the thermocouple voltage can be computed. In the actual instrument resistance R_2 is replaced by an electronic circuit, and the galvanometer position is detected with a beam-splitting mirror and two photocells. The electronic circuit adjusts the current until the galvanometer shows no deflection. The milliammeter is fitted with a recording pen and thus automatically plots the thermocouple voltage on a strip chart.

Accuracy of Temperature Measurement

Very high precision is possible in temperature measurement, but great precautions are necessary to achieve this precision. By ordinary methods it is relatively easy to reproduce temperatures to ±1°C; but, unless the instruments are accurately calibrated, the true temperature will probably not be known to better than about two or three times this value. The precision of control with automatic equipment is less than this. A well-adjusted controller will control the temperature of a furnace to within ±5°C, but usually a lack of uniformity in the temperature of the furnace means that the temperature spread in a large specimen will be somewhat greater than this. For most applications this is satisfactorily accurate. If the temperature is close to a critical point in the metal, or if reaction rates or other processes are being studied, it may be necessary to take greater precautions to assure better control.

Thermocouple Cold Junctions

The emf generated by a thermocouple is a function of the temperatures of both the hot, or measuring, junction and the cold, or reference, junction. For the most precise measurements the cold junction is maintained at 0°C in an ice bath. In less precise work the cold junction is held at room temperature. Satisfactory compensation for this temperature difference may be made by adding to the emf generated by the thermocouple the emf that would be generated by the same couple if one junction were at the ice point and the other at room temperature. With base metal couples it makes practically no difference whether the emf is added to the measured emf or whether room temperature is added to the temperature computed from the tables, but with noble metal couples, which do not have a linear relationship between temperature and emf, it is important that emf's and not temperatures be added.

Provision is made for making this addition automatically in a large number of commercial instruments designed for the measurement of thermocouple voltages. In some instruments it involves merely a mechanical readjustment of the zero point so that room temperature is indicated when the measuring junction is at room temperature; in others an emf corresponding to room temperature is added electrically to the value indicated by the instrument. Some of these methods are described briefly below.

Compensating Leads. A complete thermocouple installation is shown schematically in Figure 4. It includes a thermocouple proper, compensating lead wires, and, if an ice bath is used for the cold junction, a pair of lead wires of the same metal, such as copper, extending from the cold junction to the measuring instrument. The total emf characteristic of the temperature of the measuring junction is developed between the measuring junction and the reference cold junction. The function of the compensating leads is to place the cold junction of the thermocouple circuit at a convenient place where its temperature may be measured or controlled. If an ice-point cold junction is used, the lead wires should be brought only to that point; both leads from there to the voltage-measuring instrument must be

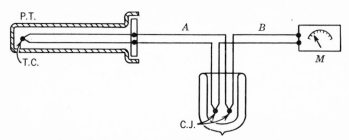

Figure 4. Complete Thermocouple Assembly. Thermocouple T.C. is contained in protecting tube P.T. Compensating leads *A* run to the cold junction C.J., and copper leads *B* from there to the voltage indicator *M*.

made of the same metal (usually copper) if proper readings are to be obtained. If cold-junction compensation is provided in the voltage measuring instrument itself, the compensating lead wires must extent to it.

For base-metal thermocouples the lead wires are invariably made of the same materials as the thermocouple itself, and flexible stranded insulated leads for this purpose may be obtained from commercial supply houses. Noble-metal couples are expensive, and special compensating base-metal lead wires made of a copper-nickel alloy and of pure copper are used for them. These leads together have the same thermoelectric power as the noble-metal couple, but the metals do not compensate individually so that it is necessary to have both the platinum-to-copper–nickel alloy and the platinum–rhodium-to-copper junctions at the same temperature if correct readings are to be obtained.

In use, caution must be exercised to be certain that the lead wires are properly connected to the thermocouple. A convenient way is to connect the lead wires to the measuring instrument, join the free ends, and heat that temporary junction with a match to be sure that the temperature indication of the instrument increases. Next, this junction is broken, the thermocouple connected to it, and the same test applied. The temperature indication of the instrument should again increase. If it does not, the connection should be changed at the thermocouple-lead wire junctions and not at the instrument.

A convenient method of arranging a cold junction at 0°C is illustrated in Figure 5. Two glass tubes large enough to receive the thermocouple wire and an insulated lead wire are fitted through a cork stopper in a small Dewar flask filled with ice and water. The thermocouple lead wire junction is placed at the bottom of the tube, and care is taken to insure that the wires are insulated from each other above this point. If the thermocouple is to be changed frequently a few drops of mercury may be placed at the bottom of the tube to make an electrical contact. All that is necessary to make a temperature measurement is to dip the thermocouple and instrument lead wires into the mercury. This method has the disadvantage that in time water will condense in the tubes and permit the possibility of spurious readings because electrolytic emf's may be generated here. For more permanent installations the thermocouple and lead wires may be fastened to each other permanently and the tube closed with sealing wax.

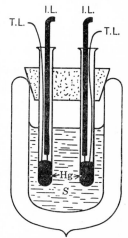

Figure 5. Cold-junction Device. The glass tubes are immersed in a mixture of ice and water (S) in a Dewar flask. Contact is made between the thermocouple leads T.L. and the insulated instrument leads I.L. with a few drops of mercury at the bottom of the glass tubes.

A number of methods are used in commercial instruments to provide compensation for the thermocouple cold-junction temperature without using an ice bath. This may be accomplished either manually or automatically.

If a cheap millivoltmeter is used, reasonably satisfactory temperature readings may be obtained by setting the zero of the instrument to indicate room temperature, and this procedure is satisfactory if room temperature is reasonably constant. Many of the better millivoltmeters accomplish this correction automatically with a Bréguet spiral or bimetallic spring connected to one of the control springs of the moving coil.

Figure 6a shows schematically one method of obtaining cold-junction compensation in a manually operated potentiometer. With the auxiliary slide wire R_4, a voltage equal to the one that would be produced by the thermocouple with one junction at the ice point and the other at room temperature can be added to the thermocouple voltage electrically. This may be accomplished automatically by the circuit indicated in Figure 6b. The resistance of coil R_4 changes with temperature whereas that of coil R_5 is independent of temperature. Thus, as the temperature of the coils change, an effect similar to that of moving the slider on coil R_4 in Figure 6a is produced, and by

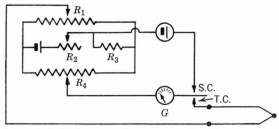

Figure 6a. Manual Cold-Junction Compensator for Potentiometer. A voltage equal to the one required for cold-junction compensation is added to the thermocouple voltage by properly positioning the slider on resistance R_4. Other symbols the same as in Figure 2b.

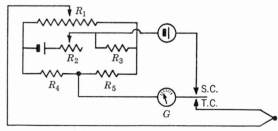

Figure 6b. Automatic Cold-Junction Compensator. Resistances R_4 and R_5 replace resistance R_4 of Figure 6a. The resistance of R_4 is temperature dependent, so that the voltage added to the thermocouple voltage depends upon the temperature of resistance R_4, which should be the same as the temperature of the thermocouple cold junction.

selecting suitable values for the coils compensation for changes in room temperature can be achieved.

A word of warning is necessary in connection with the use of automatic (as opposed to manual) cold-junction compensators. They are exceedingly useful for temperature measurements where the utmost precision is not required, and they are necessary where the instrument is used to control temperatures for long periods of time. However, when they are built into the temperature-measuring device, it can be used only with the kind of thermocouple for which cold-junction compensation is provided. False readings will be obtained with any other kind of thermocouple. Furthermore, the thermocouple cannot be used with an ice bath to control the cold-junction temperature.

In a few instruments of the potentiometer type it is possible to remove the cold-junction compensator but, in general, the factory must make this change. If it is probable that the millivoltmeter or potentiometer will be needed for use with different kinds of thermocouples, it should be procured without automatic cold-junction compensation.

There is one method that will permit a standard millivoltmeter or potentiometer with automatic cold-junction compensation to be used with a different kind of thermocouple from the kind for which the instrument was designed. By connecting a thermocouple of the kind the instrument was designed to use, and holding its reference junction at the ice point, the instrument will always indicate 0°C or zero millivolts. Any other kind of thermocouple can then be connected, and the voltage indicated by the instrument will be correct.

RADIATION PYROMETRY

Radiation pyrometers are the only instruments that can be used to measure temperatures above those at which thermocouples can be used, and frequently are more convenient than thermocouples for use at lower temperatures. They are of two types: (1) the *optical pyrometer,* where the brightness of a given wavelength of light emitted by a hot object is visually matched with some standard source, and (2) the *total radiation pyrometer,* where the radiation in a wide band of wavelengths is focused on an absorber whose temperature rise is measured with a vacuum thermocouple or thermopile.

For temperatures above 1500°C the International Temperature Scale is defined in terms of the optical pyrometer and Planck's radiation law.*

* The International Temperature Scale of 1948 for temperatures above the gold point is defined by the equation

$$\frac{J_t}{J_{Au}} = \frac{e[c_2/\lambda(t_{Au} + T_0)] - 1}{e[c_2/\lambda(t + T_0)] - 1} \tag{4}$$

where T_t and J_{Au} are the radiant energies per unit wavelength interval at visible wavelength λ emitted per unit time by a unit area of black body at the temperature t and at the gold point t_{Au}, respectively, c_2 is defined as 14,380 micron degrees, T_0 is the temperature of the ice point in degrees Kelvin, and e is the base of natural logarithms.

Until 1948 the International Temperature Scale defined elevated temperatures in terms of the optical pyrometer and the somewhat simpler Wien's radiation law. The following approximate formula, based upon Wien's law,[3,4] may be substituted for equation 4 without significant error:

$$\ln \frac{J_t}{J_{Au}} = \frac{c_2}{\lambda} \left[\frac{1}{1336} - \frac{1}{t + 273} \right] \tag{5}$$

The disappearing filament optical pyrometer consists of a telescope for producing an image of the hot object in the plane of a filament whose brightness can be adjusted, a method of measuring the filament current, and a filter to permit the brightness comparison to be made at a given wavelength of light (usually 0.63 micron). The temperature measurement is made by adjusting the intensity of the light from the filament until it is invisible against the image of the hot object.

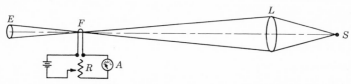

Figure 7.   Disappearing Filament Optical Pyrometer.   The image of the hot source S is superimposed on that of a hot filament F with the lens L.   The brightness of the filament is adjusted with rheostat R until it cannot be seen against the hot source.   The current flowing through the filament is then read with ammeter A.

Two methods are in common use for adjusting the brightness of the filament.   In the Leeds and Northrup optical pyrometer (Figure 7) the current passing through the filament is varied to give the brightness match.   This current is then determined by measuring with a potentiometer the voltage drop it produces across a standard resistor. It requires accurate control of the filament characteristics so that a given current produces a standard brightness.   In the Pyro optical pyrometer (Figure 8) the intensity of an illuminated spot is matched

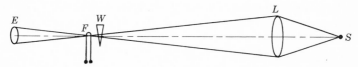

Figure 8.   The filament is at constant brightness, and the apparent intensity of the source is varied with the optical wedge W, until a brightness match is achieved.

to the intensity of the hot object by inserting a calibrated optical wedge, while the filament is maintained at a constant brightness.

Although the scale of these pyrometers is based on Planck's law, they are empirically calibrated.   The Leeds and Northrup optical pyrometer is calibrated by measuring the current I necessary to match the brightness of black bodies at three known temperatures so that the constants in the equation

$$I = A + BT + CT^2 \tag{6}$$

may be determined. A similar method may be used to relate the thickness of the optical wedge to temperature where this method of brightness matching is employed.

The scale range of these optical pyrometers may be readily changed by interposing a neutral absorber in front of the telescope used to examine the hot object, and such instruments are usually provided with at least two scale ranges. In instruments where the filament is operated at a standard current and the brightness match obtained by an optical wedge, the scale range may also be changed by changing the filament current.

It is obvious that great errors in reading can result if appreciable light absorption occurs between the hot object and the objective lens of the telescope. Such absorption may occur in smoky and dusty air, but a more common source in laboratory work is a dirty furnace window or lens in the pyrometer itself. Great precautions should be taken to avoid errors of this type if good temperature readings are to be obtained. (The correction for a clean, clear glass window is negligible.) It should be noted, however, that no corrections are necessary for distance between the hot object and the instrument itself. The brightness match is based upon an equality between the energy emitted per unit of surface in the image and in the filament. At greater operating distances the image of the object is smaller so that its intensity remains the same.

Emissivity Corrections

Most optical pyrometers are calibrated to read the temperature of black-body emitters. Under many laboratory conditions the hot object meets the requirements of being a black body rather well. For example, temperature readings made through a small aperture in a dark furnace, or upon the surface of graphite, should be quite accurate. On the other hand, readings made upon highly reflecting objects that are illuminated may be in error by 100°C or more. This error occurs because highly reflecting objects are less perfect radiators than black ones. The emissivity $E\lambda$ of a substance is defined as the ratio of the intensity of radiation of a given wavelength from the substance to the intensity of radiation of that wavelength that would be emitted by a black body at the same temperature. These values are always less than one. The emissivities of a number of metals are listed in Table 4, and it can be seen that they vary widely.

Corrections for emissivity $E\lambda$ may be made in several ways. Figure 9 shows a plot of the corrections that should be applied to temperatures read from an optical pyrometer calibrated for use with a black

TABLE 4

Emissivity of Various Materials for Red Light ($\lambda \approx 0.63\,\mu$)

Material	$E_{0.63\,\mu}$	Material	$E_{0.63\,\mu}$
Silver	0.07	Cuprous oxide	0.70
Gold—solid	0.13	Iron oxide— 800°C	0.98
liquid	0.22	1000°C	0.95
Platinum—solid	0.33	1200°C	0.92
liquid	0.38	Nickel oxide— 800°C	0.96
Palladium—solid	0.33	1300°C	0.85
liquid	0.37	Iron—solid and liquid	0.37
Copper—solid	0.11	Nickel—solid and liquid	0.36
liquid	0.15	Iridium	0.30
Tantalum—1100°C	0.60	Rhodium	0.36
2600°C	0.48	Graphite powder	0.95
Tungsten—2000°C	0.46	Carbon	0.85
3000°C	0.43		
Nichrome— 600°C	0.95		
900°C	0.90		
1200°C	0.80		

From Bureau of Standards T.P. 170.

body for different values of $E\lambda$ and of T. Such curves can be computed from Wien's law since

$$J_\lambda = c_1\lambda^{-5}e^{-(c_2/\lambda T_A)} = E_\lambda c_1{}^{-5}e^{-(c_2/\lambda T)} \qquad (7)$$

Thus

$$1/T - 1/T_A = \log E_\lambda/9660 \qquad (8)$$

taking $c_2 = 14,380$ micron degrees. It will be noticed that the right-hand side of equation 8 is a constant. It can, therefore, be evaluated for a given set of conditions by reading one apparent temperature of an object at a known temperature, such as its melting point. This does not mean that the ΔT to be added to the temperature readings is a constant, but over short ranges of temperature this approximation is permissible. For example, if it is desired to superheat a metal 100°C above its melting point, a temperature reading at the melting point may be taken and heating continued until the pyrometer indicates a temperature 100°C higher than that at the melting point.

Most of the emissivity values reported in Table 4 and in the literature are for polished metal surfaces. This is a condition usually fulfilled for molten metals in a vacuum or in an entirely inert atmosphere. On the other hand, the emissivity of rough metal surfaces and of those with an oxide coating is considerably higher. These surfaces will have apparently higher temperatures.

It is possible to read a temperature that is too high when examining a highly reflecting object if it is contained in a furnace or crucible that is hotter than the specimen itself, and the geometry of the setup is such that light can be reflected from the hot walls of the container into the pyrometer. Obviously even a cold mirror will appear to be hot

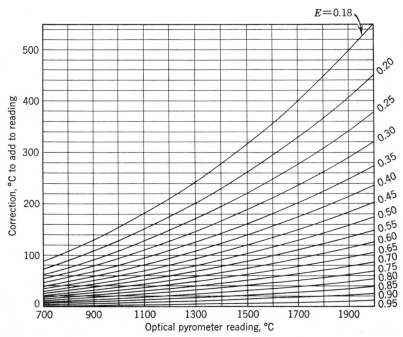

Figure 9. Corrections for Emissivity to Temperature Observed with Optical Pyrometer. The curves for emissivity values ranging from $E = 0.18$ to $E = 0.95$ show the additions to be made to the pyrometer reading. Computed for $C_2 =$ 14,350 and $\lambda = 0.65$ μ. (Bureau of Standards T.P. 170.)

if it is used to reflect the light from a hot specimen into the pyrometer. Usually this is not a serious difficulty if the specimen is examined through a small hole in the furnace or crucible cover.

If an optical pyrometer is to be used continuously for the examination of only one hot material, it can be calibrated to include the emissivity correction. Instruments are available, for example, corrected for the emissivity of molten steel.

Most optical pyrometers of the brightness matching type require the human eye for brightness matching. One company, however, makes an instrument of this type in which the brightness match is achieved photoelectrically. The brightness of the object is compared with the brightness of a standard source with a pair of photo-cells, and the brightness of the two made the same by an external self-balancing mechanism. This method has the advantage that it lends itself to the recording and control of the temperature.

Total Radiation Pyrometry

Optical pyrometers select only a short range of wavelengths for observation to measure temperature. Another class of instruments, a so-called total radiation pyrometer, uses as wide a band of wavelengths as possible. Nominally these pyrometers obey the Stefan-Boltzmann law,

$$E = K(T^4 - T_0^4) \qquad (9)$$

where E is the net energy lost by radiation per unit area per unit time, T is the absolute temperature of the black body, T_0 is the absolute temperature of the surroundings, and K is the constant of proportionality. This law applies for the total radiant energy of all wavelengths. In practice total radiation pyrometers do not use all wavelengths because of absorption of the optical system. Thus they do not strictly obey the Stefan-Boltzmann law. Accordingly, total radiation pyrometers are always empirically calibrated.

Radiation pyrometers are usually divided into two classes, depending upon their optical systems: the mirror type or the lens type. In principle, the mirror-type instrument is superior to the lens-type one since no absorption of energy occurs in the lens. In practice a dust-protecting cover must be placed in the front of the instrument so that the mirror type has little advantage over the lens type. Figure 10 shows a schematic drawing of a mirror-type radiation pyrometer. The diaphragm opening D and the sensitive element T are at conjugate foci of the mirror. The diaphragm opening acts as a secondary source, and readings, at least theoretically, are independent of the distance from the source, provided that it is large enough to cover completely the base of a cone determined by the formula

$$\text{Minimum distance of source} = MD/N \qquad (10)$$

where M is the distance from point c to source, N is the distance from point c to aperture b, D is the diameter of the aperture. This instrument does not need to be focused.

Figure 11 shows a schematic drawing of a typical lens-type radiation pyrometer. The lens focuses the energy from the object upon a diaphragm D_2, behind which is the disk of a vacuum thermocouple or thermopile. An auxiliary diaphragm fixes the solid angle of the rays incident upon D_2. E is an eyepiece used to aid in pointing the instrument at the desired portion of the object O. Although theoretically this is not a fixed-focus instrument, whenever the distance of the object is greater than ten times the focal length of the lens, refocusing

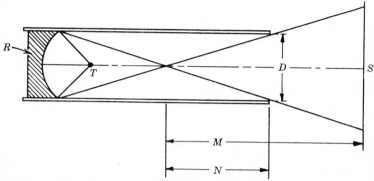

Figure 10. Mirror-Type Radiation Pyrometer. Hot source S is focused on sensitive element T with mirror R. See text for details.

is not necessary for changes in distance. In all these cases the source must be large enough to fill the aperture entirely.

The lens-type total radiation pyrometer generally uses fluorite or quartz as a lens material and has the advantage over a mirror-type instrument that satisfactory readings can be taken at a greater distance. Total radiation pyrometers have the advantage over optical pyrometers that much lower temperatures may be measured, and, since

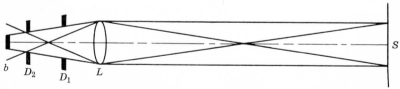

Figure 11. Lens-Type Radiation Pyrometer. The lens L focuses radiant energy from the source S upon thermocouple disk b. D_1 and D_2 are diaphragms used to define the source.

the temperature is indicated in terms of an electrical voltage, they lend themselves to the operation of automatic recording and controlling equipment of the same type used with thermocouples. In particular they are useful for the measurement of surface temperatures, where it would be difficult with thermocouples.

Since a total radiation pyrometer requires a large source of uniform temperature, it is more difficult to calibrate accurately, and the accuracy of calibration may be expected to be somewhat lower than that of either a thermocouple or an optical pyrometer. To aid in reproducibility a common way of using a total radiation pyrometer is to sight it on the closed end of a tube which is inserted into the high-temperature zone. This procedure has the additional advantage that no difficulties are encountered with smoky atmospheres.

Emissivity corrections must be made for total radiation pyrometers, but, as different wavelengths are involved, the corrections are different from those used for optical pyrometers. Emissivity values for use with radiation pyrometers may be found in the literature, but at best they can be considered to be only approximate. The best method to determine emissivity corrections for total radiation pyrometers is to make simultaneous readings on the surface in question with both an optical and a radiation pyrometer, and then to determine the true temperature by applying the appropriate correction from Table 4 and Figure 9 to the optical pyrometer reading. The corrections for the optical pyrometer are much more reliable than those available for radiation pyrometers because the wavelength is known.

OTHER METHODS OF MEASURING TEMPERATURE

Resistance thermometers are among the most accurate of temperature-measuring devices. They are extensively used in scientific work, especially at low temperatures. However, the platinum spiral that is usually used as the temperature-sensitive element is rather bulky, at least compared to the volume of a thermocouple junction, and some difficulties are encountered in compensating for the changes in resistance of lead wires with temperature. Finally, the precision of which the resistance thermometer is capable is rarely required in metallurgical work, and as a result thermocouples are generally used in applications where resistance thermometers might be used.

For many years ceramists have measured temperatures with Segar cones, ceramic bodies of rather accurately known softening temperature, which are inserted into the kiln at the time of firing. The temperature is measured by determining which of a series of Segar cones deforms to a standard shape during a given firing. These cones do not measure temperature alone but rather a combination of time and temperature, since some time is required for the standard deformation to occur, the time being a function of course of the temperature.

They do, however, provide a good measure of the extent to which the vitrification reaction, for example, has occurred in the firing of the ceramic body.

Recently a series of mixtures of substances (Tempilstiks) has become available commercially to permit the rough determination of the temperature of hot objects. These mixtures are available in the form of crayons, pills, or a paint that can be allowed to dry, and they permit the approximate estimation of the temperature of many objects by observation of melting of the substance applied. There are cases, such as the measurement of surface temperatures, where they are much more convenient and much simpler to use than the more standard methods.

For rough laboratory temperature control, and sometimes even for temperature measurement, bimetallic strips, either coupled to an indicating dial or coupled to an electrical contact, are frequently used to measure or control temperatures. These are most commonly used in the control of the temperature of low-temperature drying ovens and similar equipment.

Occasionally it is convenient to measure temperature by observing the conditions under which a phase change occurs in a pure substance. An example is in conducting observations in a furnace adapted to a microscope or X-ray camera. The voltage that must be applied to the heating coil to produce a phase change that occurs at a known temperature can be observed for several substances, and a calibration curve prepared that will permit the temperature to be set with reasonable accuracy at any desired value by controlling the applied voltage.

REFERENCES

1. H. A. Wilhelm, H. J. Svec, A. I. Snow, and A. H. Danne, "High Temperature Thermocouples," AECD–3275 (a declassified publication of the United States Atomic Energy Commission).
2. G. R. Fitterer, "Pyrometry of Liquid Steels and Pig Iron," *Temperature, Its Measurement and Control in Science and Industry*, p. 496, Reinhold Publishing Corp., New York, 1941.
3. R. J. Carruccini, *J. Research Natl. Bur. Standards*, **43**, 133 (1949).
4. H. F. Stenson, *J. Research Natl. Bur. Standards*, **42**, 209 (1949).

Two very generally useful reference books on the general topic of temperature measurement and control are:

(1) *Temperature, Its Measurement and Control in Science and Industry* (a Symposium sponsored by the American Institute of Physics), Reinhold Publishing Corp., New York, 1941.

(2) *Pyrometric Practice*, by Paul D. Foote, C. O Fairchild, and T. R. Harrison, Bureau of Standards Technical Publication 170 (1921). (In spite of the age of this book the procedures described herein are still authoritative and useful.)

Detailed information on temperature measuring, controlling, and recording equipment may be obtained, for example, from the following manufacturers:

Tempil Corp., 123 W. 22nd St., New York, N. Y.
The Bristol Co., Waterbury 20, Conn.
The Foxboro Co., Foxboro, Mass.
General Electric Co., Apparatus Division, Schenectady, N. Y.
Illinois Testing Laboratories, Inc., Chicago 10, Ill.
Leeds and Northrup Co., Philadelphia 44, Pa.
Minneapolis-Honeywell Regulator Co., Industrial Division, Philadelphia 44, Pa.
The Pyrometer Instrument Co., Bergenfield 1, N. J.
Tagliabue Instruments Division, Newark, N. J.
Wheeler Instrument Co., Chicago 7, Ill.

In general, thermocouples can be obtained from the foregoing companies, as well as from a large number of houses that specialize in supplying thermocouples, compensating leads, and accessories.

CHAPTER THREE

Control of Temperature

As the power supplied to a furnace increases, the temperature rises, and more heat is lost by convection and radiation. Thus an equilibrium temperature exists for each amount of power supplied. Whenever a specimen is to be heat treated, the temperature of the furnace must be controlled by automatically or manually controlling the power input to the furnace. The power may be controlled by supplying it uniformly at a suitable level, or by interrupting it periodically so that over a period of time the average power level is correct. A complete installation for controlling temperature requires also a thermocouple or other device to measure the temperature of the specimen. Frequently another thermocouple is needed to measure the temperature at some point in the furnace (it may be different from the temperature of the specimen!).

In this chapter, we shall deal first with the problem of controlling the power input to a furnace and then with methods for automatically measuring and controlling the furnace temperature. Rough control of furnace temperature can be accomplished merely by setting the power to some predetermined value, but accurate temperature control is almost always accomplished with some kind of automatic temperature-measuring instrument.

METHODS OF CONTROLLING FURNACE POWER

A simple device for controlling the power supplied to a furnace is the *series rheostat* shown in Figure 1. It is cheap, and it is frequently

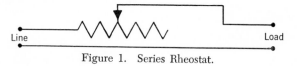

Figure 1. Series Rheostat.

supplied with small laboratory furnaces. By roughly calibrating a series of settings against ultimate temperature it is possible to repro-

duce temperatures fairly well. The disadvantages of this device are
that it is wasteful of power, the equilibrium temperature varies with
line voltage fluctuations, and, finally, very long times are required to
reach the equilibrium temperature characteristic of a given setting.
This latter difficulty can be overcome by setting the rheostat for a
high temperature until the desired temperature is reached, and then
setting the rheostat back so that the desired temperature is just maintained.

A more refined method of controlling the voltage supplied to a furnace is to use an *autotransformer* (Figure 2). This instrument is

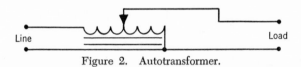

Figure 2. Autotransformer.

efficient and commonly used for very small laboratory furnaces, but
for larger ones the cost of the transformer becomes prohibitive. Auto-
transformers are rarely used for control of furnace power in sizes
much larger than one kilowatt and they operate best when the voltage
setting is changed frequently. When they are used for long times at
a fixed setting some deterioration of the contacts may occur, and a
fixed ratio transformer is to be preferred.

Large furnaces, and some quite small laboratory furnaces, especially
those operating at much less than 110 volts, are frequently operated
with *tapped transformers* (Figure 3).

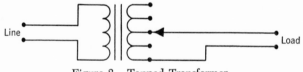

Figure 3. Tapped Transformer.

A very convenient way of controlling rather heavy loads with a
small autotransformer is by the use of a *saturable core reactor* (Figure
4). It consists of a coil wound around an iron core and connected in
series with the main power circuit. An auxiliary coil wound on the
iron core of the reactor is supplied with direct current from an autotransformer and a rectifier. When the auxiliary coil is not energized
(no direct current flowing), the iron core causes the main coil to have
a high impedance, and no heating current passes through the furnace.
Turning up the autotransformer magnetically saturates the iron core

and in effect removes it from the circuit, the impedance of the reactor is thus decreased, and the current to the furnace increased.

These are the most common of the methods used to provide temperature control in a furnace while providing a continuous supply of
power. After equilibrium is reached, the temperature of the furnaces
changes only if the line voltage changes, if room temperature changes,
or if the heat losses change for other reasons. Changes in line voltage
are usually serious, so that a constant temperature can be obtained

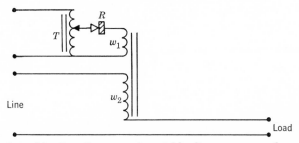

Figure 4. Saturable Core Reactor. A variable direct-current voltage is applied
to winding w_1 with autotransformer T and rectifier R. This varies impedance of
winding w_2.

for only relatively short periods of time. However, for small furnaces
it is possible to use a *constant voltage transformer* to supply an autotransformer (Figure 5). This method provides an exceedingly constant temperature in small furnaces and is particularly useful for
furnaces of small heat capacity, or for single-crystal furnaces.

The power supplied to a furnace, and thus its temperature, may also
be controlled with a current interrupter, which varies the fraction of

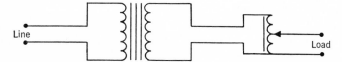

Figure 5. Constant Voltage Transformer Feeding Autotransformer.

the time that power is supplied to the furnace. Such a device is illustrated schematically in Figure 6. The notched disk is driven by a
small motor and actuates a switch that controls a power relay. In
commercial instruments the fraction of the time that power is supplied
to the furnace is continuously variable from 0 to 1. For this method
of power control to be satisfactory, the furnace must have a reasonably
large heat capacity so that its temperature does not drop measurably
during the off part of the cycle.

The devices described thus far suffer from the disadvantage that the furnace temperature is strongly influenced by line voltage fluctuations. One ingenious device illustrated in Figure 7 provides power proportioning, yet the power supplied is almost independent of line voltage fluctuations. It consists of a small bimetal thermostat surrounded by a small auxiliary heater powered by the same voltage used

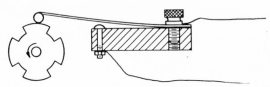

Figure 6.   Current Interrupter.   The notched wheel is driven by a motor.   By using different wheels, the fraction of the time that power is available can be varied.

for the large furnace and connected in parallel with it. The bimetal contactor can be adjusted to make contact at a range of temperatures. Both the furnace and the bimetal heater are heated until the bimetal contactor reaches temperature. Both furnaces are then turned off until the contactor temperature falls sufficiently. Since the heater has a very small heat capacity compared to the large furnace, the power is turned off and on frequently—the higher the setting of the thermostat, the greater proportion of the time it is on. Furthermore, if the line voltage is low, the auxiliary heater must remain on a greater fraction of the time to keep the bimetallic regulator at the proper temperature.

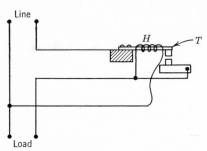

Figure 7.   Input Controller.   The heater H is wound around the bimetal strip T. The circuit is opened as the bimetal strip is heated. By adjusting the spacing of the contact points, the fraction of the time that power is supplied can be varied.

A very rough method of power control, which is sometimes convenient, is possible with furnaces constructed to operate on either 110 or 220 volts. Normally these furnaces heat to about 1000 to 1100°C when the rated voltage is applied. However, if the windings are connected for 220 volts and only 110 volts are applied, the maximum temperature will be only about 500°C.

AUTOMATIC TEMPERATURE CONTROL

The preceding methods are convenient for the rough automatic control of temperature for long times or for its precise manual control for short times. In most installations, however, temperature control is accomplished by measuring the furnace temperature with a thermocouple or radiation pyrometer and controlling it to the desired value by suitable instruments, often in conjunction with power-control equipment of the type described above. Temperature control has become in recent years an advanced engineering science, particularly in complicated industrial applications. No attempt will be made here to describe the theory of control, or even to cover all possible cases. Rather, a few examples of methods that are useful in the laboratory will be described. We shall limit ourselves to a discussion of the control of temperature in electric furnaces since these are almost exclusively used for laboratory work.

The instrumentation required for automatic temperature control is almost independent of the method of temperature measurement. A thermocouple, a radiation pyrometer, or a resistance thermometer will give an electrical signal that can be interpreted in terms of temperature by instruments described in the previous chapter. These can also permit comparison of that temperature with the desired temperature and close or open a circuit accordingly.

It might be pointed out that the ability of various controllers to handle electrical loads varies widely. Many instruments require auxiliary relays to control even small furnaces, since the contacts inside the instrument have a capacity of only a few amperes. Other instruments are available that will handle moderate loads, up to 35 to 50 amperes, and may thus be used to operate small furnaces directly without auxiliary equipment. Most temperature controllers have their control contacts in circuits that are separate from those used to operate the instrument. A few instruments designed for the operation of laboratory equipment require only a single connection to the power line, and have terminals from which large relays or small furnaces may be operated directly.

On-Off Control

The simplest method of automatically controlling the temperature of a furnace is to turn the power off when it reaches the desired temperature and to turn it on again when the temperature falls below the desired value. This is on-off control, illustrated schematically in Figure 8. The temperature can be measured with a thermocouple, and the control instrument actuates a simple circuit breaker that opens when the temperature indicated by the thermocouple is above the control point and closes when the temperature is below the control point. The power supplied to the furnace is either completely on or completely off. If the instrument is sufficiently sensitive, and the thermocouple is properly located, this method will provide satisfactory control. In most cases, because of the time required for heat flow, on-off control leads to marked fluctuation in temperature. The fur-

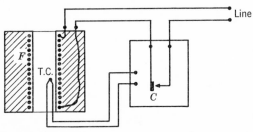

Figure 8. Simple On-Off Control. The thermocouple output is fed to the controller C, which opens the power circuit when the furnace is above the control temperature, and closes it when the furnace is below the control temperature.

nace windings become very hot before the thermocouple in the interior of the furnace reaches the control temperature. Then, even if the power to the windings is turned off, the interior of the furnace will continue to heat for some little time. Similarly, when the thermocouple inside the furnace has cooled to the control point again, and the controller again calls for power, it will be some time before heat from the windings again reaches the center of the furnace; and it will cool seriously below the control point.

Two-Position Control

Two-position control is a modification of on-off control that markedly reduces the temperature swing. Instead of turning the power completely on and off it is changed from a high level that will just heat the furnace above the desired temperature to a low level that will not quite heat the furnace to the desired value. A simple method of accomplishing this is shown in Figure 9a.

The adjustable resistor in series with the furnace keeps some current flowing through it all the time, and this current is adjusted so that it is insufficient to heat the furnace to the control temperature. When the furnace falls below the control temperature, the closing of the contacts short-circuits the rheostat and allows a larger current to pass through the furnace and heat it above the control temperature. The spread between the two power values must always be sufficiently great so that, regardless of line voltage fluctuations, the attainable temperature limits lie on either side of the control point. Both the high and the low currents may be controlled by the scheme shown in Figure 9b.

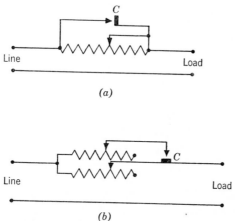

(a)

(b)

Figure 9. Two Methods of Two-Position Control. The power supplied shifts from a high to a low value. In (a) only the low power level can be controlled. In (b) both the high and low value can be controlled. C is the contactor in the temperature controller.

Many automatic temperature controllers are equipped with three contacts, marked H, C and L. The H (high) and C (common) contacts close when the temperature is too high, the C and L contacts close when the temperature is too low, and both contacts are commonly open when the furnace is at temperature. A controller of this type may be used as an on-off or two-position controller with a so-called three-wire relay, as shown in Figure 10. The relay coil is energized by closing the L-C contact, and holding contacts keep it energized after the L-C contact breaks. When the H-C contact is made, the relay coil is short-circuited through resistance R, and the relay drops open. This method of operation prevents relay chatter, but since there is a definite spread between the high and low settings the temperature fluctuation may be reasonably great.

There is danger with any controller of this type that the furnace will seriously overshoot and perhaps be burned out if the thermocouple burns out or breaks. Many temperature controllers are equipped with so-called thermocouple burn-out protection, a circuit that causes the controller to indicate a very high temperature and thus turn the furnace off if the thermocouple circuit opens. Another way of achieving the same end is to set the mechanical zero on the potentiometer galvanometer slightly above zero, so that if the thermocouple circuit burns out the galvanometer will read high, and no power will be supplied to the furnace. Another method that is expensive but warranted if the furnace or specimens are valuable is to use two controllers and thermocouples, and two relays in series in the power line.

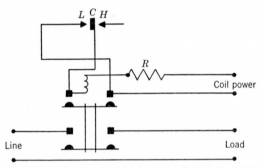

Figure 10. Three-Wire Relay for Use with Controller Having H, C, and L Contacts. Relay closes with momentary contact between L and C and opens when H and C contacts close.

If the second controller is set a few degrees above the first one, it will assume control if the first controller fails for any reason, and will prevent the furnace from overheating seriously.

When a controller of the on-off type is used the best control is achieved when the heating period is about equal to the cooling period. If, for example, the heating current used is much greater than that necessary to heat the furnace to the control temperature, the furnace will be heated rapidly from the minimum temperature to the control temperature, at which time the power will be turned off. However, the stored heat will cause the temperature to overshoot the high side. Cooling then occurs relatively slowly so that the average temperature will be somewhat above the desired value.

Anticipating Devices

The temperature control in a furnace can be greatly improved if some means is provided for reducing the power input to the furnace as the temperature rises toward the control point. Many methods for doing this have been devised. One of the simplest is to place the power-controlling thermocouple near the windings instead of in the center of the furnace.

If there is a long thermal path between the furnace windings and the control thermocouple, the windings will be superheated when the power is finally turned off and supercooled when the power is turned on again. By placing the controlling thermocouple very close to the windings the power cycle is shorter, and the spread between the maximum and minimum temperature of the windings is greatly reduced. The greater part of this fluctuation is smoothed out as the heat diffuses to the specimen inside the furnace so that the specimen temperature remains very constant. By surrounding the specimen with a block of material having high thermal conductivity and high heat capacity (for example, a heavy block of copper) and separating this block from the winding or other primary source of heat by thermal insulation, the temperature fluctuation may be further minimized. This system very effectively "filters" the fluctuations in temperature encountered at the windings, so that an almost completely constant temperature is obtained inside the block. The high heat capacity of the block serves to make the temperature uniform with respect to time, and its high thermal conductivity provides uniform temperature at different positions inside the block. Two separate thermocouples must be used, one for controlling temperature, and one for measuring the temperature of the specimen, the so-called control and measuring thermocouples. These are necessary because the temperature indicated by the control couple bears little relation to the temperature of the specimen, which finally is being controlled. What is actually done of course is to adjust the control setting for the control couple until the specimen is at the desired temperature. In general, the control temperature must be set 10 to 100°C higher than the desired specimen temperature.

Another method of anticipation is to place the control thermocouple in a small heater or furnace that has a much smaller heat capacity than the working furnace, and that is connected in parallel to the power supply of the working furnace. The principle of operation is identical with that of placing the thermocouple close to the furnace windings. Since the auxiliary heater has a small heat capacity, the temperature falls rapidly when the power is shut off, so that the thermocouple promptly calls for power. The temperature of the large working furnace does not change so rapidly; thus its temperature fluctuates over a narrower range of temperatures. The effects of thermocouple position on temperature of the specimen are summarized in Figure 11.

Anticipation may also be provided by a suitably connected pair of thermocouples of different thermal capacity and an electrical heating

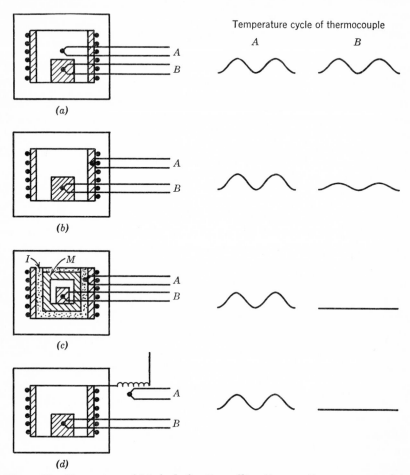

(a)

(b)

(c)

(d)

Figure 11. Comparison of Methods for Controlling Furnace Temperatures. A is the thermocouple used to control the furnace temperature, B is a thermocouple inserted in the specimen. Temperature swing in specimen is reduced by placing control thermocouple near windings (b), by shielding specimen with thermal insulation I, and a metal block M (c), or by placing control thermocouple in a series or parallel auxiliary furnace of small heat capacity (d).

element enclosed in an evacuated glass envelope [1] as illustrated in Figure 12. The heating element is energized by the same power supply that operates the working furnace; thus the furnace and the heating element operate together. The two thermocouples in the anticipator and the control thermocouple in the furnace are connected in series so that the emf of the thermocouple of less heat capacity is added to that of the control thermocouple, and that of the thermocouple of greater heat capacity is subtracted. With the furnace turned off, both the low heat capacity (1) and the high heat capacity (2) thermocouples are at room temperature. When the temperature is rising, thermocouple (1) is hotter than thermocouple (2) so that the net emf of the pair is added to that of the control couple proper, and the power to the furnace is turned off before the desired control temperature is reached, and overshooting is prevented. When the tem-

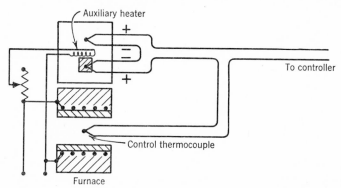

Figure 12. Thermocouple Anticipator for Reducing Temperature Fluctuation.

perature is falling, thermocouple (2) is warmer than thermocouple (1); the net emf of the pair is thus subtracted from that of the control couple, the power circuit is closed earlier than it otherwise would have been, and undershooting is prevented.

Several commercial devices that minimize temperature fluctuations in furnaces are available. One operates essentially like the instrument just described. Another operates in conjunction with a power interrupter or proportioner of the cyclic type. A controller with *H-C-L* contacts is used. The power proportioner is fitted with a drive so that the percentage of time that power is supplied to the furnace can be controlled by an electrical signal. While the furnace is below temperature the percentage of time that power is supplied is continuously increased until power is on all the time or the furnace reaches temperature. When the furnace goes above the desired control temperature, the power input is continuously decreased until eventually the control temperature is again reached. By a series of approximations of this type a setting is finally automatically reached where the power proportioner holds the furnace at the desired temperature without operation of the controller. Small changes in line voltage are then automatically compensated for by minor readjustments in the fractional time power is supplied to the furnace.

Proportioning Control

In proportional control an attempt is made to make the power supplied to the furnace proportional to the difference between the actual temperature and the desired control point. The intention is to supply the precisely correct power at the control point, only slightly more at temperatures just below the control point, and only slightly less at temperatures just above the control point.

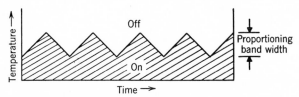

Figure 13. Operation of Proportioning Controller. As the furnace temperature increases, the fraction of time that the furnace is on decreases, until at a high enough temperature it is off all the time.

This may be done by interrupting the power with an input controller of some type. Usually the arrangement is to have the power on half the time and off half the time at the control temperature. If the temperature falls below the control value the power is then supplied somewhat more than half the time.

There are several things that can be varied in this kind of control: the frequency of the on-off cycle, the rate at which the on-off ratio changes with temperature, which controls the temperature range over which any proportioning at all is supplied. The frequency of the cycle must be matched to the heat capacity of the furnace; a small furnace requires a short cycle. If the on-off ratio changes only very slowly with temperature, overshooting or undershooting is indeed diminished, but a very stable power supply is needed to maintain a uniform temperature. If the line voltage decreases, the temperature will also decrease. If the proportioning range is reduced the temperature becomes less dependent on line voltage, but in the limit the method becomes identical with on-off or two-position control (Figure 13).

Program Controllers

It is frequently desired to program a furnace through a sequence of temperatures rather than hold it for long times at a uniform temperature. For example, it may be desired to heat a specimen slowly to one temperature, hold for a given time, heat to a second temperature, and then cool at a definite rate to room temperature. Programs such as these are readily carried out with so-called program controllers.

A simple programming controller can be devised in the laboratory quite readily by motorizing the control point setting knob of most of the standard temperature controllers with a variable speed drive. There are commercially available several instruments which use cams

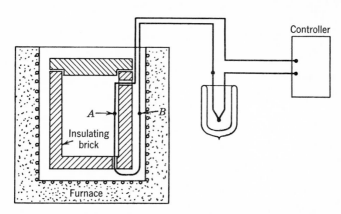

Figure 14. Device for Slowly Cooling or Heating Furnace. The differential thermocouple has one junction in contact with the specimen and one in contact with the furnace wall. The temperature controller keeps the temperature differential constant. The auxiliary thermocouple in an ice bath is used only if the temperature controller has an automatic cold junction compensator that cannot be removed. (After C. S. Smith.[2])

especially cut for any desired temperature program to adjust the position of the control point with time as desired. The only restriction is that the furnace should be able to follow the temperature changes as rapidly as the controller calls for them.

An ingenious method of slowly cooling a furnace in a controlled fashion has been described by C. S. Smith,[2] and is illustrated in Figure 14. It is particularly useful for obtaining cooling curves to detect transformations but also finds other applications. It is an arrangement where the temperature difference between the specimen and the furnace is maintained at a constant value with the aid of a differential thermocouple and an automatic temperature controller. The specimen is contained in a refractory container of low thermal conductivity such as insulating brick, and the whole assembly is placed in a furnace. A differential thermocouple is arranged to have one junction inside the container next to the specimen, and the other junction next to the furnace wall. The output from the differential thermocouple is fed to an automatic temperature controller that is set for the desired temperature difference between the specimen and the furnace walls. By suitably adjusting the polarity of the thermocouple, the controller will supply power to the furnace to keep its temperature at all times at the desired amount above or below the specimen temperature. The rate of heating or cooling the furnace is controlled by the thermal conductivity of the refractory block that isolates the specimen.

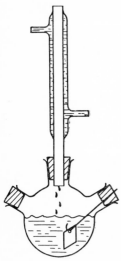

To be used in this way the temperature controller may not have automatic cold-junction compensation. However, if the controller to be used does have automatic cold-junction compensation it can be neutralized by inserting in the circuit an additional thermocouple of appropriate materials that has one junction at the ice point and the other junction at the temperature of the cold-junction compensator of the controller. The polarity should of course be adjusted so that when this compensating thermocouple alone is in the circuit the controller will indicate the temperature of melting ice.

Figure 15. Method of Heating Specimens at Accurately Controlled Low Temperatures for Long Times.

Other Methods of Temperature Control

It is possible to achieve very precise temperature control by immersing specimens in or above boiling liquids in an apparatus similar to that shown in Figure 15. Unfortunately there are relatively few liquids that have well-defined boiling points, are stable for long periods of time, and are cheap enough to be used in the quantities necessary. Water, carbon tetrachloride, several of the chlorinated solvents, benzene, and toluene are examples of liquids that may be useful.

REFERENCES

1. M. J. Manjoine, *Materials and Methods,* **22,** 459 (1945).
2. C. S. Smith, *Trans. Am. Inst. Mining Met. Engrs.,* **137,** 236 (1940).

CHAPTER FOUR

Refractories

Refractories may be defined broadly as non-metallic materials which stand very high temperatures without melting, excessive deformation, or compositional change. For present purposes certain materials, while strictly not refractories from a high temperature standpoint, are included since they are used in some applications like a refractory; Pyrex glass is an example. There are many requirements for refractory materials, but for the metallurgist the following are probably the most important: (1) ability to provide thermal insulation, (2) to act as a high temperature structural material, (3) to support the metallic windings of electric resistance furnaces, and (4) to act as a container for liquid metal.

In order to evaluate refractories in the light of the main requirements cited above, something about the following properties must be known:

1. Melting point.
2. Thermal conductivity.
3. Strength at elevated temperatures.
4. Thermal coefficient of expansion.
5. Resistance to thermal shock.
6. Chemical inertness to liquid metals and to surroundings.
7. Electrical conductivity at elevated temperatures.

Resistance to thermal shock is a derived quality, depending principally upon coefficient of thermal expansion, thermal conductivity, and upon mechanical strength, elastic modulus, and plasticity. Although strength at elevated temperatures is of prime interest in industrial uses where large, heavy structures are involved, it is not usually a significant factor in the metals laboratory. Because of the fundamental importance of melting point, coefficient of thermal expansion, thermal conductivity, and electrical resistivity in the use of refractories in the laboratory these properties are listed (where available) in Table 1 for most of the important refractories, together with

TABLE

SOME PROPERTIES AND PRINCIPAL APPLICATIONS OF

Refractory	Composition	Melting Point, °C	Coefficient of Thermal Expansion $\times 10^6$, °C	Thermal Conductivity, Cal/sec/cm/°C $\times 10^4$	Electrical Resistivity, ohms/cm^3
Alumina	Al_2O_3	2050 1900 *	6–9 (20–1000°C)	89.7 (425°C) 72.5 (540°C) 59.6 (980°C) 55.2 (1425°C)	3×10^{13} (at 300°C)
Beryllia	BeO	2530	8–9 (100–1000°C)	1910 (200°C) 1000 (600°C) 383 (1400°C)	8×10^{13} (1000°C) 3.5×10^{10} (1600°C)
Clay-graphite	$C + xSiO_2yAl_2O_3$	1600 *	....	....	....
Diatomaceous earth	85% SiO_2	1095	....	2.41 (95°C) 3.45 (650°C)	....
Fire clay (dense)	$xSiO_2yAl_2O_3$	1600 *	7 (980°C)	34.5 (980°C)	10.8×10^3 (1000°C) 50.0×10^3 (1000°C)
Graphite	C	3500	1.8 (RT) 2.5 (1000°C)	1650 (800°C) 2480 (400°C) 4000 (32°C)	8×10^{-4} to 13×10^{-4} (20°C)
Lime	CaO	2570	....	....	....
Magnesia	MgO	2800	11–15 (100–1000°C)	124 (20°C) 82.7 (540°C) 75 (980°C) 58.6 (1430°C)	9×10^{12} (1000°C) 7×10^9 (1600°C)
Mycalex	Glass + mica	350 *	8 (20–350°C)	13.8	2 to 12 $\times 10^{13}$
Porcelain (mullite)	$3Al_2O_3 \cdot 2SiO_2$	1850 1780 *	6.2 (980°C) 5.3 (20–1430°C)	34.5 (980°C)	20×10^3 (1000°C)

* Maximum useful temperature.

1

CERAMIC MATERIALS IN THE METALS LABORATORY

Principal Applications in the Laboratory	Commercial Shapes	Crucibles Recommended for Melting	Trade Names, Manufacturers
Building electric resistance furnace cores, melting metals	Tubes, bricks, crucibles, rods, plates, etc.	Al, Sb, Bi, Cd, Co, Cu, Ga, Au, In, Fe, Pb, Ni, Pd, Pt, Ag, Tl, Sn, Zn	1. "Alundum," Norton Co., Worcester, Mass. 2. Carborundum Co., Niagara Falls, N. Y. 3. "Triangle RR," Morganite Inc., Long Island City, N. Y.
Melting metals	Crucibles, powder, bricks, all shapes made to order	Be	1. Brush Beryllium Co., Cleveland, Ohio 2. Clifton Products, Inc., Paynesville, Ohio 3. Beryllium Corp. of America, Reading, Pa.
Melting metals	Crucibles	Al, Sb, Bi, Cd, Cu, Ga, Au, In, Pb, Tl, Ag, Sn, Zn, Ge	1. Joseph Dixon, Jersey City, N. J. 2. American Crucible Co., North Haven, Conn.
Insulation in furnaces	Powder, brick	Not used as a crucible	"Sil-O-Cel" C-3, "Sil-O-Cel," Johns Manville, New York, N. Y.
Miscellaneous	Brick, crucibles, furnace parts	Not recommended for retaining high purity in melting	1. Babcock and Wilcox, New York, N. Y. 2. General Refractories Co., Philadelphia, Pa. 3. Harbison-Walker Refractories, Pittsburgh, Pa.
Crucibles, molds, special machined shapes	Rods, tubes, blocks	Same metals indicated for clay-graphite	1. "Acheson" Graphite, National Carbon Co., New York 2. Stackpole Carbon Co., St. Marys, Pa. 3. Great Lakes Carbon Co., Niagara Falls, N. Y.
Melting metals	None	Has no obvious advantage over MgO. Could be used for melting metals. Was used with torch for platinum melting.	New England Lime Co., Adams, Mass.
Crucibles, powder for backing crucibles and for high-temperature insulation	Crucibles, brick, others	Metals indicated for Al_2O_3 plus Mn, and rare earths	1. The Norton Co., Worcester, Mass, 2. General Electric Co., Pittsfield, Mass. 3. Lava Crucible Co., Pittsburgh, Pa. 4. Westvaco Chemical Division, Food Machinery and Chemicals Corp., New York, N. Y.
Electrical insulation at mildly elevated temperatures (see Steatite)	Plates, rod, molded shapes	Not used for crucibles	1. "Mycalex," Mycalex Corp. of America, 64 Clifton Blvd., Clifton, N. J. 2. For molded parts—GE Chemical Dept., Taunton, Mass.
Tubes for vacuum or controlled atmosphere work	Tubes, bricks, furnace parts	Not ordinarily available as crucibles. May be made in place using mullite cement.	1. Coors Porcelain Co., Golden, Colo. 2. "Shamwa" mullite, Mullite Refractories Co., Shelton, Conn.

TABLE

Some Properties and Principal Applications of

Refractory	Composition	Melting Point, °C	Coefficient of Thermal Expansion $\times 10^6$, °C	Thermal Conductivity, Cal/sec/cm/°C $\times 10^4$	Electrical Resistivity, ohms/cm^3
Pyrex glass	80% SiO_2 12% B_2O_3 3% Al_2O_3 4% Na_2O	500 *	3.0 (20–300°C)	28.2 (200°C)	10^{14} at RT
Silica	SiO_2 (fused quartz)	1715 1100 *	0.40–0.48 60–1000°C	45.5 (100°C) 45.8 (1300°C)	45×10^{12} (25°C) 20×10^6 (800°C)
Silicon carbide	SiC	2700 1650 *	4.3 (980°C)	362 (650°C) 372 (980°C) 380 (1540°C)	4.1 (1000°C)
Steatite	Magnesium-silicate, $Mg_3Si_4O_{10}(OH)_2$, plus alkali earth carbonates (before firing)	1400–1600 † 1000–1200 *	7–10 (most grades) 25–700°C	50	7×10^3 to 2×10^7 (at 900°C) (10^{14} at RT)
Tercod	C + SiC	1650 *	2.7	345	9.1×10^{-3} (815°C) 7.6×10^{-3} (1205°C) 6.6×10^{-3} (1480°C)
Transite	Asbestos plus portland cement	370 *	....	....	Not considered an electrical insulator
Thoria	ThO_2	3050	8–9 (100–1000°C)	228 (150°C) 121 (400°C)	4×10^{13} (20°C) 1.2×10^{12} (500°C)
Vycor	96% SiO_2 3% B_2O_3	1500 † 900 *	0.75 (0–300°C)	Similar to fused SiO_2	
Zircon	$ZrSiO_4$	2550	4.2 (20–1550°C)	46.6 (200–1000°C)	....
Zirconia	ZrO_2	2700 2400 *	6 (at 980°C) 7 (at 1430°C) (Stabilized ZrO_2)	20.6 (1300°C)	1.2×10^3 (1200°C) 300 (1400°C) 968 (1400°C)

* Maximum useful temperature.
† Softening temperature.

1 *(Continued)*

CERAMIC MATERIALS IN THE METALS LABORATORY

Principal Applications in the Laboratory	Commercial Shapes	Crucibles Recommended for Melting	Trade Names, Manufacturers
Too numerous to mention. Can be used as crucible for low melting metals.	All shapes	Ba, Cd, In, Pb, Sn, Zn, Cs	"Pyrex," Corning Glass Co., Corning, N. Y.
Tubes for vacuum or controlled atmosphere work	Tubes, rods, plates, special shapes	Si	1. "Vitreosil," Thermal Syndicate, New York, N. Y. 2. "Amersil," Amersil Co., Hillside, N. J.
Furnace parts, hearths	Muffles, brick	Not ordinarily used for crucibles (*see* Tercod)	1. "Crystalon," Norton Co., Worcester, Mass. 2. "Carbofrax," Carborundum Co., Niagara Falls, N. Y.
Vacuum-tube insulators, electronic parts of low dielectric loss, machinable refractory for applications up to about 1000°C	Rods, blocks, machined parts	Not recommended for melting	"Alsimag," "Lava," American Lava Corp., Chattanooga, Tenn.
Melting non-ferrous metals	Principally crucibles	Same metals indicated for clay-graphite	"Tercod" Electro Refractories and Alloys Corp., Buffalo, N. Y.
Furnace shells	Plates, pipe	Not used for crucibles	"Transite," Johns Manville, New York, N. Y.
Melting metals	None	Ir, Pt, Rh	Lindsay Light and Chemical Co., West Chicago, Ill.
Furnace tubes for vacuum or controlled atmosphere work	Tubes, special shapes	Not recommended for melting	"Vycor," Corning Glass Works, Corning, N. Y.
Melting metals, tubes for vacuum or controlled atmosphere work	Crucibles, brick, furnace parts	Al, Co, Cu, Fe, Ni, Pd, Pt	1. Titanium Alloy Mfg. Div., National Lead Co., Niagara Falls, N. Y. 2. Zircofrax (Zircon-clay porcelain), Carborundum Co., Niagara Falls, N. Y.
Melting high-melting metals	Crucibles, insulating powder, tubes	Cr, Co, Au, Ir, Fe, Ni, Pd, Pt, Rh	1. The Norton Co., Worcester, Mass. 2. Titanium Alloy Mfg. Div., National Lead Co., Niagara Falls, N. Y.

some remarks about their major application and sources of supply. It will be noted that the melting point for essentially pure substances is given, but when a substance tends to break down before melting, a value is given for maximum useful temperature. The maximum useful temperature is indicated, where information is available, on more stable substances as well; naturally, a refractory may not be used right up to the melting point.

CLASSIFICATIONS OF REFRACTORIES ACCORDING TO USE IN THE LABORATORY

Containers

The most difficult refractory problem for the research metallurgist is finding a crucible which is inert to the metal being melted. Probably no crucible is ever completely inert, but the usual criterion for acceptance or rejection is whether or not any important change in the properties of the metal results from crucible contamination. Crucible contamination ranges from cases where no detectable change in properties result from melting, to drastic alteration of the metal properties accompanied by destruction of the crucible. Table 1 lists metals which are recommended for melting in the various refractories.

It is realized that considerable difference of opinion may exist on this subject. The authors have not listed every metal in the periodic table; some, like sodium, are best melted in metallic containers. In general, with the exception of the alkali and alkaline earth metals, the lower melting metals such as tin, indium, gallium, zinc, and lead may be melted in practically any refractory without difficulty. It is in regard to the higher melting metals (above about 1000°C) that some thought must be given to the possibilities of crucible-melt reaction. Carbonaceous crucibles, such as clay-graphite, graphite, and Tercod,[1] should obviously not be used with metals which form carbides. Although fused silica would be perfectly satisfactory as a crucible for most of the low-melting metals, it is rarely used chiefly because cheaper crucibles are available which are as good or, in some respects, better. The same considerations apply to fire clay, mullite, silicon carbide, steatite, and vycor.

Refractories as Materials of Construction

A second class of refractory use in the metals laboratory is a high-temperature construction material such as furnace tubes and muffles where they form the heating chamber, support for metallic windings, crucible supports, and a wide variety of similar things. In such applications, the main properties of importance are high melting point, good thermal conductivity, inertness to neighboring parts, ability to be fabricated into complex shapes, and good strength at elevated temperatures.

Thermal Insulation

Insulating materials are of considerable importance in building furnaces to avoid excessive heat loss, and hence power consumption, and to make possible maximum temperatures with a given furnace geometry. Bricks or loose powder are the most common forms of insulating refractory materials, and both have their uses, as will be described later.

Refractory Cements

Cements are used to fasten metallic windings to refractory tubes (furnace cores), to cement bricks and other parts together, to form monolithic (one-piece) linings in furnaces, to line the inside of crucibles, and for other uses too numerous to list. Most refractory cements are used with a little water to yield a pasty material, which then may be trowled or rammed in place. After air drying, they become more or less hard, but they generally do not really set or become fully hard until fired to a high temperature.

In subsequent pages, the problems associated with all four uses outlined above will be explored in detail.

PROPERTIES AND APPLICATIONS OF VARIOUS REFRACTORY SUBSTANCES

As mentioned above, Table 1 lists the most important properties of the refractories of main importance in the metals laboratory. However, the table is somewhat too terse a summary for a proper understanding of the applications of the various products listed; hence in the following section each substance is discussed in some detail.

Besides the common refractories listed in Table 1, some non-oxide materials are briefly discussed and also the use of metals as refractories.

Common Refractories

Alumina has the widest application of any refractory in the metals laboratory because of its availability in high purity, high melting point, low reactivity, fair thermal shock resistance, and very low electrical conductivity at high temperatures. It is this last property, coupled with some of the others mentioned, that makes it an almost universal material for the construction of furnace tubes and muffles upon which metallic, electrical resistors are wound. It is available [2,3,4] in a very wide variety of forms, including crucibles, tubes, rods, plates, muffles, and powder. Since it is not so resistant to basic metal oxides, like iron oxide, as magnesia, its use as a crucible for melting metals of the iron group has usually been rather unsatisfactory, particularly in air melting or where oxides of these metals are present. However, in recent years a very highly fused, high-purity alumina crucible has been available [4] which is much less susceptible to reaction with metal oxides than lower-fired, less pure crucibles. These newer crucibles have the appearance and translucent character of porcelain, and appear to offer a solution to the problem of melting moderately reactive materials without appreciably changing their composition.

Beryllia, with its very high melting point, good thermal shock resistance, extraordinarily high thermal conductivity, and high degree of chemical inertness, would be an extremely valuable refractory material were it not for its high cost due to the scarcity of beryllium, and its toxicity. It has been widely recognized since about 1945 that beryllium and its compounds are extremely toxic, many people having contracted beryllium disease and later died from breathing in only fantastically minute quantities. These facts are quite widely known today, but will bear repeating here. Beryllium and its compounds should not be handled without proper protective masks and ventilation. Which beryllium compounds and what forms of them are most toxic is a subject being assiduously studied. There is some evidence that the high-fired or ceramic grade of BeO, particularly in coarser particle sizes, is not as dangerous as the calcined or light and fluffy form. However, BeO may be used safely if great care in ventilation is taken so that traces of BeO in the air breathed is eliminated. Beryllium oxide crucibles and BeO powder are available from beryllium producers.[5] The elimination of BeO as a crucible material for the reasons cited above should work no hardship on those concerned with melting metals because it apparently has no unique application except in melting beryllium metal.

Clay-graphite is widely used as a crucible material in melting nonferrous metals. It is available [6] in an extremely wide range of crucible sizes and shapes. Clay-graphite, as the name indicates, is a combination of these two materials in which the graphite is bonded together by a network of clay. It couples the high thermal conductivity of graphite with the toughness and the strength of clay. Because of its duplex nature, it does not oxidize as rapidly in air as pure graphite nor is it as subject to thermal shock as pure fire clay; hence it is popular as an extremely useful crucible for melting a wide variety of metals which do not readily pick up carbon. It is possible to line the inside of the crucible with a magnesia cement, for example, and use the lined crucible for melting metals which readily form carbides or dissolve carbon, such as iron or nickel.

Diatomaceous earth, Sil-O-Cel or kieselgur, is a siliceous, cellular, granulated product used only for heat-insulation purposes. It is obtainable as a rather coarse, lightweight powder [7] and is mainly used in the laboratory for insulating furnaces or ovens. Its use at temperatures above 1100°C is not recommended. Some grades should not be used at temperatures above 850°C. At higher temperatures, its shrinkage is excessive and it will tend to react with the alumina furnace tube or muffle. However, for moderate temperatures, it is probably the most satisfactory heat-insulation material of the powder type and is the most commonly used insulating powder for lagging Nichrome (80 Ni–20 Cr type) laboratory tube furnaces. Because of its moisture content and closed cell structure, it should not be used inside a vacuum chamber because it is difficult to degas.

Fire-clay crucibles are not used very much today although they were once commonly used for non-ferrous melting. Because of their low cost they are still used in such operations as fire-assaying, where high purity and chemical inertness are of no particular importance. Clay-graphite, with its superior resistance to thermal shock and greater inertness, has largely replaced it. Fire clay is not very stable and may introduce impurities into high-purity melts; furthermore, it is not as refractory as alumina or magnesia and is limited to temperatures of the order of 1600°C or lower, depending upon the particular quality of fire clay obtained.

Graphite is an extraordinarily useful laboratory material because of its chemical inertness (except to oxygen at high temperatures), high melting point, electrical conductivity, high thermal conductivity, fair strength, which is unaffected by high temperature, and machinability.

Many refractories partake of some of these qualities and many exceed graphite in one or two of them, but none has the same high thermal and electrical conductivity or, above all, the quality of machinability. It is hard to overemphasize the importance of having a material available from which a crucible or tube, for example, may be machined to exact size in a matter of a few hours with standard machine tools. Its electrical conductivity makes possible its use as a heating element in high-temperature furnaces (see Chapter 1) or as an electrode in electrowinning processes such as the reduction of aluminum. It is also one of the few materials feasible for use as a die material for hot-pressing metal or carbide powders at very high temperatures (Chapter 9).

As a crucible, it suffers the disadvantage of wasting away rather rapidly in air at high temperatures because of oxidation, but it is often possible to protect the crucible and charge by melting in an inert atmosphere or by vacuum melting. Naturally, it cannot be used in melting metals which form carbides, but in melting metals like aluminum or copper it has the advantage that impurity pick-up from the crucible is at a minimum; and, since non-carbide-forming metals do not wet graphite, the crucible "pours clean." A graphite crucible may be used in instances where the carbide formed has limited solubility in the metal because there is no satisfactory alternative crucible.

Graphite is commercially available in rods about one-quarter inch up to about 30 inches in diameter, and as rectangular blocks; the graphite producers will supply other shapes such as crucibles and tubes, etc. Ordinarily it is preferable to keep a modest stock of rounds on hand and use them to machine special shapes as occasion arises, unless the facilities for graphite machining are not available, or very large shapes are required. If shapes must be very large, machining large crucibles from solid bar stock might result in excessive waste. Most machine shops dislike doing graphite machining because it is very dirty work. Graphite dust tends to get into the moving parts of machine tools and to cause excessive wear, and it may also cause trouble in electrical equipment such as electric motors. For most graphite machining jobs it is advisable to bring a large vacuum cleaner to the machine and mount the suction tube near the tool post to remove most of the dust at the point of origin.

Since graphite has a very low coefficient of expansion and high thermal conductivity, it may be heated and cooled as rapidly as desired without fear of its cracking. This property makes possible its use as a mold for casting metals, and it is much used for this purpose.

For general work where a moderately fine-grained and fairly dense graphite is desired as in crucibles, molds, and high-temperature dies, the so-called CS grade of one manufacturer [8] has been found satisfactory. This grade is available in rounds, the most generally useful form. For work requiring a more dense, extremely fine-grained grade of graphite, C–18 [8] is recommended, but this is available only in rectangular blocks about a foot square by 3 inches thick. It should be borne in mind that in any of the round grades of graphite, such as AGR, AGX, or CS, the larger the diameter, the coarser the structure, and the weaker the material.

For high-temperature insulation of graphite, as in Arsem furnaces or in induction heating of graphite in the air at temperatures much above 1000°C, carbon black powder is by far the best insulation material. It not only has a high insulation value, but it also protects the graphite from oxidizing. A satisfactory grade of carbon black, called "Norblack," is available from one of the suppliers of induction heating equipment.[9]

Lime (CaO) is rarely used as a refractory because it is not stable in the air at ordinary temperatures. However, it is possible that for melting some highly reactive metals it might find limited application. By working with dry CaO in limited batches, so as to expose as little of the material as possible to the water and CO_2 in the atmosphere, it is quite feasible to dry-press crucibles of CaO and then fire them to a high density in air at temperatures close to 2000°C. After being cooled to room temperature, lime crucibles should be stored in cans with tight covers which have been flushed out with a dry inert gas, such as nitrogen or argon. In this way lime crucibles may be kept indefinitely until ready for use. There are no lime crucibles or other refractory parts available commercially; one must make them himself.

Magnesia (MgO) is one of the most useful refractories for metals research because of its high melting point, chemical stability, cheapness, and availability. Unfortunately, it is not readily available in the form of crucibles of high purity. There are many manufacturers [2,10,11] who supply magnesia crucibles, but they usually contain rather large quantities of "binders" such as fire clay or silica. Often these crucibles instead of being pure white are nearly a milk-chocolate brown. Fortunately, it is not difficult to make crucibles in the laboratory if a small hydraulic press or universal tensile testing machine and a high-frequency furnace are available (see below).

Magnesia powder of high quality is readily available from several suppliers.[2,12,13] Besides using magnesia powder for making crucibles or other ceramic shapes, it has been customary in many laboratories to use a rather impure and hence cheap grade of magnesia as a thermal insulation material for high-frequency melting. Magnesia crucibles are particularly useful in melting iron or steel because their basic character resists the slagging effect of FeO. They are equally suitable for nickel or cobalt or their alloys. Because of its poor thermal shock characteristics, MgO cracks rather readily with the rapid heating or cooling rates characteristic of induction heating. However, if the crucible is surrounded by a tightly packed layer of refractory powder, such cracks that form cause no serious harm as long as the crucible remains in place. The melt cannot penetrate very deeply into a crack because it soon reaches a zone below the melting point because of the steep temperature gradient. Surface tension prevents metal from leaking out through fine cracks.

Mycalex [14] consists of mica particles bonded by a low-melting glass. It is a unique material in the electrical field as it has a very high dielectric strength, low power loss characteristic, stands moderate temperatures up to 350°C, is moldable (like a plastic), machinable, and is available in large plates up to several feet square. One prominent use is in vacuum technology for bringing power leads through a port or opening in a vacuum tank. Because of its glass-like nature, it has no appreciable vapor pressure, and since it is an excellent electrical insulator it is ideal for such purposes. Unlike steatite, however, its use is limited to relatively low temperatures.

Porcelain as used in the metals laboratory is generally a high-quality chemical porcelain of the *mullite* type; it is chemically $Si_2Al_6O_{13}$ or $3Al_2O_3 \cdot 2SiO_2$. However, as manufactured, mullite ware contains excess clay to bring the firing (vitrification) temperature down to a commercial range. Porcelains of this type are gastight and are largely used as furnace tubes through which various gas atmospheres may be passed, or which may be evacuated while being heated. With gases in the tube at essentially atmospheric pressure, such tubes may be used at temperatures close to 1600°C; evacuated, they can stand about 1400°C without collapsing. Zircon porcelains are also available, but the properties of these are in general similar to pure zircon listed in Table 1. Some commercial "combustion" tubes, as the tubes of this type are usually called, are labeled "sillimanite" or "sillimanite (mullite)" presumably indicating that the mullite-type body was made from the mineral sillimanite rather than being a synthetic mixture of Al_2O_3 and SiO_2. Sillimanite, Andalusite and Kyanite are all minerals of the same composition ($Al_2O_3 \cdot SiO_2$) but of various crystal structures.[15] When any of these minerals are heated to the neighborhood of 1000°C, they break down into mullite and excess silica. Small crucibles and boats mainly suited to chemical analytical work are also available. Although larger crucibles more suited to melting metals could be made from mullite porcelain, this is not customary, probably for a variety of reasons. Like most complex refractories (as contrasted with pure oxides) porcelain has a tendency to be somewhat unstable chemically toward metals. In addition, porcelain is not very resistant to thermal shock, is rather expensive, and has no advantage over alumina or magnesia.

Mullite is also available as a heavy refractory in brick or special shapes, suitable for lining large furnaces and building up furnace walls. Its good strength just below the melting point, rather low thermal conductivity, and high abrasion resistance, coupled with high melting point (above ordinary fire clay), makes it an excellent all-round material for general furnace work. Mullite cements are in common use (see below).

Pyrex glass [16] requires no description here because it is such a familiar material. It is perhaps enough to say that Pyrex may be used as a crucible up to about 500°C for melting small amounts of low-melting metals. However, unless all the Pyrex container is uniformly heated to the melt temperature, the glass is likely to crack if hot metal is poured over a comparatively cold lip at the top of the crucible. It is feasible to make low-temperature ovens by winding resistance alloy wire over a layer of asbestos paper wrapped around a Pyrex tube.

Silica as a pure substance is generally used in the laboratory in the form of fused quartz or, more properly, fused silica. Vycor,[16] essentially fused silica, is discussed later. Before the utility of fused silica is described, a few comments should be made on granular silica crucibles, sometimes called sand crucibles. They are entirely similar in nature to the silica brick refractory used so extensively in the roofs of open-hearth steel-melting furnaces. Such silica or sand crucibles are subject to two drawbacks which are serious enough virtually to eliminate them as serious contenders for an important place in the metals laboratory. One is the polymorphic transformations at 573 and 870°C, where low quartz passes to high quartz and then to tridymite, respectively. These transformations are accompanied by substantial volume changes which tend to crack the crucible on heating or cooling. The second drawback is that silica is not particularly stable, and is subject to partial reduction by many metals. It also tends to react with various metal oxides because of the acid nature of SiO_2 and the generally basic nature of metal oxides. One laboratory with which the authors are acquainted avoided the crucible-reaction problem by lining silica crucibles with magnesia cement. The main advantages in this procedure were the low cost of the silica crucibles and the ease with which the coating of cement was applied as compared to fabricating a pure magnesia crucible. This technique, although apparently successful with small crucibles, might prove to be unsatisfactory if used with crucibles several inches in diameter.

Fused silica should not be used at temperatures higher than 1100°C, and then only for short periods of time. It is better to limit the temperature to 1000°C. Long exposure even at 1000°C results in devitrification caused by transformation of the amorphous silica to the crystalline crystobalite, with an accompanying volume change. This change to a crystalline form of quartz results in a chalky structure which is very weak and porous.

The prime advantages of fused silica are:

1. Gas-tight.
2. Mechanically strong.
3. Chemically resistant, particularly to most aqueous solutions and gases.
4. Extraordinarily low coefficient of expansion.
5. Electrically insulating.
6. Withstands heating to 1000°C.
7. Transparent (only in small sizes in certain grades).

Because of its low coefficient of expansion there is no thermal shock problem with fused silica; it can be heated or cooled at practically any desired rate without cracking. Fused silica may be divided into two categories, opaque and transparent.

The opaque grade is available in much larger sizes than the transparent and is many times less expensive. In most applications both grades are used in the form of tubing or pipe. The opaque form is available in two grades, sand-surface and satin-finish. The latter is available in smaller sizes up to perhaps 2 inches in diameter, whereas the sand-surface tubes or pipes are available up to about 30 inches in diameter. The satin-surface tubing is dimensionally better controlled, whereas the wall thickness and eccentricity of the sand-surface material may vary by ⅛ to ⅜ inch, depending upon size. There are three major suppliers [17,18,19] of fused-silica tubes, but not all of them make all sizes and grades.

The properties of the transparent fused silica (fused quartz) are identical with those of the opaque grades except for the property of transparency. The transparent property is due to careful selection of raw materials; high-grade quartz-crystal pieces, melted down, are used instead of a fairly pure silica sand. In addition, care is taken to exclude most of the bubbles, since much of the opacity of the other grades of fused silica is caused by very many small air bubbles throughout the wall. The transparent silica is quite thin in wall compared to the opaque, and may be sealed to glass through a graded seal; such a procedure is not feasible with the thick-walled fused silica. In general, the only reason for using the thin-walled transparent quartz is for reasons of visibility and because it is better for all glass-blowing operations.

Fused silica is available in several standard shapes, including plates, rectangular boxes, tubes closed at one end, crucibles, rods, and beakers.

Its use in crucibles is more or less limited to a few specialized operations in the chemical laboratory. It is not attractive as a metal-melting crucible because of the devitrification tendency, and because of the reactivity mentioned above.

For a complete treatise on the subject of silica, the reader is referred to the standard work by Sosman.[20]

Silicon carbide (SiC) is a refractory material better known as Carbofrax [3] or Crystolon [2] when used as a refractory. In these products clay is used as a binder to hold the particles of silicon carbide together in a manner entirely analogous to its use in clay-graphite. Because of the semi-metallic nature of silicon carbide, such refractories have a much higher thermal conductivity than most refractories. The main application of the refractory grades of silicon carbide is in muffles of electric or gas furnaces, where high heat transfer to the work within the chamber or muffle is important. This refractory material is also available in brick form, which, together with a special cement, allows the construction of large furnace walls at the site where the furnace is to be used. Silicon-carbide products are usually glazed to prevent oxidation in service. These glazes vary in their composition and refractoriness, so that care must be exercised in selecting the proper grade.

Steatite is a generic name for high-talc (magnesium-silicate) bodies used largely in the electrical industry for high-temperature electrical insulators and dielectric materials. Steatites may be either natural or synthetic, and in the latter type aluminum usually replaces part of the magnesium. Such bodies are made by firing mixtures of alumina, talc, and clay to a temperature of about 1400°C. Talc is essentially $Mg_3Si_4O_{10}(OH)_2$, but the natural varieties usually contain some alkaline earth carbonates as well. Many grades of steatite are more or less machinable until fired to a temperature of around 1000°C, where the water is driven off and the body becomes quite strong, hard, unmachinable, and simultaneously of higher insulating or dielectric power. Steatite, some grades of which (the natural product) are trade-named Lava,[21] is available in the form of blocks, rounds, or as machined shapes. At least one grade of steatite is available in an as-fired but machinable condition.

These materials find application in the metals laboratory as insulating sleeves in furnaces through which electric leads are passed, and generally as parts in electrical equipment subject to elevated temperatures up to about 1000°C.

A graphite-bonded silicon carbide known as *Tercod* [1] is a competitor of clay-graphite crucibles and has similar properties. Tercod crucibles, since they have no clay binder, are to be preferred to clay-graphite in a few special cases where reactive flux melt covers such as borax are necessary, as in some degassing treatments. One other manufacturer,[6] at least, makes graphite-bonded silicon carbide shapes including crucibles, but does not call them by this name. Although Tercod is used mainly in the form of crucibles, it is also available in the form of blocks, tubes, and special shapes.

Transite,[7] a trade name of one of the large refractory companies, consists of asbestos bonded with portland cement. Although this material, like many discussed here, is not a true refractory because it cannot be heated to a high temperature without decomposing, it is nevertheless used as a construction material at elevated temperatures. Its primary use in the laboratory is as furnace shells where the temperature does not rise much above 370°C; prolonged use at higher temperatures results in deterioration. Transite is available in the form of pipe 2 to 3 inches to about 3 feet in diameter. Pipe 1 or 2 feet in diameter is particularly convenient for constructing a laboratory tube furnace. It is also available as sheets in thicknesses up to 2 inches. Thin sheets of transite are often used to cover laboratory benches because of its chemical resistance and resistance to heat. A few of the commercial shapes available are given in Table 2. For a complete list of shapes, the manufacturer should be consulted. Transite is readily machinable but is rather abrasive.

TABLE 2

A FEW OF THE SIZES AND SHAPES IN WHICH TRANSITE MAY BE OBTAINED

Shape	Inside Diameter	Thickness	Length	Width	Weight/Foot
Cylinders (flue pipe)	3 to 12 in.	Varies with diameter, 0.4 in. (for 10 in. I.D.)	5 to 6½ ft.	. . . . .	13.4 lb (for 10 in. I.D.)
Cylinders (vent pipe)	3 to 36 in.	Varies with diameter, 0.4 in. (for 10 in. I.D.)	10 to 13 ft.	. . . . .	13.9 lb (for 10 in. I.D.)
Cylinders (Korduct)	2 to 6 in.	0.25 to 0.3 in.	5 to 10 ft.	. . . . .	4.8 lb (for 6 in. I.D.)
Cylinders (sewer pipe, class 1)	4 to 36 in.	0.5 in. (for 10 in. I.D.)	13 ft.	. . . . .	15.3 lb (for 10 in. I.D.)
Sheets	. . . . .	0 25 to 2.0 in.	48 in. 48 in. 96 in.	36 in. 42 in. 48 in.	. . . . .

Thoria has the highest melting point of the oxides (3050°C), is available commercially,[22] and has been used to make ThO_2 crucibles (see references 23–26 for methods). It offers little advantage over more common refractories, such as zirconia, since resistance to attack by the melt is as important as high melting point. Because it is expensive and radioactive, it is little used as a crucible material. Also its high density (9.69 grams per cc) makes it very expensive to use, since its cost per pound is quite high.

Similar in most respects to fused silica, *Vycor* [16] is 96% SiO_2 and is made by preparing a special high-silica, two-phase glass, in which the second phase is a borate glass. After the articles to be made are formed, such as a tube, the borate phase is leached out by acid, leaving a porous network of amorphous silica. By heating the shape to a high temperature, the silica sinters together, thus closing up the pores and making a gastight, transparent body resembling glass in appearance. Since Vycor consists almost entirely of fused silica except for a little B_2O_3 and a few minor impurities, its properties closely resemble those of quartz, but it is available in much larger sizes than transparent fused silica. Its cost is very much less than transparent fused quartz, and it is obtainable in diameters up to about 6 inches O.D.

Its principal uses are for vacuum-furnace chambers, and for enclosures for gas-metal reactions, beakers for high-temperature service, etc. Like fused silica, it should not be heated very hot because it is subject to devitrification; the manufacturer recommends a maximum temperature of 900°C.

Among refractory materials which should probably be more widely used as a crucible material because of its excellent combination of properties is *zircon* ($ZrSiO_4$). Zircon is characterized by very high melting point, low coefficient of thermal expansion, and moderate cost. Its low coefficient of expansion leads to excellent thermal shock resistance, which makes it particularly attractive for use in high-frequency melting where rapid heating and cooling rates are the rule. There may be some question about its use where extreme purity in a melt is required because it appears to be slightly subject to reduction by some metals. Zircon shows some dissociation into its components (ZrO_2 and SiO_2) at temperatures above 1400 to 1500°C. The SiO_2 volatilizes, so it may be a source of contamination. Crucibles of zircon are commercially available [27] in a wide variety of sizes.

"Combustion" tubes of "zircon" are also available, but these are zircon porcelain, which consists of zircon plus clay. The addition of clay allows vitrification during moderate firing, and hence makes possible the production of gastight tubes competitive with the mullite porcelain tubes referred to above. Zircon is available from the same supplier [27] in the form of bricks, rods, and other shapes.

Rather recently *zirconia* has become available commercially in the form of crucibles, tubes, and rods. Like zircon, its major application in the laboratory is in the form of crucibles and in addition as an insulating powder of very low thermal conductivity suitable for use at very high temperatures. Zirconia presents more of a problem to the fabricator than zircon because of the inversion at 1000°C, when it passes from a monoclinic form at low temperatures to the tetragonal form at higher temperatures. Fortunately, in the presence of a small amount of clay, CaO or MgO, as well as various other oxides, a cubic form of zirconia is obtained at 1700°C, which does not transform on cooling. Hence, these additions, singly or in combination, stabilize the zirconia so that the large volume change which accompanies the normal inversion at 1000°C is largely reduced. Completely stabilized zirconia has a high coefficient of thermal expansion so that best results in use are obtained with partially stabilized material. For certain applications zirconia is preferred over zircon because of its greater chemical stability and higher melting point. Although its melting point is not as high as the melting point of magnesia, it is preferable in high-temperature vacuum melting because of the tendency of magnesia to volatilize at 1600°C and higher. Zirconia is probably the most generally useful refractory for extreme temperature service in the laboratory, but it cannot be used as a core for electric resistance windings because of its large electrical conductivity at high temperatures (see Table 1). In fact, its electrical conductivity at very high temperatures is so great that electric resistance tube furnaces have been built and successfully operated using zirconia tubes as the heating element, in a manner exactly analogous to a carbon resistance or a Globar [3] furnace. Auxillary heaters are required to bring the temperature up to a point where zirconia begins to conduct. The advantage of such a furnace is the ability to secure very high temperatures in an oxidizing atmosphere. Zirconia shapes are available from at least two companies. [2, 27]

An insulating grade of zirconia powder is available [28] which may be used up to about 2400°C, and it gives very good service for insulation in vacuum as it is readily degassed.

New Low-Thermal Expansion Materials

There are three relatively new low-thermal expansion ceramic materials: cordierite, beta spodumene, and aluminum titanate. Cordierite is composed of SiO_2, Al_2O_3, and MgO in various ratios, one of which is commercially available [21] as $2Al_2O_3 \cdot 2MgO \cdot 5SiO_2$. Beta spodumene [11] is $Li_2O \cdot Al_2O_3 \cdot 4SiO_2$, and aluminum titanate is $Al_2O_3 \cdot TiO_2$. The last-named composition may be used up to 1500°C; the other two are limited to 1200°C. Besides low coefficient of expansion (it can be close to zero or even negative) some of these have unusual electrical properties which will not be described here. These substances are too new to be accurately evaluated as general ceramic materials for the laboratory, but the very low coefficient of thermal expansion suggests that they should eventually find wide application for moderately high temperature use where thermal shock resistance is important, as in thermocouple protection tubes.

Non-conventional Refractories

The refractories discussed above constitute the majority of refractory materials in ordinary use in the metals laboratory. However, there are other high-melting compounds about which, in general, comparatively little is known, although many such compounds have been somewhat investigated in recent years. Such materials are the very stable carbides, nitrides, sulphides, borides, silicides, and phosphides, which have melting points in excess of 2000°C and constitute a relatively new field in the technology of high-temperature materials. Table 3 lists a few of these compounds, with their melting points.

TABLE 3

MELTING POINTS OF SOME REFRACTORY COMPOUNDS [15]

Carbides

Boron carbide	B_4C	2350°C
Molybdenum carbide	Mo_2C	2380
Silicon carbide	SiC	2700
Tantalum carbide	TaC	3880
Titanium carbide	TiC	3140
Tungsten carbide	WC	2780
Vanadium carbide	VC	2830
Zirconium carbide	ZrC	3530

Nitrides

Tantalum nitride	TaN	3360
Titanium nitride	TiN	2900
Vanadium nitride	VN	2050
Zirconium nitride	ZrN	2950

Sulphides

Cerium sulphide	CeS	2450
	Ce_3S_4	2050
Thorium sulphide	ThS	2200
	Th_2S	2000

As yet, none of these materials has found any widespread use as a
refractory, although many have been used experimentally for crucibles
in attempting to melt metals where traces of oxygen or other impurities
found in oxide crucibles could not be tolerated. Certain compounds,
with and without added metals, have been investigated as "super-
alloys" for rocket engine components where extremely high temperatures are encountered. One of the difficulties in using most of these
high-melting compounds is their lack of resistance to oxidation. This
characteristic generally necessitates their preparation (in firing operations) and eventual use in vacuum or inert atmospheres.

Few of the high-melting compounds given in Table 3 are available
commercially, although some of them, like boron carbide and tungsten
carbide, have been used in non-refractory applications for a number
of years.

Metals as Refractories

Although refractories by ordinary definition do not include metals,
there are many metals which have melting points in the range of
refractory oxides. A partial list includes tungsten, molybdenum, tantalum, rhenium, and iridium. Of these, the first three are the most
commonly used because of availability in suitable shapes and moderate
cost. High-melting metals are not widely used as containers for molten
metals since alloying with the crucible is the rule, but there are a few
combinations which may be used. The most common example of a
metal crucible is the one used in melting magnesium, where the use
of an iron (low-carbon steel) crucible is standard practice; steel is
used because magnesium is so reactive that it reduces the most common refractory oxides.

Copper may be melted in a molybdenum crucible, but this is rarely
done because molybdenum is a more expensive crucible than the many
ordinary refractory materials which can be used, including clay-
graphite, graphite, alumina, and magnesia. In addition, melting in
molybdenum requires a protective atmosphere to prevent destructive
oxidation of the molybdenum. A major difference between refractory
metals and true refractories is oxidation resistance. Most refractories
need no protection from the air since they are already oxides (graphite
commonly listed as a refractory substance is of course an exception),
whereas refractory metals other than noble metals require very complete protection in this respect. This is of course also true for high-
melting compounds such as carbides, nitrides, sulphides, and the like.

Refractory metals, particularly molybdenum, are widely used as
resistance windings in high-temperature furnaces where most com-

monly a hydrogen atmosphere is used to protect the metal from oxidation. Tungsten may be used for this purpose also, but it is harder to fabricate than molybdenum. Platinum, or preferably a platinum-iridium alloy, is often used in small tube furnaces which require an oxidizing atmosphere and allow the attainment of temperatures in the neighborhood of 1500°C.

A different but common use for refractory metals as high-temperature construction materials is in making radiation shields for high-temperature furnaces. Molybdenum and tantalum sheet, in the form of cylinders or flat disks, is often used for this purpose. Such radiation shields are best used in vacuum furnaces where the principal heat losses are by radiation. The bright metal surfaces efficiently reflect back radiation to the center of the furnace, and the shields have the advantage over insulating refractories that there is no degassing problem.

A more detailed description of the use of refractory metals as metallic windings in resistance furnaces and in radiation shields will be found in Chapter 1.

FORMS OF REFRACTORIES AVAILABLE

Refractories may be purchased in three main forms: loose powders, brick of various types, and finished shapes, including tubes, rods, plates, and crucibles. Another class of refractory materials is the cements which are used to cement resistance wire to a furnace core, to cement refractory parts together, or to form a monolithic layer or structure which sets up hard, often without the necessity of being fired to a high temperature.

Powder

There are two main uses for loose refractory powders in the metallurgical laboratory: (1) for making crucibles or other shapes and (2) for insulating purposes. Although it is probably better in general to buy crucibles ready-made from various manufacturers (see Table 1), it is also true that frequently it is necessary to make one's own if the size and shape of the crucible must be changed from time to time, and if different crucible materials are to be investigated. Often it is difficult to obtain from manufacturers crucibles of the requisite purity, and the suppliers are frequently reluctant to supply adequate information regarding the chemical composition of their products. It has been very difficult to persuade crucible manufacturers to use pure materials. A so-called magnesia crucible, for example, might well contain as much as 10% clay or silica because it is easier to make; the behavior of a crucible containing essentially 100% magnesia and one containing 90% may be quite different. Of the various refractory oxides, alumina and magnesia are probably the most useful to have on hand for making special crucibles. Crucibles capable of melting most metals may be made from these two.

For some purposes, such as the thermal insulation of crucibles in a high-frequency induction furnace, loose powders are necessary because of space limitations. Obviously, for filling a small 1/4- to 1/2-inch-thick annulus between a crucible and the electrically insulating liner, a powder is required of good insulating properties, high melting point, and chemical inertness.

The thermal conductivity of a ceramic powder, up to temperature levels where radiation is the most important means of heat transfer, is largely a function of the thermal conductivity of the gas in the interstices between the powder particles. Austin [29] has derived an equation for the thermal conductivity of powder as follows:

$$K \cong K_g \left[\frac{3}{P} - 1 \right]$$

where K = thermal conductivity in usual units,
       K_g = thermal conductivity of the gas,
       P = void volume or porosity of the powder.

Hence the larger the void volume, the smaller the resulting thermal conductivity of the powder. In practice, it is observed that a very fine powder of low bulk density (large void volume) is a better thermal insulator than a coarser, more compact powder. The equation above indicates that the thermal conductivity of the solid itself is not a pertinent factor in the conductivity of the powder. It should be mentioned that many of the data in the literature on the thermal conductivity of powders have been found to be erroneous, and hence most published values should be accepted with caution.

At high temperatures, the thermal conductivity of powders is mostly a function of their ability to reflect or absorb radiation. In vacuum furnaces the thermal conductivity of a powder is only a function of the radiative properties as no gas is present to contribute to thermal conductivity.

A distinction must be made between calcined or "low-fired" powder and "high-fired," fused, or refractory-grade powder. The calcined or low-fired powder is usually to be avoided for either crucible making or for thermal insulation as it shrinks considerably on firing.

For lower temperature uses, up to about 1100°C, diatomaceous earth is a very efficient powder insulating material; it is available from a refractories supply house [7] under the trade name Sil-O-Cel. It has been standard practice to use this for insulating small furnaces and ovens for many years, and there is probably no better loose powder available for this temperature range. It is particularly easy to use as compared to cutting and fitting bricks, and is far less expensive.

Finished Shapes

Refractory brick may be divided into two classes, dense brick and lightweight brick. The latter is of greater interest in the metallurgical laboratory because of the ease with which it is cut to shape with simple tools, such as a hacksaw blade and wood rasp, and also because of its heat insulation properties. Most of the true lightweight brick is essentially fire clay or kaolin and hence is limited to temperatures around 1600°C.

The dense brick is used mainly in large-scale industrial furnaces and is available in a wide variety of compositions, including magnesia, alumina, chromite, fire clay, zirconia, and others. In furnaces designed for temperatures well above 1600°C, a facing of dense alumina or zirconia may be used, backed up by the lightweight fire-clay brick for superior thermal insulation.

A brick partaking of both these functions is alumina bubble brick,[2] a body composed of small hollow spherical particles of Al_2O_3, which, although not as light or as thermally insulating as some of the light-weight fire-clay brick may, however, be used at much higher temperatures. However, above 1425°C, bubble brick is a better insulator than the 1650°C type of lightweight fire-clay brick. Such brick, because of the air spaces afforded by the hollow particles, has a much lower thermal conductivity than the regular dense alumina brick.

Lightweight brick is available from several manufacturers, and is generally numbered according to the maximum Fahrenheit temperature to which it should be subjected. For example, JM–16 [7] may be subjected to a maximum temperature of 1600°F (870°C); K–23 [30] to 2300°F (1260°C), etc.

It is to be noted that in general the thermal insulation value of such brick is better the lower the temperature grade; hence, for maximum efficiency in insulating properties, the lowest number grade consistent with the requirements should be used. Also, the higher number grades are somewhat more costly. The maximum temperature for such brick is 3000°F (1650°C). The average thermal conductivity of insulating brick of this type is about 0.00069 cal/sec/cm/°C as compared to approximately 0.00345 for ordinary fire clay or 17 for dense alumina, at temperatures near 980°C.

The ease with which such brick may be cut with a hacksaw blade and smoothed to fit with a coarse file or rasp is one of its more useful features. For example, it is easy to carve out a series of split rings the thickness of the brick in order to line a fused silica tube for the preparation of a thermally insulating liner in a high-frequency induction vacuum furnace. A wash (thin slurry of alumina cement) brushed on the inside surfaces of insulating bricks helps as a radiation shield and prevents contamination from pieces of the brick being abraded or chopped off. A coat of sodium silicate will also prevent this trouble. Such a refractory lining has the advantage of being self-supporting, and it need not be contained between two walls as a loose powder must. On the other hand, the cutting of dense brick is almost impossible without a specially designed ceramic cutoff wheel.

The manufacture of *refractory tubes* used for furnace cores is best left to industrial concerns [2,3] who are properly equipped with the tools and know-how. As indicated above in the discussion of uses of various refractory materials, there are two main classes of refractory tubes: (1) those used for furnace cores for resistance furnaces, the outstanding example of which is alumina, and (2) gas-tight tubes of the porcelain type, as exemplified by mullite and zircon porcelain. The first type (furnace cores) is not gas-tight; but, if gastightness is required, a porcelain tube can be inserted through the alumina core tube. Winding electric resistance wires upon porcelain tubes is not practicable because of the relative susceptibility of the tubes to thermal shock, because of reaction between the wire and tube, and finally because porcelain tubes cannot stand as high a temperature as alumina. Alumina tubes may be used at temperatures up to about 1900°C. In purchasing refractory alumina tubes for very high temperature operation, a statement to the manufacturer should be made regarding the maximum temperature expected. Various grades of alumina furnace cores are available; some are more refractory than others because less impurity is present as binder. Formerly, for maximum temperature service in molybdenum-wound tube furnaces (above 1700°C), it was customary to heat the most refractory grade of alundum tubes to 1750 to 1800°C over a 36- to 48-hour period. During this period, considerable quantities of impurities were distilled off, thus increasing the refractoriness of the tube. However, this procedure is not necessary now as purer alumina tubes are available. Both grooved and plain tubes are available. In general the plain tubes are more satisfactory because they allow more freedom in spacing the winding of the wire.

Thermocouple insulation and protection tubes are another important refractory item for the laboratory. Insulators may be either porcelain or alumina; there is little choice between them for this application. Because protection tubes must frequently be gas-tight to exclude deleterious furnace atmospheres, a gas-tight refractory such as mullite porcelain is often used. Metals such as Inconel, however, are widely used for protection tubes, and may be pur- chased from various instrument companies. The protection of thermocouples from molten metals poses another and more difficult prob- lem because of the severe thermal shock en- countered in dipping a cold tube into a bath of molten iron or steel, for example. Graph- ite protection tubes serve admirably for many non-ferrous metals such as copper or aluminum, but are useless with iron or other high melting metals. If a thermocouple must be inserted into a metal bath where graphite may not be used, it may be pro- tected by fused silica, which is not subject to cracking due to shock. However, the life of such tubes is very short at temperatures in the neighborhood of 1600°C, and in small melts there is danger of contamination of the melt by silicon. There is also some danger of silicon contamination of the thermocouple. One technique which has been widely used to circumvent this difficulty in the thermal analysis of high-melting alloys is illustrated in Figure 1. A special crucible is constructed with a thermocouple protection tube built into the crucible. Obviously, thermal shock is not encountered here because the protection tube is always at the same temperature as the melt.

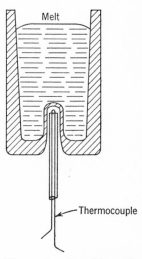

Figure 1. Crucible with Thermocouple Well.

Crucibles

Earlier in this chapter it was pointed out that in many cases cruci- bles present the most perplexing refractory problem for the metal- lurgist because of more or less reaction between the melt and the crucible.

Many types of reactions between the melt and the crucible are pos- sible, and a few such reactions are given below in generalized form,

using oxide crucibles as an illustration. Naturally, the same considerations would apply to crucibles consisting of carbides, nitrides, sulphides, etc.

$$RO_2(s) + M(l) = MO_2(s) + R(s) \tag{1}$$

$$RO_2(s) + M(g) = MO_2(s) + R(s) \tag{2}$$

$$RO_2(s) + M(l) = MO_2(s) + R(g) \tag{3}$$

$$RO_2(s) + M(l) = MO \cdot RO(s \text{ or } l) \tag{4}$$

In the reactions above R is the metallic constituent of an oxide crucible (RO_2), M is the metal being melted, and MO_2 an oxide of the
melt metal. The parenthetical s, l, and g refer to the solid, liquid, and
gaseous states, respectively. Reaction 4, indicating the formation of
a complex oxide ($MO \cdot RO$) derived from both the crucible and the
melt, can be important in a number of cases. Under the conditions of
melting, such a complex oxide or similar compound may be more
stable than either RO_2 or MO_2 so that the crucible oxide reacts vigor-
ously with the metal being melted.

In many cases, straightforward thermodynamic calculations can be
used to predict in advance the likelihood that a particular combination
of metal and crucible material will or will not be satisfactory. Many
data are available on the free energies of formation of oxides from
which such estimates are readily made. In particular, the Bureau
of Standards Tables,[31] the book by Thompson,[32] and K. K. Kelley's[33]
well-known contributions may be consulted for such work.

Consider two examples: (1) Al_2O_3 as a crucible for melting iron
at 1600°C and (2) Al_2O_3 as a crucible for magnesium at 800°C. In
the first example we consider the reaction

$$3Fe(l) + Al_2O_3(s) = 2Al(l) + 3FeO(l) \tag{5}$$

This reaction is the most probable one since FeO represents the lowest
state of the oxidation of iron, and experimentally it is found that FeO
is stable in equilibrium with molten iron. Since the melting point of
FeO is approximately 1420°C, the state of FeO is liquid. The free
energy of the above reaction is then

$$\Delta F = 3\Delta F^0{}_{FeO} - \Delta F^0{}_{Al_2O_3} \tag{6}$$

or the change in free energy of reaction 5 is the difference between the
free energies of the formation of the individual oxides on the basis

of the same number of oxygen atoms. The same standard states (ordinarily the state at 25°C and 1 atmosphere pressure) of the reactants must of course be used throughout. The free energy of formation of aluminum oxide is obtained from the reaction

$$2Al(l) + \tfrac{3}{2}O_2(g) = Al_2O_3(s) \tag{7}$$

$$\Delta F^0{}_{Al_2O_3(s)} = -376,000 + 61.56T \text{ calories/mole} \tag{8}$$

according to the data presented by Thompson.[32]   At 1600°C, $T = 1873°K$, hence

$$\Delta F^0{}_{Al_2O_3(s)} = -260,700 \text{ calories/mole}$$

The free energy of the formation of FeO is derived in an analogous manner:

$$Fe(l) + \tfrac{1}{2}O_2(g) = FeO(l) \tag{9}$$

According to Thompson,

$$\Delta F^0{}_{FeO(l)} = -55,842 - 4.12 \cdot 10^{-5}T(T - 1873)^2 + 11.36T \tag{10}$$

and, at 1873°K,

$$\Delta F^0{}_{FeO(l)} = -34,500 \text{ calories/mole} \tag{11}$$

Substituting the ΔF values in equation 6, we obtain $3(-34,500) - (-260,700)$, hence

$$\Delta F \text{ reaction } 5 = +157,200 \text{ calories/mole} \tag{12}$$

Since the reaction of interest (reaction 5) has a large positive-free energy, it seems clear that it will not proceed as written (to the right). Hence iron may be melted in an alumina crucible without the likelihood of crucible reaction, at least under the conditions assumed where no other reactions occur, such as interaction between FeO and Al_2O_3. It should be noted that these assumptions will not be valid in melting iron in air, where other reactions than the ones considered above can occur. Then both solid iron and liquid iron can react directly with the oxygen of the air to form FeO independently of possible reaction with Al_2O_3. The conditions assumed in the thermodynamic calculations would be obtained if the clean (oxide-free) iron were melted in Al_2O_3 in a completely inert atmosphere such as purified argon, or helium, or in a vacuum.

Let us now consider a case where crucible reaction does occur, and the thermodynamic calculation predicts such reaction. The data used in the following computations are also Thompson's.[32]

$$3Mg(l) + Al_2O_3(s) = 3MgO(s) + 2Al(l) \qquad (13)$$

at 800°C, $T = 1073°K$.

$$\Delta F = 3\Delta F^0{}_{MgO(s)} - \Delta F^0{}_{Al_2O_3(s)} \qquad (14)$$

$$Al(l) + \tfrac{3}{2}O_2(g) = Al_2O_3(s) \qquad (15)$$

$\Delta F^0{}_{Al_2O_3(s)}$ at 1073°K $= -376,000 + 61.56(1073)$

$$= -310,000 \text{ calories/mole}$$

$$Mg(l) + \tfrac{1}{2}O_2(g) = MgO(s) \qquad (16)$$

$\Delta F^0{}_{MgO(s)} = -158,474 + 1.17 \ln T - 0.51 \times 10^{-3}T^2 + 85.68T^{1/2}$ *

$$+ 1.044 \times 10^5 T^{-1} + 26.98T \qquad (17)$$

At 800°C or 1073°K, this gives

$$\Delta F^0{}_{MgO(s)} = -118,400 \text{ calories/mole}$$

Substituting the free energies for the formation of MgO and Al_2O_3 for the conditions under consideration, $3(-118,400) - (-310,000)$, we obtain

$$\Delta F \text{ (equation 13)} = -45,000 \text{ calories/mole}$$

Since the free energy of reaction 13 is negative, and has a rather high negative value, it indicates that molten magnesium at 800°C may react with an Al_2O_3 crucible to form some MgO and free aluminum. On this basis, Al_2O_3 would be a poor choice for a crucible for melting magnesium, at least at temperatures near 800°C.

Refractory Cements

Refractory cements are refractories such as alumina, magnesia, silicon carbide, and mullite, with binders added such as water glass or clay which allow them to set up hard on drying in air or firing at moderate temperatures. Alundum cements contain aluminum phosphate, which oxidizes to Al_2O_3 on firing. They are obtained as dry powder which must be mixed with water to the consistency of a mud in order to be applied. Some are sold in a damp form ready for

* Thompson writes this as $85.68T^{-2}$, which is an error.

ramming into place, and are often referred to as "ramming mixes." One example is the sillimanite-mullite type ramming mix. For holding resistance wires in place on alumina tubes, alumina cements are available in various grades of refractoriness. Since so many types are available, it is best to secure the appropriate manufacturer's [2,3] literature for consultation on specific applications. The wet cement is allowed to air-dry for several hours and is cured in place by slow heating of the furnace during the first few hours of operation.

Magnesia cement is not ordinarily used on furnace cores since alumina cements are better suited, but it is useful in lining crucibles such as clay graphite to prevent carbon pickup in ferrous melts or others where carbon contamination is likely. It may also be used as a patching material to repair magnesia crucibles, or as a ramming mix in preparing a built-up lining in a high-frequency furnace.

Silicon carbide cements are available to cement silicon carbide bricks or other shapes together or to repair silicon carbide muffles, bottom plates, etc.

Sillimanite or kyanite ramming mixes convert to mullite on firing. These cements are available in both dry form and damp form; the latter form has the consistency of a rather stiff modeling clay. Although the damp mix is convenient to use, it tends to dry out in the can even if damp cloths are placed over the cement and the lid replaced tightly. These mixes are used to prepare monolithic linings in gas furnaces, high-frequency melting furnaces and others, or for miscellaneous heavy repair work. It has excellent thermal shock resistance, high mechanical strength, withstanding temperatures in the neighborhood of 1700°C.

Insolute or Sauereisen [34] is a talc-water glass cement used more as an adhesive than as a refractory body. It stands temperatures in the neighborhood of 1500°C, but tends to be brittle, and is usually used in well-supported joints so that shear and bending stresses are avoided. Its very strong adhesive character makes it rather useful for certain odd jobs like fastening unlike objects together, such as metal to ceramics, but it is not always entirely satisfactory in some applications because of a tendency to crack. Generally speaking, its field of usefulness appears to be in assembling parts which must stick together reasonably well at moderate to high temperatures but are not permanent in nature. It has a rather high electrical insulating value.

A useful cement-like material may be prepared by thoroughly wetting asbestos paper, or asbestos "cement" (dry asbestos powder) used by plumbers. The wet mass may be kneaded in the hands like putty to some desired form such as a plug for the end of a furnace tube. In drying, it sets to a hard state and retains its shape. Asbestos does not withstand temperatures over 700°C without some crumbling, but for lower temperatures it is very useful. It serves well in plugging up cracks between furnace shells and protruding tubes to prevent chimney effects where the tubes are vertical.

Another homemade cement consists of plumber's asbestos cement mixed with water glass. It sets at room temperature to a rather hard impervious material which adheres well, and it has been much used in sealing the metal shells of hydrogen furnaces fitted with molybdenum windings where the entire furnace shell is filled with hydrogen. Another good cement is fine silicon carbide plus water glass with or without a little clay. It will stick to metal as well as to ceramics. Only the amount to be used immediately should be mixed.

CHEMICAL STABILITY OF OXIDE REFRACTORIES

Of the refractory materials discussed thus far, the pure oxide refractories, as seen from Table 1, are the most stable and refractory. Alumina, of the group including alumina, beryllia, lime, magnesia, silica, thoria, and zirconia, is the most stable in a wide variety of atmospheres, with the possible exception of zirconia. It is resistant to reduction by hydrogen and carbon up to about 1800°C, and in hydrogen atmospheres may even be heated to 1900°C. Magnesia tends to be reduced by both carbon and hydrogen at about 1700°C. Beryllia reacts with moisture in the air and forms volatile $Be(OH)_2$ in the neighborhood of 1250°C, thus not only losing weight but also creating simultaneously a serious health hazard. It is quite resistant to reduction by graphite, and may be heated to 2000°C in contact with graphite without serious reaction. Lime, as is well known, reacts readily with moisture at low temperatures, although the highly fused material reacts slowly with moisture in the air. Silica is rather readily reduced by heating with a variety of metals, and is characterized by several polymorphic transformations as noted above. Silica actually should not be included in this group of refractory oxides as it is far less refractory than the others; but it is placed beside the others for the sake of completeness. Thoria is very readily attacked by graphite at temperatures near 1200°C or over. Zirconia is stable in oxidizing atmospheres up to about 2200°C, but is reduced by hydrogen and carbon at these very high temperatures. Magnesia, beryllia, and zirconia are stable in vacuum up to 1600°C, 2100°C, and 2300°C, respectively.[35]

As regards interaction between the pure oxide refractories, elementary chemical principles regarding acid and basic materials apply, so that it is obvious that considerable reaction may be expected between very acid and very basic refractories such as silica and lime. Alumina, beryllia, thoria, and zirconia are rather amphoteric, having neither strongly acid nor strongly basic characteristics; hence binary combinations of these four tend to produce no low melting mixtures. Magnesia and lime are both strongly basic, and, of the group considered above, only silica is strongly acidic.

It is possible to make useful refractory products from certain combinations of these oxides, but this subject is one which falls outside the scope of this book.

LABORATORY PREPARATION OF CRUCIBLES

Slip Casting

There are two major methods of making small crucibles in the laboratory, pressing and slip casting. Unless one has had considerable experience in the preparation of slips (a thin slurry of the refractory in water with certain suspension agents) or has available the advice of a ceramist, this method is not recommended. Even experts in the ceramic field often have considerable difficulty in the preparation of a good slip, and a novice could waste much time in experimentation. The first step in slip casting is to suspend a maximum amount of finely divided refractory powder in water (sometimes other liquids) by the aid of various agents without getting the mixture too thick to pour. The slip is then poured into a dry plaster of Paris mold having the same dimensions as the outside dimensions of the crucible (allowing for shrinkage). The plaster draws away the water from the slip at the plaster-slip interface, and a thickened layer of damp ceramic forms while the inside is still very thin and fluid. With a few trials the proper time to wait for a suitable thickness is found, and then the remainder of the thin slip is poured off, leaving a shell of ceramic clinging to the mold. After several minutes of drying, the damp crucible shrinks away enough from the plaster so that it may be carefully removed. When all the moisture is eliminated by long standing in the air or by slow oven drying, the crucible may be fired to an appropriate temperature, when it becomes hard and strong, ready for use.

Pressing

There are two main techniques in pressing crucibles: (1) pressing in a steel mold and (2) tamping into a graphite crucible. In the first method a steel die, such as is illustrated in Figure 2, is used. The upper punch is slipped part way into the die, and the assembly is inverted so that the bottom end of the punch is upright. The punch may be allowed to protrude from the die by setting the die over a hole in a block of wood. The die is now ready to receive the charge of the ceramic powder.

Unlike "plastic" materials, such as clay, nearly pure refractory oxides, such as Al_2O_3 or MgO, have no plastic properties in themselves. It

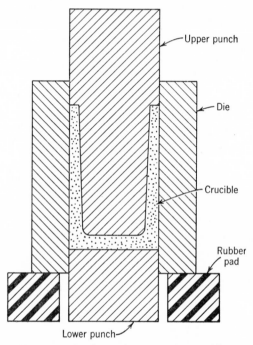

Figure 2.   Steel Die for Pressing Crucibles.

is very desirable, frequently necessary, to add some lubricant to the hard powder which allows the refractory to flow under pressure into the corners of the mold. This is accomplished by surrounding each grain of powder by a suitable lubricant. Such lubricants are usually water-soluble organic compounds such as Carbowax 4000 [36] (a polyethylene glycol), Ceremul C,[37] or other proprietary compositions, of which there are many. The amount of lubricant required is usually about 5 to 10% by weight (dry), and it is usually added as a water solution containing perhaps 20% by weight. Batches containing lubricants should always be well mixed, then dried. The powder is then ready for use or storage. The lower punch is inserted after tapping and leveling the powder and brushing away any excess from the sides of the die.

Next the die assembly is placed in a hydraulic press, such as a 10-ton or a 20-ton hand-operated hydraulic-laboratory press, and about 5 to 30 tons per square inch pressure is applied. The pressed crucible may be forced out of the die by pressing on the top punch while supporting the bottom of the die on steel blocks or on a tall ring so that first the bottom punch is forced out, followed by the crucible. If a slight taper is machined into the bottom inch or so of the die, it will aid in extraction of the crucible and minimize cracking due to elastic expansion of the crucible upon emerging from the die. By the use of pressure applied to both punches simultaneously, a double-action pressing technique is obtained which allows essentially equal punch movement at either end of the crucible, hence providing more equal compaction and densification of the ceramic body. If the bottom punch were flush with the die bottom and pressure were applied between it and the top punch only, the upper sides of the crucible would be greatly compacted, but little or no compaction of the bottom of the crucible would result, making a very weak and chalky structure at the bottom. The rubber pad or spring at the bottom of the die is a possible method of holding the bottom punch in proper starting position for pressing, but allowing relative motion between die and punch during application of pressure. Actually, after pressing has started, frictional forces are developed at the die wall sufficient to hold the die and prevent its falling down over the lower punch. If desired, the crucible could be pressed in the inverted position at the "upper" punch, now actually the lower punch.

Various refinements on the simple design shown in Figure 2 have been used; for an example, see Figure 3. Here the outside diameter of the crucible is tapered to allow easy extraction, and a separate ring is used so that pressure may be applied independently to the walls or bottom of the crucible. Such refinements are generally not necessary, but are occasionally of value in dealing with a refractory powder which does not hold together well, or where an unusually uniform pressed density is required. The die is filled in the inverted position as before but with ring C held out a short distance from the die D. On insertion of the bottom punch B pressure may be applied first to the ring C, thus securing some compaction at the top of the crucible. When the ring C is seated, as shown in Figure 3, it is prevented from further motion into the die (and cutting into the taper) by the shoulder. Pressure may be applied then as before to the punches A and B, securing consolidation along the sides and crucible bottom. After the proper pressure has been attained, punch *A* and ring *C* are extracted by hand, and the crucible is readily pushed out through the wide end of the die.

Such dies should be constructed of tool steel, preferably a non-deforming oil-hardening steel or, if a great deal of use is contemplated where wear due to the abrasive refractory powders may be an impor-

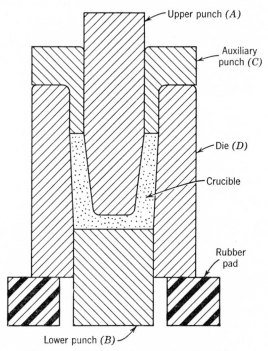

Figure 3.   Steel Die for Pressing Crucibles.

tant factor, a high-carbon–high-chromium steel may be preferable. Hard chromium plating is frequently used both to combat wear and to prevent rusting.   The hardness of the die should be about Rockwell C 40–45 and that of the plungers or punches Rockwell C 60.   This hardness difference tends to prevent possible galling and does prevent brittle failure of dies with flying fragments.

After pressing and extraction, the crucibles are ready for firing to an appropriate temperature, depending upon the composition.

Particle Sizes of Ceramic Powders

No hard and fast rules can be laid down about the particle size or size distribution for refractory powders for making pressed ware.   In general, a size around 200 mesh seems to give good results. In any nominal screen size, however, there is a range of sizes present, and sometimes powders are purchased between two sizes, such as minus 100, plus 200, indicating that all particles pass through a 100-mesh screen but not through a 200-mesh screen. This method of purchasing refractory powders, however, is rather unusual, but it is the rule in buying metal powders. Generally a refractory company offers a size such as 100 mesh or 200 mesh, indicating only the approximate size, usually meaning that all material goes through that screen; hence a rather wide range of actual particle sizes is probably present, including some fines in the subscreen sizes. In making pressed crucibles, a range of particle sizes is desirable to secure a high-pressed density, or at least some rather coarse and some rather fine material should be used. The intermediate sizes may not be important. In pressing rather large crucibles, some large particles or agglomerates approaching the wall thickness in size are desirable as they make for a stronger, more thermal shock-resisting body. Such coarse particles are called "grog" in the ceramic industry.

Tamping

The second method of making crucibles in the laboratory referred to above, the tamping technique, is carried out as follows. The "die" in this method is made of graphite, and the core or shaped punch may be made of some easily machined metal such as brass. As before, the punch is fitted into the die sleeve and the assembly inverted and the powder, previously treated with lubricant, poured in. In this method, however, the powder is placed in the space between the die and punch a little at a time and rammed in place by tamping with a rod or stick to pack the powder firmly in place. A small air hammer, if available, is very useful for this purpose; but it is not necessary. The powder may also be vibrated into place with an electric vibrator. When enough powder has been rammed to form a suitably thick crucible bottom (squared off with a reaming type of tool made to fit the die), a graphite end cap is inverted over the crucible bottom and the punch is withdrawn (see Figure 4). The die now constitutes the heater crucible for firing, and the procedure from here is identical with that described above for the steel die-pressed crucible. This is obviously a cheaper, somewhat easier technique than the former one, but it also has limitations. The firing temperature for MgO is limited to about 1600°C to 1800°C to avoid excessive reaction with graphite. The final product, although acceptable for most purposes, is not as dimensionally satisfactory as in the steel die technique. Removal of the crucible from the graphite die is simple as enough shrinkage occurs during firing to allow the crucible to drop out. By the same token, a graphite punch, if used, cannot be left in the crucible during firing as the crucible in shrinking will tighten around the punch and crack. Before use, the crucible must be fired in air at 1000°C to 1200°C to clean up graphite contamination.

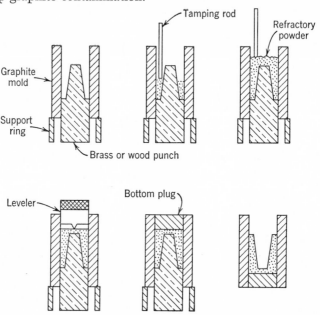

Figure 4. Steps in Ramming a Crucible.

It is quite possible to combine the ramming and steel die techniques, but this is usually done only with crucibles of the order of 4 inches in diameter or larger. The advantages are: (1) that a hardened steel die is not required and (2) that the use of a rather large hydraulic press is avoided. Generally, however, pressing does a neater job than ramming or tamping, and for smaller crucibles it is to be preferred over the tamping method despite the higher cost entailed in the construction of a hardened and tempered tool steel die. Tamping is hardly possible with small crucibles if the wall thickness is one quarter inch or less because of the difficulty of getting a ramming tool into such a small space.

Firing of Crucibles

Laboratory crucibles are most frequently made of magnesia, the crucible refractory which has widest use in metals research. Other materials such as Al_2O_3 and ZrO_2 may be handled in an almost identical manner. Since few laboratories are equipped with high-temperature ceramic kilns, it will be assumed that only high frequency induction heating is available for firing. The proper procedure is to have machined a block of graphite about an inch or so larger in inside diameter and higher than the crucible to be fired. The crucible is placed on a small block of previously fired MgO at the bottom of the graphite heater crucible, which in turn is surrounded by carbon black, as illus-

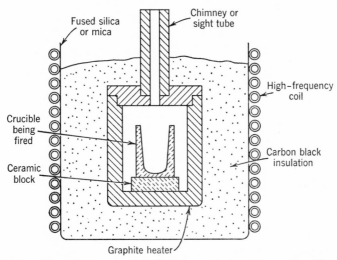

Figure 5. High-Frequency Induction Method of Firing Crucibles.

trated in Figure 5. For a 2-inch O.D. crucible, the graphite heater should be $2\frac{1}{2}$ to 3 inches in inside diameter, with perhaps a $\frac{1}{4}$-inch- to $\frac{1}{2}$-inch-thick wall. This requires a 6-inch diameter high frequency coil, allowing for about a 1-inch-thick layer of carbon black all the way around the graphite heater. The carbon black serves two functions: (1) to act as a very efficient thermal insulator and (2) to prevent oxidation of the graphite. For a unit of this size a 20-kw-high-frequency generator is desirable, but one of half this power may suffice. The chimney is required in order that the laboratory worker may see down to the crucible with an optical pyrometer. A minimum temperature of 1600°C held for about 30 minutes is required to obtain a crucible which is rather porous but serviceable; however, 1800°C is much better. After the crucible is cold enough to be removed, it may be cleaned up from adhering carbon by firing in air as mentioned above. If a 50-kw or a 100-kw motor-generator high-frequency unit is available, it is quite possible to fire several crucibles at once by piling one on top of another, with MgO plates separating them. It is important that the MgO ware not touch the graphite directly, as this contact will cause reaction with the graphite. A white smoke during firing is caused by some volatilization of MgO and probably by some reduction to Mg, followed by reoxidation to MgO. A little of this smoking during the firing of MgO ware in graphite is inevitable and need cause no great concern. Excessive white smoke means usually that the MgO is in direct contact with the graphite or that the temperature is too high.

REFERENCES

1. Electro Refractories and Alloys Corp., Buffalo, N. Y.
2. The Norton Co., Worcester, Mass.
3. The Carborundum Co., Niagara Falls, N. Y.
4. Morganite, Inc., Long Island City, N. Y.
5. Brush Beryllium Corp., Cleveland, Ohio. Clifton Products, Inc., Painesville, Ohio.
6. Joseph Dixon, Jersey City, N. J.
7. Johns Manville, New York, N. Y.
8. National Carbon Co., New York, N. Y.
9. Ajax Electrothermic Corp., Trenton, N. J.
10. Lava Crucible Co., Pittsburgh, Pa.
11. Stupakoff Ceramic and Mfg. Co., Latrobe, Pa.
12. General Electric Co., Chemical Department, Pittsfield, Mass.
13. Westvaco Chemical Division, Food Machinery & Chemicals Corp., New York, N. Y.
14. Mycalex Corp. of America, Clifton, N. J.
15. F. H. Norton, *Refractories*, 3rd ed., McGraw-Hill, New York, 1949.
16. The Corning Glass Co., Corning, N. Y.
17. Thermal Syndicate, New York, N. Y.
18. Amersil Co., Inc., Hillside, N. J.
19. General Electric Co., Lamp Dept., Cleveland, Ohio.
20. Robert Sosman, "Properties of Silica," ACS Monograph, Chemical Catalog Co., 1927.
21. American Lava Co., Chattanooga, Tenn.
22. The Lindsay Light and Chemical Co., West Chicago, Ill.
23. Wm. H. Swanger, Frank R. Caldwell, "Special Refractories for Use at High Temperatures," *J. Res. Natl. Bur. Standards*, 6, 1131–1143 (1931).
24. Oscar O. Fritsche, H. B. Wahlin, and Joseph Oesterle, "Thorium Oxide, a High Temperature Refractory," *Trans. Electrochem. Soc.*, 64, 329–339 (1933).
25. H. K. Richardson, "Small Cast Thorium Oxide Crucibles," *J. Am. Ceramic Soc.*, 18, 69 (1935).
26. D. Turner, "Special Refractories for Metallurgical Research at High Temperatures," *Trans. Ceramic Soc.*, 33, 33–35 (1934).
27. Titanium Alloy Manufacturing Co., Division National Lead Co., Niagara Falls, N. Y.

28. O. J. Whittemore, "Pure Oxide Heavy Refractories," *J. Am. Ceramic Soc.,* **32,** 48–53 (1949).
29. J. B. Austin, "Factors Influencing the Thermal Conductivities of Non-Metallic Materials," A.S.T.M. Symposium on Thermal Insulating Materials, March 8, 1939.
30. Babcock & Wilcox, Refractories Division, New York, N. Y.
31. Selected Values of Chemical Thermodynamics Properties, U.S. Bureau of Standards, Series I, II, III:
    I. Properties of Materials at Room Temperature.
    II. Transitions: Fusions, Vaporization, etc.
    III. Properties as a Function of Temperature.
32. M. deK. Thompson, *The Total and Free Energies of Formation of Oxides of Thirty-Two Metals,* The Electrochemical Society, New York, 1942.
33. K. K. Kelley, *Contributions to the Data on Theoretical Metallurgy:*
    I. *U.S. Bureau Mines Bull.* 350 (Washington, 1932)

II.	371	1934
III.	383	1935
IV.	384	1935
V.	393	1936
VI.	394	1936
VII.	406	1937
VIII.	407	1937
IX.	434	1941
X.	476	1949

34. Sauereisen Cement Co., Pittsburgh, Pa.
35. P. D. Johnson, "Behavior of Refractory Oxides and Metals, Alone and in Combination, in Vacuo at High Temperatures," *J. Am. Ceramic Soc.,* **33,** 168–171 (1950).
36. Union Carbide and Carbon Chemical Co., New York, N. Y.
37. Socony Vacuum Oil Co., New York, N. Y.

CHAPTER FIVE

Controlled Atmospheres

The objective in using controlled atmospheres is to control the composition of the metal being heated or melted. Such atmospheres may be divided into two categories: (1) that where no change in composition of the metal is desired and (2) that where an important change in composition is to be produced. The first category is probably the most common one in the metals laboratory, and it exacts more time and effort from laboratory workers than the second.

INERT ATMOSPHERES

In working with low-melting metals (below about 600°C) reaction with the air is ordinarily not severe except for the highly electropositive elements such as sodium or calcium. Aluminum may be handled satisfactorily in air even at temperatures well above its melting point because it is protected by a thin film of aluminum oxide. However, most metals and alloys react with air even at moderate temperatures, and at high temperatures the reaction can be catastrophic.

A common laboratory method of preventing oxidation or other atmospheric attack in heating or melting operations is to employ a neutral or inert gaseous atmosphere. Similar protection can be obtained with a vacuum or by covering the melt with fused salts or charcoal in some cases. These methods are discussed elsewhere in this book.

Although in the factory it is economical to use inexpensive but more or less complicated gas mixtures, such atmospheres are generally not feasible in the laboratory. Most commercial gas atmospheres are not truly inert, and many of them are useful only in heat-treating steels. Far more valuable for the laboratory are the elemental gases obtainable in cylinders or "tanks": hydrogen, nitrogen, argon, and helium obtainable from several manufacturers. Of these four, only the last two are inert to all metals. However, hydrogen and nitrogen do not react with many metals, and their lower cost often commends them for use instead of the more expensive noble gases. Anhydrous ammonia is worth brief mention, however, because as dissociated without combustion it yields a very dry mixture of 75% hydrogen, 25% nitrogen (about −51°C dew point). Ammonia is usually obtained in 100-pound cylinders about the size of a standard 200-cubic-foot hydrogen cylinder, but containing about seventeen times the equivalent hydrogen volume. A dissociator is required which consists essentially of a furnace with catalyst and auxillary equipment such as flow meters and valves. The main advantage of dissociated ammonia over tank hydrogen is its lower cost, which is several times less than that of hydrogen. Combusted ammonia of various hydrogen-to-nitrogen ratios must generally be dried before use; such gas mixtures have limited application in the laboratory as it is more convenient to use uncombusted dissociated ammonia, or more commonly one of the elemental gases mentioned above.

Cylinder Gases and Valves

In Table 1 are shown some commercial grades of cylinder gases, with the analyses provided by suppliers. This table is not intended to be a complete listing of such gases as there are other grades and purities available. The degree of purity shown in the various grades should be regarded as approximate only.

The pressure of the cylinder gases listed is of the order of 2000 pounds per square inch; hence a valve of some type must be used in order to release the gas at a useful rate. The simplest and cheapest type is a needle valve. Such valves are not very satisfactory, however, since the valve controls only the flow rate and does not reduce the pressure, although needle valves are available with a gauge which indicates the amount of gas left in the tank. An undesirable feature of needle valves is that, if the gas flow should be stopped by some obstruction, the gas pressure can increase up to a possible maximum of the cylinder pressure. More satisfactory is the two-dial, diaphragm-type reducing valve. Although such valves are comparatively expensive, they do allow very good control of the rate of gas release from the cylinder and control the pressure of the gas to the line. In addition, they are equipped with gauges to show the amount of gas remaining as well as the amount of back pressure in the line. These valves may readily be adjusted to deliver gas at pressures from about 1 to 50 pounds per square inch.

The various compressed-gas companies supply their own gas cylinders and gauges, and in general one company's gauges cannot be used on another company's cylinders. Hence a laboratory using compressed

TABLE 1

SOME COMMERCIAL GRADES OF ARGON, HELIUM, NITROGEN, AND HYDROGEN WITH SUPPLIERS' ANALYSES

Gas	Company	Grade	Purity, %	Oxygen, %	Nitrogen, %	Hydrogen, %	Water, %*	Remarks
Argon	A	Welding grade	99.8	<0.005	.....	<0.01	.....	0.2% not identified
Argon	A	Lamp grade	99.6	.....	0.4	.....	.....	Total O_2, H, CO_2, hydrocarbons, <5 ppm
Argon	B	......	99.6	0.001	.....	0.001	.....	.....
Argon	C	Welding grade	99.8	<0.002	0.2	<0.01	0.002	May contain hydrocarbons up to 0.005%
Argon	C	Lamp grade	99.8	<0.002	0.2	<0.01	0.002	.....
Helium	A	Commercial grade	99.7	.....	.....	<0.01 <0.002	.....	N_2, H_2 equal amounts
Helium	Bureau M	Purified	99.8+	Nil	0.002	0.00003	−196°C dew point?	Dried over charcoal-liquid air: CO_2, 0.0006%; A, 0.00005%; methane, 0.000002%
Nitrogen	C	Water-pumped	.....	<0.3	.....	0	Saturated	.....
Nitrogen	C	Dried	.....	<0.3	.....	0	<0.002	.....
Nitrogen	C	Oil-pumped	.....	<0.3	.....	0	<0.03	.....
Nitrogen		Special	.....	<0.3	.....	0	<0.002	.....
Nitrogen	B	Prepurified	.....	<0.002	.....	<0.002	0.002	.....
Nitrogen	B	Prepurified	.....	<0.001	.....	<0.001	"Dry"	.....
Nitrogen	B	Oil-pumped	.....	<0.5	.....	.....	0.003	.....
Nitrogen	B	Water-pumped	.....	<0.5	.....	.....	Saturated	.....
Hydrogen	C	Commercial grade	99.5	"Balance"	.....	.....	.....	.....
Hydrogen	A	......	99.5	.....	.....	.....	0.5	.....

* 0.002% ≅ −55°C dew point.

gases usually deals with one supplier and buys a set of gauges from that supplier.

Because of the danger of explosion in using the same gauge for both oxygen and hydrogen, oxygen cylinders and gauges of all makes have right-hand threads whereas the threads of cylinders and gauges used for hydrogen have left-hand threads. However, oxygen valves may be used for nitrogen, argon, or helium, so that gauges of only two types are required for the four gases being discussed here. Special valves are required for acetylene, carbon dioxide, and other less frequently used gases.

Gas Flow Rates

An inert gas may be flowed over a sample being heated, or a stagnant gaseous atmosphere may be employed. In the latter case no flow occurs, but the heating chamber is filled with inert gas, and the air excluded by tight seals. Systems using a static atmosphere should be vacuum-tight, and should preferably be evacuated and then filled with inert gas. In this way a long purging period to flush out air by flowing inert gas is eliminated. This is an important consideration when rather expensive gases such as argon are used. Another advantage attending the use of a stagnant inert gas is that less contamination of the metal sample occurs. Even a rather carefully purified inert gas contains traces of oxygen, nitrogen, water, etc., which obviously are added to the metal sample in amounts proportional to the flow rate and to the time of exposure to the gas. However, in a static or non-flowing atmosphere, once the residual impurities in the inert gas have reacted with the sample, no further contamination will occur if the system is tight. Clearly, the volume of the system should be kept to a minimum to reduce the amounts of residual impurities absorbed by the specimen.

In certain cases, however, a flowing gas stream is desirable. A common use of an inert gas is in a furnace not designed to be vacuum-tight, such as a commercial heat-treating furnace; a flowing inert gas is required to keep the chamber purged of air. Some air will diffuse into the chamber through openings and cracks, but the partial pressure of air can be kept quite low if sufficient gas flow is maintained (thus maintaining the inert gas pressure slightly above atmosphere pressure).

It is necessary to keep a flow of hydrogen through a molybdenum-wound electric resistance furnace to prevent atmospheric attack of the molybdenum windings, since furnaces of this type are usually opened while the furnace is hot to put in or take out samples.

In many instances a flowing gas is used to react with a metal. A continuous addition of the reacting gas is required to replenish the gas consumed and to allow the reaction to proceed to completion. Examples are the hydrogen reduction of oxides, the carburization or nitriding of iron, and the removal of carbon from iron by damp hydrogen.

Generally it is desirable to meter the gas flow. For very small flows, the order of liters an hour, a simple counting of bubbles on the gas exit of the apparatus suffices if the head of liquid in the bubbler remains constant. With hydrogen, the exit gas is usually ignited to prevent filling the room with hydrogen; the rate of gas flow may be estimated by observing the size of the burning flame. For faster flows, and to allow a variation in flow rate, the orifice type of flow meter is more useful. It indicates the difference in pressure between the forward and exit side of a constriction in the flow line on a manometer. By reading the manometer after calibration for a particular gas, the flow rate can be determined. Flow meters may be calibrated by passing the gas into a graduated cylinder full of water inverted over a large dish or pan filled with water. The gas passing up into the graduated cylinder displaces the water in the cylinder. When some convenient interval of time has passed corresponding to displacement of a large part of the original water in the cylinder, the levels of water in the cylinder and in the pan are made to coincide, hence giving the volume of water displaced at atmospheric pressure. These flow meters may readily be made in the laboratory from glass tubing or may be purchased from laboratory supply houses. Still more elegant (and expensive) is the Rotometer,[1] where one reads the height of a floating indicator against a scale.

Desiccants

Many references will be found in the literature to the use of P_2O_5 as a desiccant. Although there are few substances which have the drying power of P_2O_5, it is also true that it is extremely unpleasant and messy to handle. In addition, it becomes so pasty due to deliquescence that it tends to constrict and channel gas flow so that the gas contacts only a small portion of the desiccant surface.

Anhydrous magnesium perchlorate has nearly as good drying power as P_2O_5, and is far better to handle, remaining dry and pourable even after absorbing large quantities of water. Care must be taken to keep it from contact with mineral acids, salts which hydrolyze to mineral acids, and flammable materials, since under these conditions there is danger of an explosion. Activated alumina [2] is also a powerful desiccant, and the common grade (A) may be regenerated easily by passing air through it while heating to 175 to 315°C. A less stable grade (C) has a higher moisture capacity, but must not be reactivated above 175°C.

If liquid nitrogen is available in the laboratory, extremely low moisture contents may be obtained by passing partially dried gas through a copper coil immersed in the liquid. Pre-drying may be necessary to prevent plugging the copper tubing with ice. If the rate of gas flow is fairly fast, the nitrogen will boil away rapidly, making this method impracticable. Cooling the gas to low temperatures will produce the moisture vapor pressures shown below in Table 2. These same temperatures correspond to the "dew point" of water in a gas; actually, the water vapor is in equilibrium with ice rather than with liquid water.

TABLE 2

VAPOR PRESSURE OF ICE AT VARIOUS TEMPERATURES [3]

Temperature, °C	Vapor Pressure, mm
−183 (boiling oxygen)	1.4×10^{-22}
−90	0.0000745
−80	0.000413
−70	0.00198 (0.002 mg H_2O/liter)
−60	0.00840
−50	0.0299
−40	0.0994
−30	0.293
−20	0.779

Table 3 lists some desiccants with the vapor pressure of water in milligrams per liter over the desiccant containing appropriately small amounts of water.

TABLE 3

DRYING POWER OF SOME DESICCANTS [4]

	Mg H_2O/Liter	H_2O Capacity, %
$CaCl_2$ (technical anhydrous)	1.5	
NaOH (sticks)	0.80	
$CaCl_2$ (granular dehydrated)	0.36	
$Mg(ClO_4)_2 \cdot 3H_2O$	0.031	
Silica gel	0.030	
Al_2O_3	0.005	13.0
$CaSO_4$	0.005	6.6
$Mg(ClO_4)_2$	0.002	60.0
BaO	0.00065	

Besides the drying power of desiccants as indicated above, the water capacity is also of importance. By capacity is meant the percentage of water absorbed without appreciably decreasing the drying power; the approximate capacity of Al_2O_3, $CaSO_4$, and $Mg(ClO_4)_2$ are indicated in the table. A third quality, speed of drying, is also of importance in evaluating the performance of desiccants. The data in Table 3 (excluding the last column) were obtained under essentially equilibrium conditions since only drying power was being investigated. The rate of gas flow used varied from 26 to 240 cc per hour per cubic centimeter of desiccant. In using small laboratory-size drying tubes, 1 to 3 liters per hour flow is slow enough to insure complete absorption.

Hydrogen

Hydrogen will reduce many metal oxides. It therefore cannot be classified as an intrinsically inert gas, but it is inert to metals which

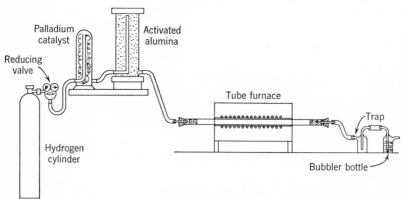

Figure 1. Gas Purification Train and Tube Furnace.

are previously clean and which do not form hydrides. Metals commonly heated in hydrogen for the purpose of preventing oxidation include iron, copper, molybdenum, tungsten, nickel, and cobalt. For many applications it is desirable to use hydrogen very low in oxygen and in water vapor. Small amounts of very pure hydrogen are readily prepared by heating various metal hydrides such as CaH_2. Where rather constant use of pure hydrogen is contemplated, a simple purification system consists of a palladium catalyst [5] followed by an activated alumina [6] drier; the palladium catalyzes the reaction $2H_2 + O_2 \rightarrow 2H_2O$, at room temperature. The water is then removed by the drying tower. Such a system can readily reduce the dew point of the residual water vapor to the neighborhood of $-68°C$ (see Figure 1).

If only rare use of purified hydrogen at low flow rates is contemplated, a homemade platinum or palladium catalyst, made by decomposing the chloride on an inert powder such as asbestos, followed by a drying tower of anhydrous magnesium perchlorate, $Mg(ClO_4)_2$, or other desiccant may be used. Palladium or platinum-treated asbestos is available from the platinum companies [7] ready for use in a purification train. If platinized asbestos is used, it must be heated to 150–600°C to become active. The heating temperature does not appear to be critical, but temperatures in the neighborhood of 1000°C poison the

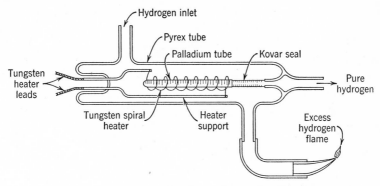

Figure 2. Palladium Valve for Hydrogen Purification.

catalytic behavior by creating a tightly bound hydrogen-absorbed layer on the metal surface. Both platinum and palladium catalyze the reaction $2H_2 + O_2 \rightarrow 2H_2O$ by an alternating oxidation and reduction of the metal surface.[8,9]

Copper turnings at 600°C have been used for the same purpose; apparently the same oxidation-reduction reaction mentioned in connection with platinum and palladium occurs with heated copper. Presumably other metals such as iron would behave similarly.

A more elegant method for the purification of hydrogen is to take advantage of the great permeability of palladium for hydrogen. Hydrogen may be passed through heated palladium, but impurities such as water vapor, oxygen, and nitrogen remain behind. In practice a palladium tube closed off at one end is heated to 600°C and is surrounded by the hydrogen to be purified at some pressure in excess of the pressure at which it is desired to draw off the purified hydrogen. If hydrogen at atmospheric pressure is needed, the impure hydrogen could be supplied at about 2 atmospheres (or 1 atmosphere gauge pressure). The palladium may be obtained [7] sealed to a Kovar tube ready for sealing to Pyrex glass (see Figure 2). After use, the palladium tube should be cooled to room temperature in vacuum to avoid beta phase embrittlement.

The heating coil, preferably of 20 to 30 mil tungsten wire, should not come too close to the palladium-Kovar joint as continued heating might deteriorate it. Also, excessive heat at the Kovar-glass joint might cause cracking of the glass. It is important that the temperature calibration of the tungsten coil be carried out in a hydrogen atmosphere (rather than in air) as the thermal losses are much greater in a hydrogen atmosphere.

Both pure copper and a copper-gold alloy containing 37.5% gold have been used as a solder for the palladium-Kovar seal. Inert arc welding has been used also. The side tube leading to a constriction where excess hydrogen is burned serves as a safety valve in case excess pressure should inadvertently be used on the hydrogen line, but, more important, it sweeps out the accumulation of water vapor and other gaseous impurities that otherwise would collect around the outside of the palladium tube.

An empirical formula for calculating the passage of hydrogen through palladium sheet at 600°C is

$$\frac{\Delta V}{\Delta t} = 0.00083 \frac{A}{d} (\sqrt{p_1} - \sqrt{p_2})$$

where $\dfrac{\Delta V}{\Delta t}$ = cubic centimeters of hydrogen/second,

A = area of palladium sheet (one side) in square centimeters,

d = thickness of palladium sheet in millimeters,

p_1 = pressure of impure hydrogen in millimeters,

p_2 = pressure of purified hydrogen in millimeters.

If a palladium tube is 10 cm long, 1 cm in diameter, with a wall thickness of 0.5 mm, it will pass about 2.16 liters of hydrogen per hour if there is a one atmosphere difference in pressure between the impure and pure hydrogen. Experience has shown that hydrogen purified in this manner is about as pure as can be prepared.

Other temperature levels have been suggested for heating the palladium, such as 300°C, but lower temperatures are not as desirable since the rate of gas put through is much less. Higher temperatures may be feasible, but there is apparently not much known about the effect of higher temperatures. It would be expected that other gases such as oxygen might tend to diffuse through at sufficiently high temperatures. Nickel has been used in a similar manner, but much larger surfaces are required.[10]

Oxygen may also be removed from hydrogen by the ferro-chromium technique described later for the purification of nitrogen.

The safest procedure in handling hydrogen in a gas train of the type shown in Figure 1 is to start the gas flowing while the furnace is cold. After 2 to 3 minutes of flow a test tube is inverted over the exit tube of the bubbler bottle at the end of the train and a sample of hydrogen collected in the test tube. A lighted match is applied to the open end of the inverted test tube (held away from the exit tube). If a non-explosive mixture is present in the train, the gas in the test tube will burn quietly, and the flame can be used to ignite the exhaust gas. If an explosive mixture is present the test tube gas will explode with a characteristic whistle or pop, and no sustained flame will be obtained to light the exhaust gas. The possibility of an explosion is completely eliminated if the exhaust gas is always lighted by a sustained flame of hydrogen burning in the test tube.

In case no exit trap is used on the end of a tube furnace with a hydrogen atmosphere another technique of handling the atmosphere may be used. The hydrogen is ignited inside the rubber stopper at the entrance end of the furnace tube by removing the rubber stopper and stopper tube from the furnace tube. The rubber stopper assembly with the burning hydrogen is replaced in the furnace tube (the central portion of which may be at some high temperature), and the hydrogen is allowed to burn along the inside of the furnace tube until it reaches the open end. This practice is not recommended except for open-ended furnace tubes where there is no interference with the smooth flow of the burning hydrogen. Generally, it is better to exhaust the exit hydrogen through a small opening, or better through a bubbler trap if a dry atmosphere is wanted, in order to prevent back diffusion of air into the furnace atmosphere.

Refractory cylinders about 2 to 3 inches long of low-weight firebrick cut to fit loosely into either end of the furnace tube are highly desirable in order to keep the extremes of the furnace tube cool. In this way, rubber stoppers may be safely used without danger of melting the rubber and without the necessity of water cooling, if the furnace tube projects 6 inches or so from either end of the furnace. Metal radiation shields have been frequently used for this purpose, but they are usually not as efficient as the lightweight firebrick. However, metal radiation shields are very useful in work where brick might prove objectionable because of evolved gases or for other reasons. Aluminum foil or polished sheet for cold zones as described above, or molybdenum for areas where the temperature is high, are recommended materials.

Many investigators have encountered difficulties by failing to realize that hydrogen can readily reduce silica or silica-containing refractories such as porcelain. Hence if a porcelain-tube furnace is used with a hydrogen atmosphere at temperatures of 1000°C or above, the reduced silicon may contaminate the samples being heat-treated. It is comparatively easy to introduce a few per cent silicon at the surface of metals like iron under these conditions. This contamination can be largely obviated by placing the samples in an alumina tube or other container not subject to hydrogen reduction.

Nitrogen

Nitrogen finds limited application as an atmosphere for metals which do not form nitrides, or dissolve nitrogen. A nitrogen atmosphere is satisfactory for the heat treatment of copper and its alloys, and may also be used for steel or certain iron alloys if traces of nitrogen are not objectionable. It could also be used as an atmosphere for nickel, cobalt, lead, zinc, palladium, silver, and perhaps a few others. There is less objection to nitrogen in heat treatments conducted below the melting point than in melting operations where the likelihood of nitrogen going into solution or forming nitrides is much greater. Nitrogen may react slowly with such metals as iron, tantalum, niobium, titanium, zirconium, vanadium, calcium, aluminum, chromium, lithium, thorium, and uranium.

Table 1 shows that several grades of purity are available, most of which require further purification before use in critical applications in the laboratory. The most common method of removing oxygen and water vapor is to pass the nitrogen through a drying tower to remove water and then over copper turnings at about 600°C to remove oxygen.

Dushman [3] gives some figures for the pressure of oxygen over $Cu + Cu_2O$ at equilibrium conditions as a function of temperature:

°C	°K	Oxygen Pressure in Millimeters
627	900	2×10^{-10}
727	1000	1.48×10^{-8}
827	1100	5.21×10^{-7}
927	1200	9.77×10^{-6}
1027	1300	1.15×10^{-4}

In order to keep the oxygen pressure as low as possible, a temperature of about 600°C is probably satisfactory. Although lower temperatures would give lower oxygen contents at equilibrium, the rate of approach to equilibrium becomes slower the lower the temperature.

Oxygen is more completely removed by chromium, as the pressure of oxygen over $Cr-Cr_2O_3$ is the order of 10^{-24} at 900°C and the order of 10^{-21} at 1000°C.[3] Comparatively cheap ferro-chromium can be used in place of pure chromium. Instead of passing hydrogen or nitrogen, etc., over finely divided ferro-chromium heated to 900°C or somewhat lower, an alternative procedure is to surround the specimen being heated in crushed ferro-chromium of about 30-mesh particle size. Naturally, the ferro-chromium should be arranged so that it is not actually contacting the specimen. This method has the advantage that oxygen is removed at the location of the specimen; hence there is no possibility of oxidizing the samples because of oxygen introduced subsequently to the purification train. But it has the disadvantage that the chromium must be heated to the same temperature as the sample. Hence if chromium or ferro-chromium were used to surround a sample at 1200°C, it would not have nearly the purifying power that it would have at 800°C, for example.

Argon and Helium

When a truly inert gas must be used, the choice lies between *helium* and *argon*. Helium costs about one half as much as argon, is lighter, and hence tends to escape more readily from a gas system if proper care is not taken to make it gas-tight. This, however, is not a very strong argument in favor of argon, as any inert gas system should be essentially vacuum-tight if the atmosphere must be pure. Helium also has about ten times the thermal conductivity of argon. This means that helium will conduct heat away to colder parts of the furnace much more rapidly than argon, which makes it an ideal gas with which to "break" a vacuum furnace when it is desired to cool the vacuum furnace quickly after a heat.

Argon is available in lamp grade and welding grade. Some typical compositions are shown in Table 1. Aside from the fact that the lamp grade may contain more nitrogen, there is not much difference between the two.

Probably the most efficient way of purifying argon or helium is to pass it over calcium turnings at 600 to 650°C in one tube furnace and in another at 350°C. The calcium should be placed in an iron pipe (to prevent reaction with ceramic materials), and the ends of the pipe closed with a standard pipe cap, which in turn is fitted with a flare fitting for copper tubing. The first furnace at 600 to 650°C takes out all gaseous impurities but hydrogen, whereas the 350°C furnace removes hydrogen, since calcium hydride is stable at this temperature. Such a double calcium furnace system operated at the temperatures indicated will prepare inert gases with negligible contents of oxygen, nitrogen, and hydrogen (the order of 10^{-6} mm).[11] A temperature higher than 650°C would reduce the oxygen and nitrogen content further, but 650°C is preferred because of the greatly increased rate of oxidation of iron by air at higher temperatures, and because oxygen diffuses through iron rather rapidly at high temperatures, thus reacting with the calcium to form CaO. Mallett [12] has found that passing noble gases over 60-mesh titanium chips or powder at 850°C is a very effective means of removing nitrogen and oxygen. Rather recently an exceptionally pure grade of helium has become available from the Bureau of Mines and from the Air Reduction Company (see Table 1). It has been purified by passing it over activated charcoal at liquid air temperatures. The availability of this pre-purified helium of high quality makes it more attractive for many purposes than argon which is not available in an equivalent state of purity. However, there are data which suggest that, as delivered in commercial cylinders, this grade is not much better than normal purity helium, hence the figures in the table.

ATMOSPHERES FOR CHANGING THE COMPOSITION OF METALS

Adding Constituents

The most common examples of adding constituents to metals are the processes of carburizing and nitriding. In the former, carbon is added to the surface of a metal (usually iron) by deposition from a gaseous atmosphere containing hydrocarbons such as methane. In the laboratory where rather small samples are the rule, and where high purity is desired, carburizing is frequently accomplished by passing a carrier gas such as hydrogen through some liquid hydrocarbon like dipentene or heptane. By controlling the temperature (and hence the vapor pressure) of the liquid hydrocarbon, the partial pressure of the hydrocarbon in the effluent gas may be controlled. If too much hydrocarbon is used in the carrier gas, the hydrocarbon is decomposed in the furnace much faster than it can be absorbed by the metal, resulting in the production of soot. This is undesirable as the soot coating prevents the intimate contact between gas and metal.

In small-scale metal-gas reactions of this type, a small laboratory tube furnace of the type shown in Figure 1 is convenient. In carburizing high-purity iron, Mehl and Wells [13] found it necessary to use an inside furnace tube of pure iron to avoid the introduction of silicon into the samples by hydrogen reduction of silicon-containing refractories, since they were using hydrogen as the carrier gas. In this work, either dipentene or dipentene plus a little benzene was used to carburize samples in the range between 0.1 and 1.4% carbon, the benzene being used for higher carbon contents. An outline of their experimental carburizing conditions is given in Table 4. Hydrogen was passed at a rate of one cubic foot per hour.

TABLE 4

CARBURIZING PROCEDURE OF MEHL AND WELLS

Desired Carbon Content, %	Temperature of Samples, °C	Time, hr	Hydrocarbon	Hydrocarbon Temperature, °C
0.1–0.4	850 ?	24–50 hr	Dipentene	0–35
0.9–1.0	850	75 hr	1 to 3 cc C_6H_6 to 30 cc dipentene	35
1–1.1	900	75 hr	1 to 3 cc C_6H_6 to 30 cc dipentene	35
1.2–1.4	1000	75 hr	1 to 3 cc C_6H_6 to 30 cc dipentene	35

For introducing very small amounts of carbon of the order of 0.001 to 0.01%, as in studying the yield-point phenomenon in iron, hydrogen may be bubbled through heptane at room temperature with the iron samples at 650°C. For very thin sheets or wire a few mils in thickness, a treatment period of an hour is enough to introduce sufficient carbon to produce the yield point in iron samples. If a specimen temperature of about 720°C (just below the iron-carbon eutectoid temperature) is used for heating the iron, the time of heating can be shortened to about 5 minutes, but in this case the heptane should be cooled to dry-ice temperature ($-78°C$) to lower the vapor pressure of hydrocarbon sufficiently to avoid soot formation on the samples.

Nitriding of some metals may be accomplished by direct reaction with purified nitrogen gas. Other metals, like iron, are more readily nitrided by ammonia, which may or may not be previously dissociated with the aid of a catalyst. Naturally, ammonia could not be used when the metal, like zirconium, forms a hydride, unless the hydride is not stable at the nitriding temperature.

A wide variety of metallic additions may be added to a metal specimen by passing a carrier gas such as hydrogen containing a gaseous halide over the sample. As in carburizing and nitriding, all additions made in this manner form surface coatings which in most cases can be diffused into the sample during a subsequent heat treatment. Chromium, silicon, molybdenum, and many other elements have been used for surface coatings on steels and other metals by such gas-phase reactions, usually involving a chloride of the coating metal but occasionally some other halide.[14, 15, 16] It should be emphasized that this technique is fraught with many experimental difficulties as there are numerous variables to be controlled. Although it has proved to be a feasible technique for the deposition of many metals, it cannot be recommended as a method to be set up and operated in a straightforward manner like electroplating. Metal carbonyls have also been used in a similar fashion.[17, 18] In some instances, instead of using a carrier gas, the chamber surrounding the sample is evacuated and the carbonyl added to the vacuum chamber, preferentially depositing on the hot sample which is heated by high frequency induction. By this technique, coating the chamber walls is avoided as the carbonyl is decomposed only upon a hot surface.

Removing Constituents

There are not so many cases where an atmosphere has been used to remove constituents from metals. It is obvious that such a process is a diffusion-limited one, and can be used only where the element to be eliminated has a high diffusion rate and where the samples to be treated are quite thin, perhaps the order of 0.10 inch thick or less.

The most common example of the removal of constituents from metals by atmosphere treatment is the decarburization and denitriding of iron by wet hydrogen. The hydrogen is saturated with water vapor at temperatures between room temperature and about 60°C, depending upon the moisture content desired, and passed over the specimen contained in a tube furnace. Often metallurgical considerations (desire to maintain a small grain size, etc.) prevent the heating of the specimen into the gamma range, and a suitable specimen temperature is about 720°C. At this temperature, carbon contents of the order of 0.05% can be reduced to less than 0.001% in 6 to 8 hours. Nitrogen is simultaneously removed. In contrast to the above figures, the rate of carbon removal by dry hydrogen is much slower, as shown by Campbell et al.,[19] who treated iron at 950°C for 7 days and reduced the original carbon content (0.018%) only to 0.009%. They remarked that with moist hydrogen the carbon was completely removed. The exact mechanism of the reaction is in doubt. Slight amounts (0.005%) of oxygen are introduced into the specimen by this treatment, but the amount is usually too small to be important. It should be emphasized that wet hydrogen is essential; dry hydrogen is essentially inert under these conditions.

Metal powders to be used in powder metallurgy work are often deoxidized by passing dry hydrogen over them while heating to some temperature below the sintering temperature.

In principle it is possible to remove oxygen from solid metals such as iron, copper, and nickel, whose oxides are not very stable, but in practice this technique is not very easy. Since, as in the decarburization of iron by wet hydrogen, the process is diffusion limited, the thickness of the samples cannot be large or the deoxidation process becomes too lengthy to be practicable. As pointed out above, there is considerable danger of introducing silicon and other metallic impurities during a long soak at high temperatures in a dry hydrogen atmosphere. However, if adequate precautions are taken, it is possible to reduce the oxygen content of many metals to about 0.001% without introducing significant amounts of other impurities. Wells et al.[20] treated iron in dry hydrogen at 1200°C for 250 hours and found the following impurities: Si 0.002%, C 0.0012, O_2 0.002, N_2 0.003, H_2 0.005. The authors stated that "both carbon and oxygen were removed" by this treatment. The iron samples were 0.125 inch thick and were supported on previously hydrogen-treated iron supports resting on high-purity magnesia. The samples and support were both placed in a hydrogen-purified Armco iron tube. J. G. Thompson,[20] in discussing the foregoing procedure, suggested that an increase in copper, manganese, tin, and carbon is possible from impurities in the iron tube.

REFERENCES

1. Fischer and Porter Co., Hatboro, Pa.
2. Aluminum Ore Co., E. St. Louis, Ill.
3. Saul Dushman, Scientific Foundations of Vacuum Technique, John Wiley and Sons, New York, 1949.
4. J. H. Bower, "Comparative Efficiencies of Various Dehydrating Agents Used for Drying Gases," J. Research Natl. Bur. Standards, 12, 241–248 (1934).
5. Baker & Co., Newark, N. J.
6. The Pittsburgh Electrodryer Co., Pittsburgh, Pa.
7. American Platinum Co., and Baker and Co., Newark, N. J.
8. D. L. Chapman and P. W. Reynolds, "The Catalytic Combination of Hydrogen and Oxygen at the Surface of Platinum," Proc. Roy. Soc. (London), 156A, 284–306 (1936).

9. D. L. Chapman and G. Gregory, "The Catalysis by Palladium of the Union of Hydrogen and Oxygen," *Proc. Roy. Soc.* (*London*), **147A**, 68–75 (1934).
10. J. L. Snoek and E. J. Haes, "Laboratory Production of Very Pure Hydrogen," *Applied Sci. Research*, **A2**, 326–328 (1951).
11. Leo Epstein, Personal Communication, Knolls Atomic Power Laboratory, Schenectady, N. Y.
12. M. W. Mallett, "Purification of Argon," *Ind. Eng. Chem.*, **42**, 2095–2096 (1950).
13. Robert F. Mehl and Cyril Wells, "Constitution of High Purity Iron Carbon Alloys," *Trans. Am. Inst. Mining Met. Engrs., Iron & Steel Div.*, **125**, 429–472 (1937).
14. E. A. Beidler, C. F. Powell, J. E. Campbell, "The Formation of Molybdenum Disilicide Coatings on Molybdenum," *J. Electrochemical Soc.*, **98**, 21–25 (1951).
15. C. F. Powell, J. E. Campbell, and B. W. Gonser, "The Formation of Refractory Coatings by Vapor Deposition Methods," U.S. Air Force Project Rand Report R-137, March 25, 1949. (Includes available literature survey on depositing Ti, Zr, Cb, Ta, Mo, W, Hf, Th, Cr, U, R, Ru, Rh, Os, Pt.)
16. C. F. Powell, J. E. Campbell, and B. W. Gonser, "The Deposition of Tantalum and Columbium from Their Volatilized Halides," *Trans. Am. Electrochemical Soc.*, **93**, 258 (1948).
17. B. B. Owen and R. T. Usher, "Plating Chromium by Thermal Decomposition of Chromium Hexacarbonyl," *Trans. Am. Inst. Mining Met. Engrs., Inst. Metals Div.*, **175**, 693–698 (1948).
18. J. J. Lander and L. H. Germer, "Plating Molybdenum, Tungsten and Chromium by Thermal Decomposition of Their Carbonyls," *Trans. Am. Inst. Mining Met. Engrs., Inst. Metals Div.*, **175**, 648–692 (1948).
19. E. D. Campbell, J. F. Ross, and W. L. Fink, "The Relative Efficiencies of Dry and Moist Hydrogen on the Decarburizing of Steel at 950°C," *J. Iron and Steel Inst.*, **108**, 179–185 (1923).
20. C. Wells, R. A. Ackley, and R. F. Mehl, "A Dilatometric Study of the Alpha-Gamma Transformation in High Purity Iron," *Trans. Am. Soc. Metals*, **24**, 46–74 (1936).

CHAPTER SIX

Vacuum Systems

Many operations involving the heating or melting of metals are most conveniently carried out in a vacuum in order to prevent reaction with the atmosphere. Although for some purposes the use of an inert gas is convenient, since it involves a simpler technique and does not require expensive equipment, vacuum offers the advantage of securing more positive protection from the atmosphere. This is true because it is not so easy to purify a gas to the same degree of freedom from oxygen and nitrogen as is readily secured in a good vacuum system. For example, the fractional amount of residual gas in a system evacuated to 10^{-5} mm of mercury is $10^{-5}/760$ or 1.32×10^{-8} or 0.00000132%. Needless to say, it is not a simple matter to purify a noble gas to an equivalent purity. Even more important, there is no satisfactory method of quickly ascertaining, when using a purified gas, whether the residual gas content is 0.001 or 0.0001%. However, with a vacuum gauge the purity of the atmosphere (gas pressure) may be read continuously. Still another advantage is that in high-temperature operations, such as melting metals at temperatures in excess of 1000°C, the only appreciable heat loss is by radiation; conduction and convection losses are eliminated. This means that much greater thermal efficiency results, and, for the same expenditure of power, considerably higher temperatures may be reached.

PUMPING SYSTEMS

In any high-vacuum system, both a mechanical pump and a diffusion pump are necessary for satisfactory operation at pressures below about 10 microns (0.010 mm) of mercury. The mechanical pump is required to remove the air in the entire vacuum system down to the region where the diffusion pump operates. In the case of the generally used oil diffusion pumps, this means about 100 microns (0.1 mm) of mercury.

Mechanical Pumps

Although there are several makes of mechanical pumps, all are very similar in operation in that an eccentric cam squeezes out a cresent-shaped volume of air at each revolution. Figure 1 shows a typical example of a two-stage pump. Gas is drawn through the entrance I

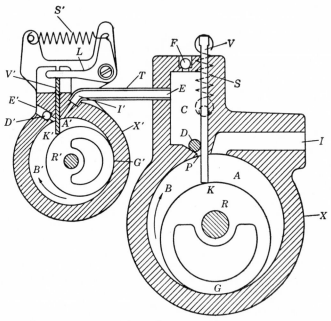

Figure 1. Schematic Diagram of Working Principle of Cenco Hypervac Pumps. I, I', intake; E, E', exhaust; D, D', exhaust valve; C, interstage; F, interstage exhaust valve; V, V', vane; S, S', vane spring; L, vane lever; R, R', rotor; X, X', stator; A, A', intake chamber; B, B', exhaust chamber; P, exhaust port; K, K', contact line of vane with rotor; G, G', contact line of rotor with stator; T, connecting tube. (Central Scientific Co.) (Dushman.[10])

into the crescent-shaped chamber A while on the other side of the eccentric R, gas at B is being squeezed through the valve D into chamber C, where it at first exhausts through valve F to the atmosphere. However, when the pressure in the exhaust chamber C falls to well below atmospheric pressure, the gas is sucked into the second stage at A^1, which operates in exactly the same way. The second-stage pump evacuates chamber C and acts as a forepump to the main stage since the pressure differential between B and A is reduced by the action of the second stage. This, in turn, means less tendency for any gas to leak past the oil seal at G, separating the first stage into a low-pressure and a high-pressure section. Vanes V and V^1 prevent the compressed gas from riding all the way around the cam, forcing the gas to go out the exit ports.

The efficiency of such pumps obviously depends a great deal on the fit of the various parts, and in particular requires a very close fit between the rotating cam and the cam housing. The oil in which such pumps are bathed not only acts as a sealing medium but also as lubrication. The pump oil after long use becomes contaminated by dissolved air and water, water being particularly troublesome, making it necessary to discard the old oil or treat it for removal of impurities.

For many pumping systems, particularly where diffusion pumps of reasonably high forepressure tolerance are used, the use of two-stage mechanical pumps is hardly necessary. There is no need to use a mechanical pump with a guaranteed ultimate vacuum of 0.1 micron if 75 microns of forepressure at the diffusion pump is adequate for satisfactory operation.

Besides evacuating the system to the pressure level where the diffusion pump operates, the mechanical pump also maintains the operation of the diffusion pump by keeping the exit end of the diffusion pump below the critical pressure required for operation. The size of the mechanical pump is fixed by two considerations: (1) it must be large enough to carry off the gas removed from the entire system fast enough to maintain the required forepressure at the diffusion pump, and (2) it should be of sufficient capacity to evacuate the chamber from atmospheric pressure to the required low level in a reasonable length of time, perhaps 5 to 10 minutes. There are several manufacturers of satisfactory mechanical pumps. Some specialize in smaller sizes; [1,2] others concentrate on larger pumps suitable for chambers of several cubic feet capacity.[3,4,5]

Diffusion Pumps

The first diffusion pumps were constructed of glass, and they used mercury as the pumping medium. Many such pumps are in use today. Figure 2 shows a typical example. Mercury in the boiler at the bottom of the pump is heated to the boiling point, while the pump is evacuated continuously by a mechanical pump connected at point A. Mercury vapor rises in the vertical tube, and is projected downward through the jet B as it starts to condense. After passing through the water-cooled jet area, the mercury is fully condensed and runs back into the boiler. The molecules of air that find themselves in the region of the jet are knocked downward and are eventually removed via the forepump opening to the mechanical pump. Most mercury diffusion pumps are rather small, seldom having a pumping speed of over 20 liters per second at one micron or thereabouts, and are usually much slower. Larger, metal diffusion pumps using mercury have been built, but their only advantage over the more common oil diffusion pumps is their ability to operate with higher forepump pressures. Also, large

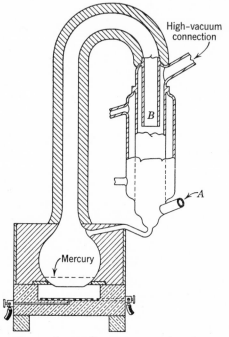

Figure 2.   Glass Diffusion Pump.   (Dushman.[10])

mercury pumps are not readily available commercially. The smaller, glass diffusion pumps employing mercury as the pumping fluid are normally used in *static systems* where a very low pressure is generally required, and where the amount of gas movement is small. *Kinetic systems* depend upon high pumping speeds to produce a low pressure. There are usually a few leaks which may be either true leaks or virtual leaks arising from gas evolution inside the system. One danger of kinetic systems should not be overlooked: the possibility of passing a large amount of gas through the system, but at very low pressure because of high pumping speed, thus contaminating the specimen with oxygen or nitrogen or both. The mere fact that the chamber pressure is low does not necessarily indicate satisfactory operation unless it can be shown that with the pumps blocked off the increase in pressure due to leaks is negligibly small, a few micron-liters per hour.

For the great majority of metallurgical operations, a kinetic system requiring a large-capacity diffusion pump is used. Such pumps nor-

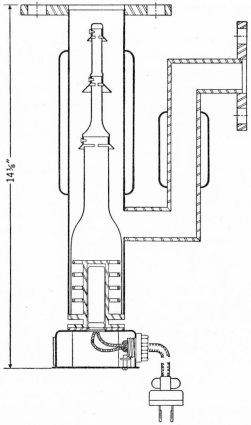

Figure 3.   Design of Three-Stage All-Metal Oil-Vapor Pump.   (National Research Corp.)   (Dushman.[10])

mally use a stable organic compound, usually an oil or ester such as one of the butyl phthalates or octyl phthalates, but there are other types such as certain chlorinated hydrocarbons. Such pumping fluids are available at vacuum equipment supply houses.[6,7] Certain silicones[8] have been much used for pumping oils in oil diffusion pumps and are less susceptible to thermal cracking or oxidation than the esters and other organic compounds. Silicones suffer somewhat, however, from a lower pumping speed as compared to the oils, and in addition tend to "poison" vacuum gauges more readily than the other oils so that they do not read correctly. Presumably such poisoning is due to the formation of a stable silica film on vacuum gauge filaments, thus markedly affecting their electron-emitting or heat-dissipation characteristics.

A section through a typical metal diffusion pump is shown in Figure 3. In this pump there are three different jets mounted at different heights along the "umbrella" or jet system. The pump fluid (in this

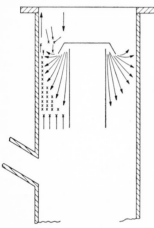

pump an organic oil) is vaporized in the boiler at the bottom of the pump, and the vapor rises inside the jet system, strikes the various jets or vanes, and is deflected downward as shown in Figure 4. In its downward path, air molecules are ejected down toward the bottom of the pump and are eventually removed through the forepump or mechanical pump. This is a very elementary description of a rather complex phenomenon; for a complete quantitative description the reader is referred to the exhaustive work by Dushman.[10]

Figure 4. Jet in Metal Diffusion Pump. (Dushman.[10])

Certain oil pumps are "fractionating" pumps which allow the higher vapor pressure components of the pumping fluid to boil off and condense in a special chamber where they do not affect the ultimate vacuum obtainable. The lowest vapor pressure components are retained in the main pumping area near the jets, thus allowing the attainment of somewhat higher vacuums than in a non-fractionating pump. This feature is not important unless one is interested in vacua of less than 0.001 micron, lower than necessary in most metallurgical experimental work.

An advantage of the oil diffusion pump over mercury pumps is that for much work no vapor trap is required, whereas a cold trap is generally necessary when a mercury pump is used, to prevent mercury from diffusing throughout the system. (Mercury at room temperature has a vapor pressure of about 3 microns.) The commonly used diffusion pump oils vary in vapor pressure at 25°C from about 10^{-2} to 10^{-5} micron.

The speed of a diffusion pump is largely a function of the area of the pump opening, constant efficiency of jet design and other pump variables being assumed. A popular 4-inch-diameter oil diffusion pump,[6] for example, has a speed of about 275 liters per second at 0.1 micron, but at 1 micron this speed falls off to about 65 liters per second. Similarly, a 2-inch-diameter pump of a different make [7] has a pumping speed at 0.1 micron of about 70 liters per second. Both pumps have a maximum speed of about 22 liters per second per square inch of opening.

In any diffusion pump, whether mercury or oil, there is a certain threshold forepump pressure which must be reached before the pump will operate. Higher pressures cause too much back diffusion of gas in the opposite direction to allow effective pumping action. For many oil diffusion pumps this limiting pressure is about 100 microns.

There is a class of metal diffusion pumps called *booster pumps*, which, although limited to higher ultimate pressures, can operate satisfactorily at higher forepump pressures, about 500 microns. Such booster pumps may be used by themselves if a pressure of a few microns is satisfactory, or, more commonly, they are used between a mechanical pump and a diffusion pump on systems subject to surges of gas sufficient to choke the diffusion pump. Very large diffusion pumps, as big as 32 inches in throat diameter, have been built which have pumping speeds of the order of 15,000 liters per second.

In general, oil diffusion pumps have an ultimate vacuum of about 0.001 micron, although a few of special design may be used for lower vacuums to about 0.00001 micron. For practically all metallurgical work 0.1 to 0.01 micron is adequate, and much work is done with pressures in the micron region. As regards manufacturers of oil diffusion pumps, there are only two which are well known [6,7] and who can be consulted for specific information regarding their pump characteristics.

VAPOR TRAPS

Traps are an important feature of vacuum systems using mercury diffusion pumps, and are used to prevent mercury from entering the rest of the system. Oil pumps generally require no cold traps, but metal baffles are usually advisable to prevent oil vapors from entering the vacuum chamber and condensing in the area near the mouth of the diffusion pump. If a vacuum valve is used between the diffusion pump and the chamber, a baffle or a trap may not be required since the valve acts as a baffle, but usually not so efficiently. In large systems where there is considerable refractory material present, as in vacuum melting furnaces, dust traps are often used to prevent abrasive particles from entering the pumping system. Even here, however, the use of traps is questionable unless the dust content is quite high, because the diffusion pump acts as a trap and generally prevents solid particles from reaching the mechanical pump, where scoring of moving parts could occur. Figure 5 shows several types of traps used for different purposes.

Mercury traps are cooled to below the freezing point of mercury. This is ordinarily accomplished by dipping the trap into liquid air or preferably liquid nitrogen, a safer material to handle. Two traps of

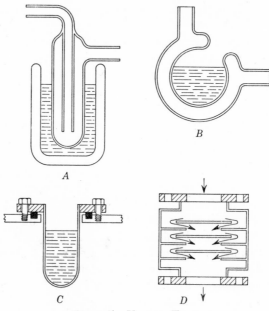

Figure 5. Vacuum Traps.

this sort are shown in Figures 5A and 5B. Cold traps are also used for freezing out other readily condensable gases, such as water vapor. In this case, the trap may be a cold "finger" or a tube inserted into the vacuum chamber (see Figure 5C). Figure 5D shows schematically a baffle often used with oil diffusion pumps as outlined above. Such baffles are ordinarily water cooled by copper coils on the outside of the baffle chamber to aid in condensing the oil.

VACUUM MEASURING DEVICES

Probably the oldest and most commonly used vacuum measuring device is the McLeod gauge (Figure 6). It is an absolute instrument whose calibration is calculated from the geometry of the instrument.

If V and P signify volume and pressure, respectively, and subscripts o and f refer to original and final, then $V_o P_o = V_f P_f$, from Boyle's law. V_f and P_f are measured when taking a reading, and V_o is known from the size of the gauge; hence P_o, the pressure desired, immediately fol-

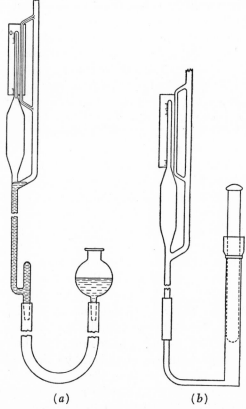

(a)   (b)

Figure 6. McLeod Gauge. (a) Form with reservoir that can be raised or lowered. (b) Form with plunger. (Dushman.[10])

lows. The gauge is ordinarily calibrated so that by always reading at a constant compression P_f of the gas, P_o is read directly from the calibration chart since each V_f corresponds to a definite P_o. However, for most vacuum measuring applications in kinetic systems the McLeod gauge is inadequate or unsatisfactory. In the first place, the McLeod gauge is not continuously reading; it is necessary to take a sample of gas and compress it so that a readily measurable mercury head is developed, corresponding to the new pressure of the gas. The operation of reading the gauge may take as much as 1 to 2 minutes, during which time conditions may be changing in the vacuum chamber. Also, it does not read condensable gases such as water vapor, oil vapors, or other similar gases because Boyle's law does not even approximately apply. Still another disadvantage is that it cannot be used as a leak-detecting device as can most other continuously reading gauges. The McLeod gauge finds its sphere of usefulness primarily as an instrument with which other devices may be compared under steady-state conditions. It has a definite function also in quantitative low-pressure gas systems, where it is necessary to know with some precision the total pressure of a gas mixture.

The useful range of the McLeod gauge is from a few millimeters of mercury to possibly 1×10^{-6} mm. Such a range is not feasible on one instrument, however. More commonly, the range is from about 1 mm (1000 microns) to 1×10^{-3} mm (1 micron).

The Pirani gauge [6] is typical of the continuously reading vacuum gauges useful in the range from about 1000 microns to 1 micron, thus blanketing the same range as the more common McLeod range. It works on the principle of measuring the electrical resistivity of a thin hot wire (usually tungsten) inserted in the vacuum system, and operates as follows. Where the vacuum is rather poor many air or other gas molecules are present, and the wire can readily give up its heat by increasing the kinetic energy of the gas immediately surrounding the wire. This loss of temperature in the wire is, of course, reflected at once in decreased electrical resistivity which may be measured readily by a suitable electrical circuit such as a Wheatstone bridge. In practice, it is customary to use a similar tungsten wire permanently sealed off in a very high vacuum as one arm of the bridge, so that any changes in room temperature are nullified by corresponding resistivity changes in the standard wire. (See Figure 7.) As in most vacuum gauges, it is customary to calibrate the gauge for air, as air usually constitutes the major residual gas left in a vacuum system. The response of the gauge depends largely upon the thermal conductivity of the residual gas; the higher the conductivity, the greater the reading in the Wheatstone bridge meter. Since hydrogen has a very high thermal conductivity, hydrogen may be used as a probe in leak hunting, as will be described subsequently. The Pirani gauge is very sensitive, responding rapidly to changes in pressure in the system, and can be a very satisfactory instrument up to the threshold of the high vacuum range, about one micron. Beyond this point it is not sensitive, and other gauges must be used. It should be added that it has been the experience of many people that the Pirani gauge does not stand up well in a "dirty" system such as a vacuum melting furnace, where, besides residual air, moisture, and traces of oil vapors, some metallic vapors are encountered. Under these conditions, a Pirani tube (containing the wire whose resistance is being measured) becomes contaminated, its resistance is changed, and the gauge no longer reads correctly. Contaminated tubes can sometimes be made to read correctly by heating the wire to 800 to 900°C in high vacuum.

The *thermocouple gauge* [6,7] covers the same range as the Pirani gauge, and operates on a similar principle. Like the Pirani, the thermocouple gauge makes use of changing temperature in a fine

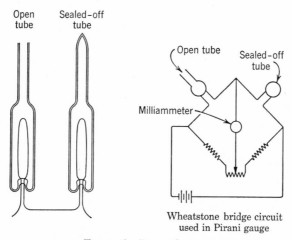

Figure 7. Pirani Gauge.

tungsten wire due to impingement of gas molecules on the wire; but, instead of measuring the resistance of the wire, the thermocouple gauge measures the temperature of the wire by means of a very fine thermocouple spot welded to the wire. The sensitivity of the gauge obviously depends upon the heat capacity of the wire and thermocouple, both of which must be very small for maximum sensitivity. Like the Pirani, the thermocouple gauge is subject to error from contamination, and some care must be exercised in placement of the gauge with respect to contaminants from the heating chamber. A trap may be used to avoid "plating" the wire with volatile materials (see Figure 8). Such a trap is also advisable with a Pirani gauge, but, regardless of the pressure-measuring device, the use of a trap suffers from the disadvantage that a pressure gradient is created, causing readings not equivalent to those obtained in the vacuum chamber.

The thermocouple gauge as offered commercially consists of a metal tube with reduced neck fitted with standard ⅛-inch-pipe threads suitable for screwing into a metal system, and a control box to measure the pressure (Figure 9).   The all-metal construction and general rugged nature of the gauge make it particularly adapted to metallurgical work.

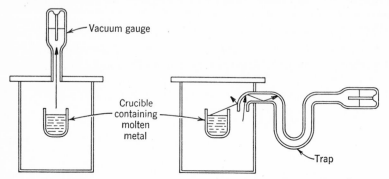

Figure 8.   Metal Vapor Trap for Vacuum Gauge.

For the measurement of high vacuum (below one micron) more sensitive instruments must be used.   Of these, the *ion gauge* [6, 7, 9, 11] is the most generally used.   The most common ion gauge is the hot cathode type, consisting of a triode—cathode, anode, and grid (see Figure 10).

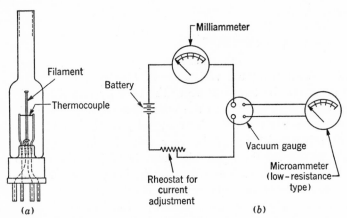

Figure 9.   Thermocouple Gauge and Auxiliary Circuit.   (Dushman.[10])

The cathode is a filament heated to a high temperature in order to supply electrons.   The electrons are accelerated to the grid between the filament and the anode, or plate.   Because of the nature of the field in the vicinity of the grid, the electrons are deflected to the grid, but in passing to the grid the residual gas in the ion tube is partially ionized because of collisions with the electrons. The ions created between the grid and the plate pass to the plate, creating an ion current which can be measured by a suitable microammeter. Hence the greater the amount of gas, the more ionization, and the more ion current. The use of an ion gauge to read pressures in the vicinity of one micron or higher is not feasible because the filament burns out rapidly under these conditions. The ion gauge is capable of extreme sensitivity, and may be used to measure vacua down to about 10^{-8} mm of mercury. Naturally, with such extreme sensitivity, contamination of the ion tube becomes increasingly troublesome, and calibration is a vexing problem. However, for most work extreme accuracy of reading is not necessary, and all that one need know is the order of magnitude of the vacuum, whether it is about 10^{-5} mm or 10^{-6} mm, etc. Besides possible contamination of the ion tube, stability of the ion gauge circuit is a troublesome matter. Fortunately, in the range up to 10^{-6} mm, these difficulties are not overwhelming, particularly if it is not required to know the degree of vacuum with high precision. In the usual range of metallurgical high-vacuum work, 10^{-3} mm to 10^{-5} mm, ion circuits and tubes are quite reliable and do not demand too much of the user if reasonable care is taken in avoiding tube contamination as with a cold trap or even a mechanical trap. However, the use of a cold trap results in lower readings since moisture and other readily condensable gases are removed before they affect the gauge.

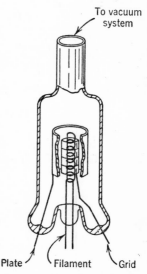

Figure 10. Ion Gauge. (Guthrie and Wakerling.[13])

The *cold cathode ion gauge* or Philips gauge operates on a principle similar to that of the hot cathode (thermionic) ion gauge, except that the electrons are given off by positive ion bombardment. A high potential, the order of a few thousand volts direct current, is impressed between the cathode and the anode, creating a cold gaseous discharge. The cathode and the anode are placed within a magnetic field, which has the effect of increasing the total path of the ionizing electrons so that the discharge can be maintained at much lower pressures than in an ordinary Geissler discharge tube (see Figure 11). The tube body, M, contains a ring-shaped cathode R located between the anode plates *P*. *H* is the permanent magnet supplying the required magnetic field. A commonly used commercial model[6] has a range of 0.02

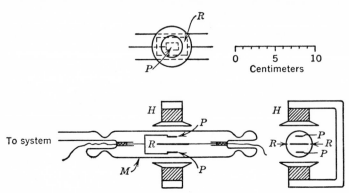

Figure 11. Cold-Cathode Ionization Gauge. (Dushman.[10])

micron to 25 microns, a very useful range for metallurgical applications. Other similar instruments[11,12] have been built with a wider

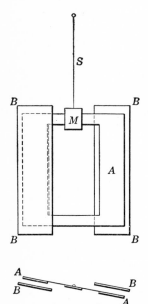

Figure 12. Diagrammatic Sketch of Knudson Type of Gauge. (Dushman.[10])

range, reading to lower pressures, but apparently it is not feasible to use a gauge of this type below about 10^{-7} mm of Hg because of the difficulty of maintaining the discharge. Cold cathode gauges have practical advantages over thermionic ion gauges in that (1) they are simpler in circuit and simpler to operate, and (2) they are not as subject to damage due to inadvertently admitting high pressures to the gauge. Gauges of this type have much to recommend them.

The *Knudsen gauge* has recently become commercially available,[6] and like the McLeod gauge it is an absolute instrument which theoretically, at least, requires no calibration. This gauge, although not new, has not been in wide use probably because it is somewhat difficult to build and is not quite as convenient to handle as a Pirani or ion gauge. The Knudsen gauge works on the principle of thermal activation of residual gas molecules in a vacuum system impinging upon a light vane vertically suspended (*S*) in the vacuum to be measured. On each side of the vane is a heating coil, which is heated to

some standard temperature in the neighborhood of 300°C. The gas
molecules in the immediate vicinity of the heated coils (*B*) take on
more kinetic energy, and some of them hit the freely suspended vane

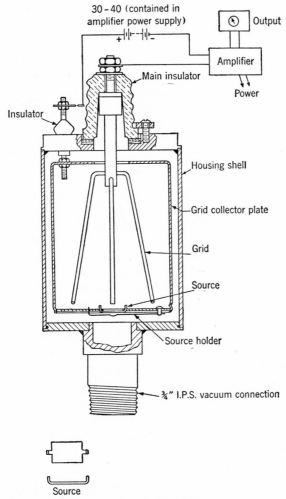

Figure 13.   Diagram of Ionization Chamber of Alphatron Gauge.   (National Research Corp.)   (Dushman.[10])

(*A*), thus turning it through a small angle (see Figure 12).   A mirror
(*M*) is mounted on the vane, and the deflection of the vane is measured
in a manner entirely analogous to that of a deflecting galvanometer
mirror.   It is a very rugged instrument, which is not harmed, as are
many other vacuum gauges, by inadvertently admitting atmospheric

pressure to the system. In addition, it is not subject to contamination and hence can be counted upon to stay in calibration. For this reason it makes a satisfactory standard instrument for checking Pirani and thermocouple gauges as well as other gauges in its range of measurement. Another advantage of this instrument is that, unlike most vacuum gauges, it reads the same pressure regardless of the species of the gas molecules in the vacuum chamber. The usual useful range is from 10^{-3} to 10^{-5} mm.

Like any vacuum measuring device the Knudsen gauge has its limitations and disadvantages. As offered commercially [6] the gauge has two ranges, from 10^{-3} to 10^{-4} mm and from 10^{-4} to 10^{-5} mm. In changing from one range to another it requires about 15 minutes to achieve thermal equilibrium; hence, in changing scales there is a considerable period when pressure readings may not be taken. The gauge is rather large and cumbersome as compared to an ion gauge, and unlike the latter, which is read remotely, the Knudsen gauge reading is taken at the point where the gauge is located in the vacuum system. The gauge should be mounted in such a manner that it is quite free from vibrations, particularly those of large amplitudes.

For several years, an instrument called the *Alphatron* has been available at one of the vacuum instrument specialty houses.[7] This is an ion gauge of special type. The gauge proper, which is fitted to the vacuum system, contains a radium source, which is an abundant emitter of alpha particles. The gas in the gauge is bombarded by the alpha particles and is thus ionized (Figure 13). As in an ion gauge, an ion current is measured by a suitable circuit containing a sensitive meter. One of the outstanding advantages of this gauge is its linear scale, making it equally sensitive in both high and low ranges.

The range is particularly broad, 10^{-3} to 10^4 mm, and is one which can be duplicated by no other known instrument. Since the radiation emitted by the radium is for all practical purposes a constant, the ionizing effect is a constant, and hence elaborate circuitry to provide a constant ionizing (grid) current is eliminated. This results in a very stable and dependable instrument.

Location of Vacuum Measuring Devices

In any kinetic vacuum system there is a pressure gradient from the mouth of the diffusion pump to the farthest recess of the chamber being evacuated. This gradient is particularly steep if the vacuum system includes bends or apertures of smaller diameter. It is of course desirable to locate the vacuum measuring device (gauge) as close as possible to the area in the vacuum chamber where it is desired to know the pressure. In general the vacuum gauge is better located in a spot where the vacuum would be poorer rather than in a place where the reverse is true, so that one is operating in a conservative manner and not obtaining a very optimistic reading as would be the case if a reading were taken at the mouth of the diffusion pump. For example, in a tube furnace, if one end of a gas-tight ceramic tube is fitted with a diffusion pump, the vacuum gauge should preferably be at the other end of the tube.

VACUUM SEALS

The technology of making vacuum seals of various kinds has been brought to a rather high degree of perfection in recent years. Much of this practical know-how has been the result of trial and error in the field of cyclotron "engineering" and in other fields of applied physics, including nucleonics.

No attempt can be made here to make anything approaching a complete index of the various known methods of making high-vacuum seals. Rather, some well-proved methods used successfully in a few laboratories will be illustrated. For a more complete discussion of this subject, the reader is referred to the book by Guthrie and Wakerling.[13]

Vacuum seals may be divided into the following principal types:

1. Flanges.
2. Small tube to large chamber.
3. Electrical leads.
4. Windows.
5. Introduction of motion into a vacuum chamber.

The five seals listed above are those most frequently used in metal vacuum systems and, in every case, involve the use of rubber gaskets. The outline drawing in Figure 14, representing a typical vacuum system, illustrates use of the flange seal in several places in the system. In the following section description is limited to demountable seals rather than to permanent seals such as welded or soldered joints since these last require little discussion.

There are several configurations of flange seals possible; the more common ones are shown in Figure 15. In type *a*, a rectangular groove is cut in a flange mounted on the vacuum chamber in which is placed a square cross section rubber gasket of medium hardness, preferably in a continuous ring. If the diameter of the gasket must be over 18 inches it would be more convenient to obtain a long strip cut to length and to make a lap joint. Although such joints in rubber gaskets

are generally satisfactory, they sometimes are leaky and should be
checked from time to time. Cementing the ends with rubber cement

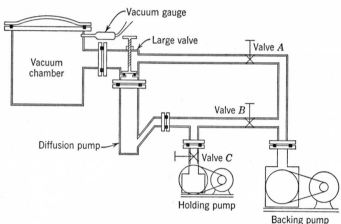

Figure 14. Metal Vacuum System.

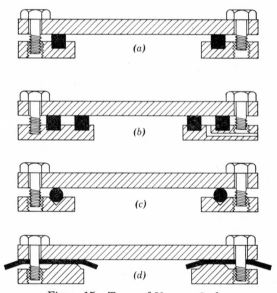

Figure 15. Types of Vacuum Seals.

is recommended by some, but there is a question of the effectiveness
of such cementing; at worst it does no harm. The rubber should be
recessed into the groove to a depth of about one half the thickness of
the rubber. An excellent finish in the groove is by no means necessary,

but it should not be very rough; a surface which feels smooth to the
hand is satisfactory. The actual thickness of the square rubber gasket
is not critical. There is no reason for using a larger gasket than $\frac{1}{4}$
inch, and anything less than $\frac{1}{8}$ inch would necessitate too great care
in obtaining very flat surfaces. The lid or cover is generally secured
in place by ordinary cap screws which pass through the cover and
either may be threaded into the chamber flange as shown or may be
fastened with nuts. The lid should not be tightened excessively to
the point where the two metal pieces almost touch, but a snug fit
obtained by tightening with a small wrench is satisfactory. Excessive pressure quickly ruins the gasket. Where the cover is in a horizontal plane, no screws at all are necessary if the rubber gasket and
lid are both fairly plane, as atmospheric pressure will apply ample
force to hold the lid securely in place.

It should be mentioned here that it is important that the gasket
groove be quite plane, but frequently warping occurs during welding
or hard soldering to the chamber wall. Hence it is desirable that
the flange be machined flat and the groove made *after* the welding or
soldering operation. In welding, a stress relief anneal before machining should be employed. Welding both inside and outside tends to
make tighter joints. With flanges up to a foot or so in diameter, six
cap screws equally spaced around the flange are adequate; but for
larger flanges it is probably desirable to have the screws spaced about
6 inches apart.

Before type a is left, a frequently used modification of it should be
discussed; this is the double gasket type (b) shown in Figure 15.
This is an elegant device which allows one to do two things which
cannot be as readily done with the single gasket seal. The small hole
leading into the space between the two gaskets allows the introduction of a probe gas for leak hunting, and if the inner gasket is leaking
a small mechanical pump can be applied at the outside of the probe
hole to hold the fort until the run is over. Obviously, only the inner
gasket acts as a seal. Although this technique is very ingenious and
probably useful once in a great while, it is a refinement of dubious
value in most cases. In the first place, there is no additional guarantee
against a leak as compared to the simpler single gasket method, since
there is only one gasket acting as a seal. Second, seals of this type
rarely cause trouble. Third, it is readily possible to check a single
gasket seal for leaks, although it takes a little longer.

Going on to type c of Figure 15, this is one type of O-ring seal much
used recently. O-rings are complete rings of circular cross section,
and are available in a wide range of sizes from commercial suppliers.

For a not exorbitant amount, a laboratory engaged in vacuum work can keep a supply of several sizes of O-rings on hand to be used on jobs requiring gaskets up to about 16 inches in diameter.

The suppliers of O-rings [14] have prepared manuals which give the correct groove size and design for rings of all sizes. The availability of these rings greatly simplifies the procurement of gaskets which otherwise have to be cut as needed from a large piece of rubber, with consequent waste and loss of time when replacement is required.

Type d (Figure 15) is probably the simplest method, and for most work is quite satisfactory. It consists only of a rough-cut piece of rubber sheet held against a flat surface as the lid shown, by means of a raised portion on the flange. The dimensions of the raised portion are not critical. This method does not result in as neat-looking seal as in the first two methods, and has the somewhat minor objection that a rather large amount of rubber is exposed to the vacuum, but except where the rubber is likely to get hot this is not a serious fault. To prevent excessive squeezing of the flat rubber into or out of the seal, the raised edge on the flange is lightly roughed by sand blasting or by a somewhat coarse lathe cut.

Although natural rubber has been used successfully for much vacuum gasketing work, Neoprene is more desirable because of its resistance to diffusion pump oils. In some applications where water cooling is difficult, Silicone rubber seals have been used. The low shear strength of this material makes it unattractive for most applications except where maximum temperature resistance is of prime importance.

Probably the neatest method of *sealing a small tube into a large chamber*, as in the case of the Pirani tube, is by means of the *compression gland* shown in Figure 16 (available commercially).[7] A tube to be sealed into the vacuum system is gripped by the rubber gasket D whose inside diameter is only slightly larger than the outside diameter of the tube (not shown). By tightening nut A slightly, which bears against washer C (to prevent twisting the rubber gasket), the rubber is necessarily compressed tightly against the smooth base of the seal body B and the tube, thus effecting a vacuum-tight joint. The insertion and removal of the tube is greatly facilitated if a very thin film of vacuum grease is applied to it. A very good feature of this type of seal is the rapidity with which a tube may be inserted into or removed from the vacuum chamber. The main requirement is that the tube to be sealed in fit rather snugly inside the rubber ring. A quarter turn or so of the nut A is usually adequate to effect a seal; it is quite easy to crush a glass tube if the tightening is overdone. A good test for adequate seal pressure is to tug lightly at the tube as if to remove it from the seal; if a gentle pull meets resistance it is probably sealed satisfactorily.

The same seal, although mainly used for small tubes of the order of $\frac{1}{4}$ to $\frac{1}{2}$ inch in diameter, has been successfully used in applications

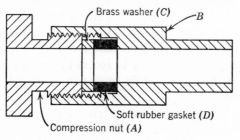

Figure 16. Compression Gland.

where the tube is up to about 4 inches in diameter. An example is the sealing of a porcelain furnace tube to a metal water-cooled chamber into which samples are pushed to be cooled before removal into the air.

There are many devices which have been used to seal *electrical leads* into vacuum chambers, including expensive (and fragile) metal-

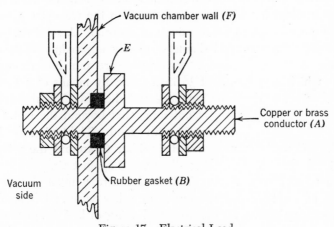

Figure 17. Electrical Lead.

to-glass seals. The scheme shown in Figure 17 has found rather wide application and has the advantage that it is simple, cheap, and readily made by any laboratory shop. The electrode A can be of any diameter large enough to carry the current required and may be made of copper or brass. A shoulder E on electrode A is pulled up tight against rubber gasket B, which is partially (about one half way) seated in the Mycalex [15] disk F, by means of the nut on the opposite (vacuum) side of the disk. Either end of the electrode is usually threaded to fasten the power leads. Mycalex is probably the best material to use except from the standpoint of machinability, but it can be machined with some wear on cutting tools. It has an advantage over plastics like bakelite and polysterene in that it stands a much higher temperature without gassing or decomposing. This is a distinct advantage in furnace construction, where the non-conducting plate can "see" a high temperature. It is not necessary to recess the gasket as shown, but it is desirable because it prevents the gasket from spreading when drawn tight. The plate of Mycalex or other non-conducting material is sealed against a flange, as shown in Figure 15. This method of sealing in electrodes has been used for all kinds of applications, including conducting high-frequency power of many kilowatts, or the low current of thermocouples, using appropriate-sized conductors.

Smaller current-carrying conductors, such as wires, may be handled in a somewhat simpler manner, as outlined in Figure 18. Part a shows the same compression gland assembly shown in Figure 16, but fitted with two non-conducting bolt-shaped pieces which could be made of plastic, Lava (steatite), or other ceramic material. In a typical application where it is desired to seal thermocouple wires into a system, two holes somewhat larger in diameter than the wire size are drilled through the ceramic or non-conducting material. A solid rubber disk is obtained whose outside diameter closely approximates the inside diameter of the gland body. Two holes are punched through the rubber, which may be about ⅛ inch thick, by means of a needle or by a hot wire and the assembly made as indicated. The non-conducting fittings preferably project out somewhat beyond the metal gland parts to prevent possible contact with gland. Tightening the hexagonal headed nut A compresses the rubber C around the wires and against the gland body, sealing all passages against air.

Figure 18b shows a somewhat similar arrangement designed for the use of multiple thermocouples or other wires. Obviously, by tightening cap screws D, the non-conducting disk A compresses rubber B around the wires and seals them as in Figure 18a. Incidentally, it is a good idea to make provision in many vacuum systems for a general-purpose "port" of this type so that, if it is desired to measure temperatures or to introduce a small amount of power into the chamber, one can do so. The port, of course, need not be used; but it is ready for quick use if necessary. Such a port might be 2 to 3 inches in diameter, and it is sealed into the vacuum chamber, using one of the standard flange seals.

Windows through which one can visually observe what is going on inside a vacuum chamber are frequently required. As in most of the vacuum seals described thus far, here again there is no unanimity of

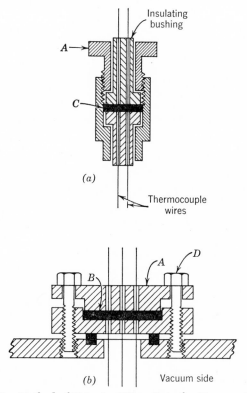

(a)

(b)

Figure 18. Method of Bringing Wires Out of a Vacuum Chamber.

opinion on the best method of accomplishing a seal. The window construction shown in Figure 19a has been found entirely reliable, and has the advantage that windows may be changed in a matter of minutes. Actually, it is the flange seal again, with the refinement of a retaining ring added to support the glass, and designed so that no wax or fastenings to the glass are required. A brass ring *A*, machined with a recess somewhat larger in diameter than the glass disk *B*, is tightened against the glass by means of four machine screws which are threaded into chamber wall or cover *D*. Since the glass is thus pushed against the yielding rubber gasket *C*, there is no danger of breaking the glass, provided it is rather thick. For diameters of glass in the neighborhood of an inch or two, a thickness of ¼ inch is recommended. Where heat is involved, as in a vacuum furnace, Pyrex glass is desirable. Even where very high temperatures are involved in a chamber at some distance from the window, the authors have found Pyrex to be entirely

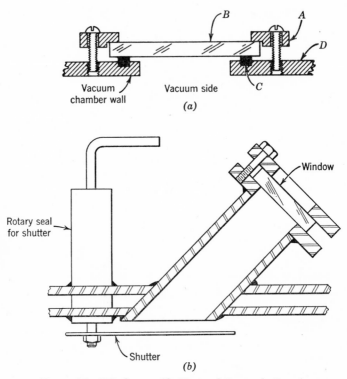

Figure 19. Windows. (*b*, National Research Corp.)

satisfactory. There appears to be no reason for the use of fused quartz in a well-designed unit. Pyrex windows of excellent quality made to any desired diameter are available from one of the optical supply houses.[16] The diameter of a window is largely a matter of individual preference, and is governed mainly by (1) the size of the available space for a window, and (2) the distance from the window at which one desires to look inside. Clearly, if the eye is put very close to the window, there is no reason to use one over about one inch in diameter.

In applications where material may be evaporated on the window, various devices have been used to keep the window clean or even to

clean it. Shutters operated from the outside by turning a rod projecting through the chamber wall, and which interpose a piece of sheet
metal between the window and the source of "dirt," Figure 19b, are
not entirely satisfactory because frequently the second or two of exposure required to see the operation is enough to cloud the window
even though the shutter is normally closed. "Windshield wipers" are
not very satisfactory when the film covering the window is of a metallic
nature, although steel wool on a wiper works well in some cases.
Probably the most satisfactory solution is to use as a shutter a rotating
disk carrying several windows like the chambers of a revolver. One
then looks through two windows: the normal external window which
seals the vessel, and the inside window mounted on the periphery of
the disk. When clouding of the inside window occurs, the disk is
merely turned by means of a rotating seal to the next window, and
so on.

Introduction of Motion into the Vacuum Chamber

One of the simplest methods of securing limited rotation (about 90
degrees) of a rod into a vacuum system is by the obvious expedient
of clamping a rather soft rubber tube around the rod and around a
tube projecting from the vacuum chamber, as shown in Figure 20.
This technique, although relatively simple, is not very universal in
application, and does not compare in utility to the more elegant and
ingenious *Wilson seal,* illustrated in Figure 21.

The Wilson seal allows unlimited motion of translation and unlimited rotation. The solid rod of rather smooth finish makes a
vacuum-tight seal with a rather thin (about $\frac{1}{8}$ inch thick) rubber
washer which is forced against the rod at an angle of about 30 degrees.
The rod must be lightly lubricated with a not-too-thick vacuum grease.
It is not necessary to apply any pressure by means of the hold-down
nut. All that is required is to seat the washer against the rubber
firmly, thus forcing the normally flat rubber washer to assume the
shape shown. Ordinarily hand tightening is all that is necessary if
the threads are rather loose fitting (as they should be). As with the
compression gland, it is best to make the metal parts of the seal out
of brass to avoid rust. Such seals allow vacuums of about 0.001
micron.

A rotating seal based on the ability of a metallic bellows to bend
readily is illustrated in Figure 22. This ingenious seal, built to allow
complete rotation (but not translation), is made by a bellows with a
universal joint and a wobble shaft, so that a twisting at one end of the

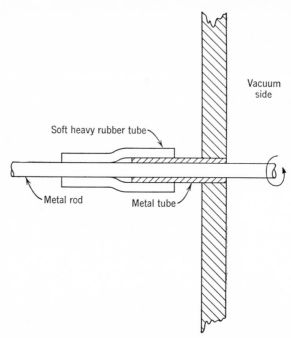

Figure 20.   Simple Method for Partial Rotary Motion.

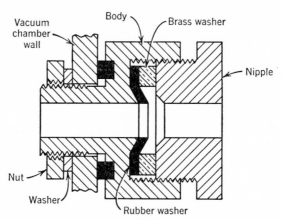

Figure 21.   Wilson Seal.

seal causes only a bending of the bellows, thus carrying the turning motion through the entire seal. Rotary seals of this type are available commercially.[7]

Another very common method of securing motion of translation in a vacuum system, particularly a glass system, consists of pushing a

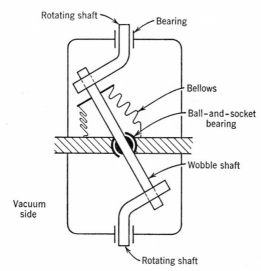

Figure 22. Transmission of Rotary Motion by Bellows Seal. (Guthrie and Wakerling.[13])

steel rod along a horizontal tube by means of a solenoid or alnico magnet on the outside (Figure 23). For example, the steel rod inside the evacuated tube may be used to push samples into or out of a furnace.

Magnets may also be used for rotation, as illustrated in Figure 24. If a disk must be slowly rotated inside a glass jar or tube, this rotation

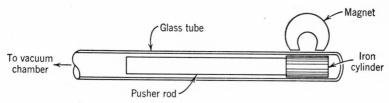

Figure 23. Obtaining Sliding Motion by Magnet.

is readily accomplished by maintaining an alnico magnet on the periphery of the disk (close to the glass). By holding a similar magnet outside so that a repulsion between the two magnets is generated, the disk may be turned to any desired position.

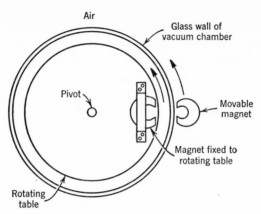

Figure 24. Rotary Motion by Magnets.

VACUUM VALVES

Vacuum valves are important adjuncts to many vacuum systems. Although their use is sometimes not actually necessary, the convenience and efficiency of operation made possible by their use justifies a brief discussion of this subject. Closing a valve at the high vacuum end of a diffusion pump allows one to open the vacuum chamber to the atmosphere without shutting down the diffusion pump, thus saving the cooling time and reheating time of the diffusion pump. By using a small holding pump to allow continuous operation of the diffusion pump, the regular backing pump may be used to evacuate the vacuum chamber. The small holding pump may then be cut off by a suitable valve and the regular backing pump turned on by opening a similar valve (see Figure 14).

In normal operation the large vacuum valve is open, and smaller valves A and C are closed, but valve B is open. If there is no objection to running the holding pump at all times when using the equipment, valve C could be eliminated. However, it would probably pay if valve C were installed in order to save wear on the small mechanical pump. If an operation is completed and it is desired to open up the chamber to remove some samples and put in others, the large valve is closed, and the holding pump started, and valve C opened. Valve B may now be closed, and valve A is still closed. The pumping system is now isolated from the tank and there is no danger of oxidizing the oil in diffusion pump since it is held under vacuum by the holding pump. The chamber may now be broken to the atmosphere by opening a small valve in some convenient location in the chamber wall or between the chamber and the large valve. If it is assumed that one is ready to pump down again, valve A is opened and the backing pump started. When the vacuum gauge shows a pressure in the neighborhood of 100 microns, valve B may be opened, valves A and C shut off, and the holding pump stopped.

There has been considerable improvement in the design and availability of vacuum valves, particularly in large valves 4 inches in diameter or over. Smaller valves were never too much of a problem as water and some gas valves of certain types were more or less adaptable to vacuum use. This was not so true of large (low impedance) valves where conventional designs suitable for water or steam applications were hopelessly large and cumbersome for vacuum application, to say nothing of the difficulty of making them vacuum-tight.

Two types of large valves used to block off diffusion pumps are shown in Figure 25. It is clear from these designs that it is necessary that these valves be built in the form of an elbow, but for many applications this is desirable where the pumping port for the vacuum is located in the side of the chamber as in Figure 14. In the type of Figure 25a, handle E mounted on a rod threaded in the lower portion raises and lowers a plate B which closes the valve opening A, fitted with a recessed rubber gasket. The rod passes through a stuffing box or gland D, which could be a Wilson seal or some other arrangement involving a tight-fitting rubber gasket. The section C is a fixed nut which engages the thread on the rod and allows the raising and lowering of the sealing plate B. Obviously, plate B must be fastened loosely to the end of the valve stem so that it does not revolve as the stem is turned, and so that it has necessary freedom in seating on the rubber gasket.

The valve shown in Figure 25b is about the same as in Figure 25a, but it is sealed by a bellows instead of a stem seal. The bellows type of right angle valve is available commercially [7] in sizes about $\frac{1}{2}$ inch in diameter and over.

For sizes less than 4 inches in diameter, it would probably be less expensive to use a converted "Globe" valve, as explained below, particularly if the pumping speed were not very high.

Straight-through valves are somewhat more difficult to construct than the right-angle valve discussed above. A design [17] for one such diffusion pump valve is outlined in Figure 26. This valve is small and has a short path compared to the opening size, hence it allows minimum resistance to fast pumping. It consists of a rectangular vacuum-tight box (A) with longitudinal rectangular grooves (B) cut along the long sides. In this groove slides a plate (C) in the center of which is a cam (D). On either side of the central plate lie two sealing disks (E) fitted with a rubber gasket well recessed into gasket

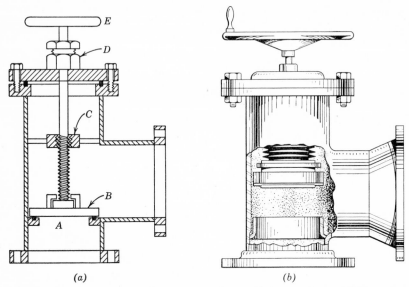

Figure 25. Two Right-Angle Vacuum Valves. (b, National Research Corp.)

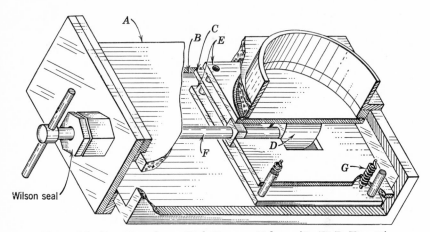

Figure 26. Low-Impedance High-Vacuum Valve. (L. D. P. King.[17])

grooves in the two plates. The plates are mounted so that they are free to move in a direction normal to the central plate (C) containing the cam. To the central plate is fastened a rod (F), which slides through a Wilson seal at one end of the box. When the plate assembly is pulled back all the way, the valve is open and amounts to a short length of pipe with a box in the center of the pipe. When the rod is pushed all the way in, the opening of the valve is closed and by twisting the cam 90 degrees, the two sealing disks are pushed against the box sides just outside the pipe holes to seal the valve above and below. If atmospheric pressure is admitted to one side of the valve with vacuum on the other side, the valve cannot be opened because the springs (G) tending to pull the two sealing plates to the central plate are not strong enough to work against atmospheric pressure. The pressure must be equalized on either side of the valve before it can be opened. In addition, if the valve contains air at essentially atmospheric pressure and if there is vacuum on either side, the valve cannot be opened for the same reason. In this case it is necessary to pump out the valve by opening a small bleeder line to the forepump or to an independent mechanical pump. Although this valve is small and offers a minimum of resistance to gas flow, it is admittedly a costly valve to build, and suffers in comparison to the angle valve because of its complexity and because it cannot operate against atmospheric pressure. This last objection is not a very cogent one as in normal operation, using an auxiliary pump as described in Figure 14, it is not necessary to open against atmospheric pressure.

Quarter swing valves are another type of low impedance valve used between vacuum chambers and metal diffusion pumps. They are essentially "butterfly" valves adapted to vacuum applications, and as made commercially [6,7] may be opened against atmospheric pressure (see Figure 27).

A straight-through valve of the forepump line type is shown in Figure 28a. This is a modification of the common Globe valve or water valve, but the stem packing here consists of a Wilson seal or equivalent rubber gasket seal, and the disk is fitted with a medium hardness rubber to make a vacuum-tight seal on the metal seat. Valves of this type used in vacuum work are usually not over 1 to 2 inches in diameter and are used in forepump lines where high conductance is not necessary.

It is quite easy to convert a bronze globe valve to a vacuum valve by this method. Occasionally the bronze body will not be vacuumtight, but this can usually be remedied by painting it with Glyptal [9] or by tinning. It will be noted that, unlike the valve of the first example cited, there is a marked constriction inside the valve at the seat, so that the opening is smaller than the inside diameter of the valve body.

Vacuum   valves of the "Globe" type are commercially available [3] in the range between 1 and 4 inches in diameter.

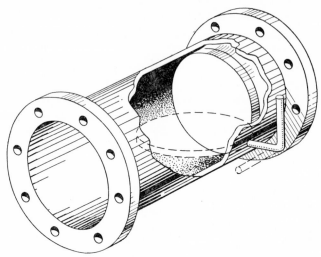

Figure 27.   Quarter Swing Valve.   (National Research Corp.)

Figure 28*b* shows a very compact right-angle valve [18] commercially available in the range of ⅝ to 1½ inches inside diameter which utilizes a bellows for sealing the stem.

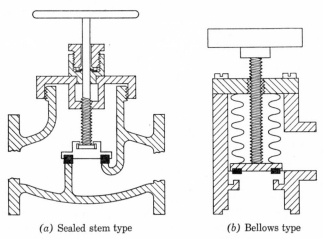

(*a*) Sealed stem type   (*b*) Bellows type

Figure 28.   Smaller Vacuum Valves.

For smaller applications in the neighborhood of ¼ to ½ inch in diameter, *Kerotest valves* [19] built for refrigerator service may be used.

These are co-called diaphragm valves because a diaphragm instead of a bellows is employed to seal the stem. Otherwise it is similar in operation to the valve sketched in Figure 28b. Experience indicates that they are not always reliable for vacuum work, but in general they seem to give satisfactory service.

Needle valves are generally used only for breaking a vacuum system to air or to some inert gas. Because of their small size they are not useful for passing gas at low pressures (for regular vacuum valve service). For bleeding in a gas at a slow rate in a rather small system, however, they are very useful. Generally one needs to break the vacuum slowly to prevent a great gust of gas from being driven into the evacuated chamber. On a large system of several cubic feet, a globe valve modified as indicated above is better because it would take too long to bring the pressure up to atmospheric pressure with a needle valve. Another advantage in the use of needle valves in rather small systems is the fact that they are readily fitted with a hose nozzle, a convenience for introducing various compressed gases into the vacuum chamber.

It is important to mount the needle valve into the vacuum system in such a way that atmospheric pressure pushes down on the needle rather than lifts it up from the seat. A cursory examination of the valve makes it obvious which end should be mounted at the vacuum system.

VACUUM-SYSTEM DESIGN

Elements of a Vacuum System

The principal elements of a vacuum system are the chamber to be evacuated, the diffusion pump, and the mechanical pump. Obviously, the larger the chamber, the larger the mechanical pump must be in order to exhaust the chamber in a reasonable length of time. Since large chambers present more opportunities for leaks, and because usually larger scale operations inside the chamber cause a larger evolution of gas, the diffusion pump must be larger, which also requires a larger mechanical pump.

From the above elementary considerations it is clear that before a choice of a suitable diffusion pump or mechanical pump can be made, one must know (1) the size of the chamber to be evacuated, and (2) the amount of gas which might be evolved during the operation. This last question is often difficult to answer with any precision, and frequently the amount of gas generated must be assumed, or judged from past experience.

Pumping Speed and Conductance

In the following section it is assumed that air is the gas being pumped, as the values of the constants in the conductive formulas are those for air. For a more detailed discussion of this subject, the reader is referred to the books by Guthrie and Wakerling [13] and by Dushman.[10] The various formulas used for calculation of conductance are taken from Guthrie and Wakerling.

The amount of gas to be removed in a vacuum system is conveniently given as micron liters, and the rate of gas flow as micron liters per second. Obviously, the amount of gas in a system is proportional to the product of the volume of the system times the pressure, where generally volume is measured in liters and pressure is measured in microns.

The pumping speed of a system, S, is related to the rate of flow of gas, Q, and pressure, P, by

$$S = Q/P \qquad (1)$$

where S is in liters per second, Q is in micron liters per second, and P is in microns. This formula is of prime importance in calculating the size of the diffusion pump required for a particular job. Let us assume that the speed of the diffusion pump is 300 liters per second and the pressure required inside the chamber is one micron. Since $S = Q/P$, 300 micron liters per second of gas could be evolved or permitted to leak in without exceeding a pressure of one micron. If the chamber size was 100 liters, the amount of gas (on the average) generated in a second's time would cause a pressure rise of 3 microns. Hence a chamber of this size would require a larger pump if the gas flow were as stated, and 1 micron pressure were required.

If Sp is the speed of the pump, S is the speed of the system, and C is the conductance of the system in liters per second, then:

$$1/S = 1/C + 1/Sp \qquad (2)$$

This is of course analogous to the conductance of an electrical system where the reciprocal of the total conductance is equal to the sum of the reciprocal individual conductances.

The flow of gas through a pipe can be *molecular flow* (at very low pressures) or *viscous flow* at higher pressures, for a system of any size. Formulas for molecular flow are applicable when $PD < 15$, where D is the pipe diameter in centimeters and P is the average pressure in microns. Viscous flow applies when $PD > 500$. In intermediate ranges where the nature of the flow may be both viscous and molecular, it is good practice to assume the worst conditions and design diameters and lengths to be on the safe side.

In order to calculate the conductance of a long circular pipe where the pressure is rather high, as at the fore end of a diffusion pump where viscous flow would be expected, the formula

$$C = 0.182D^4P/L \qquad (3)$$

may be used where P is the average pressure in microns between the mechanical pump and the forepump. C as before is in liters per second. D is the diameter of the pipe in *centimeters*, and L is the length in *centimeters*.

For very short pipes, the conductance is more limited by the aperture of the pipe than by the resistance to flow in the pipe itself. In most forepump connections, however, where viscous flow is ordinarily encountered, the aperture correction to viscous flow through pipes can ordinarily be neglected as the path between mechanical pump and diffusion pump is generally rather long and sudden changes in diameter are not common.

The conductance (for molecular flow) through a long circular pipe is given by the simple formula

$$C = 12.1D^3/L \qquad (4)$$

where the symbols have the previous meaning and dimensions. This formula serves to point out the great importance of the diameter of the pipe in the high vacuum end of the system where the diffusion pump connects to the vacuum chamber, as the conductance varies as the third power of the diameter. Hence with the same length a difference between a 4-inch and a 6-inch pipe results in a greater conductance of the 6-inch pipe by a factor of over three.

In calculating the conductance in the diffusion pump side of the system where molecular flow obtains, the formula for the conductance of the diffusion pump connection must usually be modified since Equation 4 holds strictly for long pipes, where L/D is about 100. If L/D is 20, the error is only about 10%; but where L approximates D in the diffusion pump connection, as is ordinarily the case, C calculated in the above expression may be too large by a factor of about three. This is because the resistance of such a short pipe is small compared with the resistance generated by the opening itself. The effectiveness of the aperture in reducing pumping speed depends upon the ratio of the pipe opening to the chamber diameter (the diameter of the region from which gas is flowing). One can write

$$1/C = 1/Cp + 1/Cap \qquad (5)$$

where C is the total conductance, Cp is the conductance of the pipe, and Cap the conductance of the aperture. Cp is calculated by Equation 4, and Cap may be calculated by

$$Cap = \frac{9.11D^2}{1 - D/D_0} \qquad (6)$$

where D_0 is the diameter of the region from which the gas is flowing.

Elbows or bends in a vacuum line usually are equivalent (in reducing conductance) to adding 2 to 3 diameters to the length of the pipe in viscous flow; bends have no appreciable effect under the conditions of molecular flow.

In calculating the size of an adequate diffusion and mechanical pump for a system of certain size and desired pressure characteristics, it is necessary to start with the high-vacuum end and work backwards. A diffusion pump of the right size having been decided upon, a pipe connection to the vacuum chamber should be chosen whose conductance is at least equal to the pumping speed of the diffusion pump. All that remains then, knowing the total gas flow in micron liters per second (which like current in an electrical circuit is constant throughout) is to choose a mechanical pump capable of handling this amount of gas while maintaining a safe forepressure to the diffusion pump.

Example of Computing a Vacuum System

Let us assume that the vacuum chamber has a 20-liter capacity and is 20 centimeters in diameter, that the desired pressure in the chamber is 0.1 micron, and that the gas evolution (real and virtual leaks) is 10 micron liters per second.

Since $S = Q/P$, we have $S = 10/0.1 = 100$, or the pumping speed of the system must be at least 100 liters per second at the chamber entrance. If the pumping speed of the system did not depend upon the conductance of the pipe connecting the vacuum chamber to the diffusion pump, all that would be necessary at this point would be to chose a diffusion pump capable of at least 100 liters per second speed at a pressure of 0.1 micron. Let us assume temporarily that such a pump is adequate and try a diffusion pump mouth connection pipe 10 centimeters in diameter and 10 centimeters long. Since $PD = (0.1)10 = 1$, molecular flow obtains since $PD < 15$. Therefore the formula $C = 12.1D^3/L$ applies for the conductance of the pipe. Substituting numerical values, $C = 12.1 \; 1000/10$ or $C = 1210$ liters per second for pipe conductance. Since it is a very short pipe, it is necessary to take account of the aperture conductance in the formula

$$Cap = \frac{9.11D^2}{1 - (D/D_0)}$$

Putting in the appropriate figures,

$$Cap = \frac{9.11(10)^2}{1 - (10/20)}$$

where $D_0 = 20$, since that is the diameter of the tank. Cap is found to be 1820 liters per second.

The total conductance is given by $1/C = 1/Cp + 1/Cap = 1/1210 + 1/1820$, whence $C = 726$ liters per second. To find out the pumping speed possible with this conductance applied to the pump of 100 liters per second speed, we write

$$1/S = 1/Sp + 1/C = 1/100 + 1/726$$

and S is about 88 liters per second, or somewhat lower than the desired pumping speed of 100 liters per second.

The next largest pump available has a pumping speed of 275 liters per second. Taking the same 10 by 10 cm pipe as before, and substituting in the pumping speed formula above, we find that the larger pump yields a total pumping speed of 200 liters per second, more than adequate.

Turning attention now to the forepump system, let us examine what is needed for the mechanical pump and its connection to the diffusion pump. The diffusion pump, according to the manufacturer's literature, will not operate with a back pressure greater than 100 microns. Since $S = Q/P$, $Q = 10$, and $P = 100$, $S = 0.1$ liter per second, or a mechanical pump of 0.1 liter per second is required to maintain 100 microns at a gas evolution rate of 10 micron liters per second. However, since the diffusion pump will just operate with this backing pressure, a somewhat faster mechanical pump should be used to insure satisfactory operation. If a pump of 0.2 liter per second capacity is used, the forepressure will be $P = Q/S = 10/0.2 = 50$ microns.

Looking now at the forepump-diffusion pump connection, let us try a pipe of 2 cm inside diameter and 25 cm long. Taking 50 microns as the forepump pressure, $PD = (50)(2) = 100$, which falls in the region of viscous and molecular flow. Calculating the conductance both ways, for molecular flow we have $C = 12.1(8)/25$ or about 3.87 liters/second, while with viscous flow $C = 0.182\ 1600/25$ or about 11.7 liters per second; hence molecular flow is more restrictive. $1/S = 1/C + 1/Sp = 1/3.86 + 1/0.2$, where $S = 0.19$ liter per second or barely adequate. A somewhat larger pipe would be desirable but might not make much difference in practice.

There is still left the calculation of the time required to pump down the 20-liter vacuum chamber from atmospheric pressure to 100 microns required for diffusion-pump operation. If the 0.2 liter per second mechanical pump requires an excessive time to do this, then a larger pump should be used even though it may be otherwise adequate as a backing pump.

An approximate formula for calculating pump-down time is given by $t = (2.3V/S)f$, where f may be 4, 5, or 6, etc., depending upon how many factors of 10 are required to reduce the pressure from 1000 mm (assumed to be atmospheric pressure). V is the volume of the container in liters, and S is the mechanical pump speed in liters per second. Although this formula obviously is not exact, it is close enough for practical purposes. In the example at hand, then, since the pressure must be reduced from atmospheric (assumed to be 1000 mm) to 10^{-1} mm (100 microns), the pressure is reduced by four factors of 10. $S = 0.2$ liter per second and $V = 20$ liters. Hence $t = (2.3)(20/0.2)4 = 920$ seconds or about 15 minutes. This is probably a little too long; hence it would be preferable to use a mechanical pump of higher capacity, perhaps 0.5 liter per second, which would allow a pump-down to 100 microns of about 6 minutes. This would have the additional advantage that the forepressure to the diffusion pump would be lower, allowing more satisfactory operation, since if bursts of gas should be given off, the forepressure might climb to 100 microns or higher with the 0.2 liter per second pump; this would not be nearly as likely with the larger pump.

There are various other pumping speed and conductance formulas which apply in various situations and with other geometry than discussed above. For a complete discussion of this subject the reader may refer to standard works [10,13] on vacuum technology.

LEAK HUNTING

It is an unfortunate fact that much of the time of the vacuum technologist is spent in hunting leaks, particularly directly after completion of a new vacuum system. However, armed with a definite procedure in locating leaks, leak hunting is usually successful and the task is not particularly onerous. Several techniques are available. It may be assumed that a Pirani or thermocouple gauge, or the equivalent in a continuous reading instrument, is attached to the system. If the pressure upon pump-down hangs up at some pressure over 100 microns, the major leak may be partially isolated by the use of valves if available. By comparing the readings of gauges in different parts of the system it is possible to decide whether the trouble lies in the pumping system or in the vacuum chamber. If multiple gauges and valves are not available, then one has to proceed to step two as in the case where the general location of the leak was discovered by the isolation technique. Here one admits air to the part of the system being checked and applies about 10 pounds of air pressure to the system; the mechanical pump connection may have to be plugged off or the gas pressure reduced to the point where it barely exceeds the leakage pressure through the pump.

A heavy soap solution is painted on all suspicious joints, and a careful watch is made for bubbles. This technique may sound crude, but it is surprisingly sensitive, and with a little care leaks of the order of a few microns may be located. Generally this method yields results fairly quickly, and if one or two large leaks are found, it is best not to waste time looking for other leaks until these are remedied. As soon as the vacuum gauge reads 100 microns or lower, another technique can be used which is more sensitive and more rapid than the soap bubble method. Before going on to the second method, a word of caution may be in order. If a leak is very large, the soap solution may be blown away from the leaky spot so fast that no bubble builds up. Hence it is necessary to look closely at the soap solution in the crevice being tested to make sure that an unbroken film of solution remains undisturbed at the point being checked. A leak large enough to blow away the solution is usually noisy enough to be heard if the sound level in the area is reasonably low.

The second leak-hunting technique consists in probing the entire system with hydrogen or helium gas streaming slowly out of a $\frac{1}{4}$-inch rubber tube and observing the reading of the Pirani, or thermocouple gauge. When the hydrogen plays on a leak, the gauge will soon show a rapid apparent increase in pressure due to the high thermal conductivity of hydrogen as compared to air. In completely covering a vacuum system by this method it is usually necessary to have an assistant watch the gauge while one applies hydrogen gas to the various seals being investigated. This method is very effective, and only very small leaks generally escape detection. It is necessary to pass the rubber tube quite slowly over a joint at a rate of perhaps 10 inches a minute so that small leaks will not be overlooked. In this manner the leaks should be eliminated to a point where they cannot be read by the low sensitivity gauges being used, that is, to about one micron or less. Exactly the same technique can be used with an ion gauge to chase the leaks down to a much lower level—in general to as low as the gauge being employed will read.

H. Nelson [20] has developed a *hydrogen ionization gauge* which is now commercially available.[21] It consists of a permanently sealed-off ionization gauge fitted with a heated palladium tube which is part of the sealed-off gauge envelope. Since the hot palladium is permeable to hydrogen and not to other gases, only hydrogen can enter the gauge and cause a gauge deflection. A hydrogen probe is used as described above so that when a leak is encountered, the hydrogen diffuses to the gauge, entering it through the sealed-off palladium tube. Greater sensitivity is possible with this technique then with an ordinary ion gauge completely open to the vacuum system since there is a higher vacuum in the gettered gauge than normally exists in a high-vacuum system. After locating a leak, the hydrogen is pumped out of the gauge by leaving the palladium hot long enough for degassing the tube. The sensitivity of this gauge for hydrogen is about 0.36 micron liter per hour.

The *helium mass spectrograph,* usually called the helium leak detector, offers the most sensitive method known of detecting leaks. Ordinarily these instruments are available only in large laboratories doing a great deal of vacuum work, as they are very expensive and may be used only for leak hunting.

The helium leak detector is a small mass spectrograph unit with the slit position set to be sensitive to the presence of helium. Helium is used because it diffuses rapidly to a leak, is non-combustible, and has a low background value, that is, is not present in significant amounts in the air (unlike hydrogen). A connection is made to the detector between the diffusion pump and the mechanical pump of the system being investigated, with the aid of a valve (A) which regulates the amount of gas flow to the detector (see Figure 29). The vacuum system is operated as usual, and valve A is regulated to give a pressure in the leak detector of about one micron. Hence most of the gas being evacuated from the system being leak-tested goes through the regular mechanical pump B, but some fraction of the same gas enters the leak tester as shown. By playing a probe of helium gas over the vacuum

chamber and pumping system, very small leaks may readily be found
because of the high sensitivity of the mass spectrometer. As in leak
checking with a Pirani or ion gauge, care must be taken to direct the
gas only at the spot desired in order to avoid getting a response from

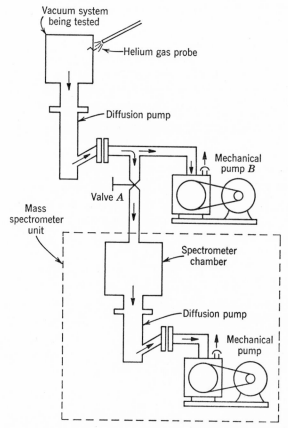

Figure 29.   Helium Mass Spectrograph Leak Detector.

neighboring areas, hence confusing the location of the leak.   This is
particularly important with the helium leak detector because of its
great sensitivity, one part of helium in 200,000 parts of air.

While the helium leak detector is in a class by itself in the ease and
speed with which leaks may be found, it is hardly a necessity since
there are other methods available (although less powerful), as outlined above.   The helium leak detector is particularly valuable in
large, complicated systems where there are many connections and
seals, and where isolation and testing of various parts of the system

are difficult or impossible, and finally in vacuum engineering operations where many parts or devices must be tested quickly and accurately.

REFERENCES

1. Central Scientific Co., Chicago, Ill.
2. Welsch Scientific Co., Chicago, Ill.
3. Kinney Manufacturing Co., Boston, Mass.
4. Beach-Russ Co., New York 7, N. Y.
5. P. J. Stokes Machine Co., Philadelphia, Pa.
6. Distillation Products, Inc., Rochester, N. Y.
7. National Research Corp., Cambridge, Mass.
8. Dow Corning Co., Corning, N. Y.
9. General Electric Company, Schenectady, N. Y.
10. Saul Dushman, *Scientific Foundation of Vacuum Techniques*, John Wiley and Sons, New York, 1949.
11. Miller Laboratories, Lathams, N. Y.
12. Ernest C. Evans and Kenneth E. Burmaster, "Philips Type Ionization Gauge for Measuring of Vacuum from 10^{-7} to 10^{-1} mm of Mercury," *Proc. I.R.E.*, **38**, 655 (1950).
13. A. Guthrie and R. K. Wakerling, *Vacuum Equipment and Techniques*, National Nuclear Energy Series, McGraw-Hill Book Co., New York, 1950.
14. Linear, Inc., Philadelphia, Pa.
15. Mycalex Corporation, Clifton, N. J.
16. Bausch & Lomb, Rochester, N. Y.
17. L. D. P. King, *Rev. Sci. Instruments*, **19**, 83–84 (1948).
18. Vacuum Electronic Engineering Co., Brooklyn, N. Y.
19. Kerotest Manufacturing Co., Pittsburgh 22, Pa.
20. H. Nelson, *Rev. Sci. Instruments*, **16**, 273 (1945).
21. Radio Corporation of America, Camden, N. J.

CHAPTER SEVEN

Melting and Casting

The object in the melting and casting of a pure metal is primarily to change its shape in order to secure a more convenient form for subsequent work. For alloys, melting makes possible the mixing of the desired metallic constituents to form the required composition.

Although it is recognized that the factors involved in securing satisfactory commercial castings of complicated shape constitute an important field of study, it is also a field which is rather highly specialized, and is not readily treated by a concise discussion. For this reason, this subject is not dealt with in detail here, but it is assumed that the making of a casting in the laboratory is only a means of securing a suitable sample for further study. If the metal being cast is brittle, and hence cannot be fabricated by rolling, wire drawing, etc., it must be used in the as-cast condition. In this case the casting of a finished shape, such as a tensile specimen, may be required, although for much work a simple cylindrical ingot may provide a suitable sample.

The majority of melting and casting operations are carried out in the air, with or without partially protective covers, but vacuum or noble gas atmosphere melting is needed for minimum contamination. Such refined techniques are often desirable in melting common metals like copper, iron, or nickel, and they are actually necessary for more reactive materials such as zirconium, titanium, or vanadium.

Except for the procedure of alloying, there is no essential difference between handling a pure metal and an alloy; hence in the following pages there will be no separate description of procedures for these two cases. When casting a pure metal there is of course no concern about the matter of securing a homogeneous material since no segregation of components is possible, but there is concern regarding soundness of the casting and possible contamination by the atmosphere during melting or casting.

I. MELTING

Melting Furnaces

There are four major types of furnaces for preparing alloys in the laboratory, and in the order of decreasing field of application they are:

1. High-frequency electric induction melting.
2. Gas-air combustion melting.
3. Electric resistance melting.
4. Electric arc melting.

High-frequency induction heating is the most generally useful method because it may be used over the widest temperature range and because it is rapid, clean, and convenient to use. The various types of high-frequency units have already been discussed in Chapter 1, and the discussion will not be repeated here, except for a few comments which bear directly on the problem of melting metals. For melts up to about 25 pounds, the use of spark gap equipment has much to recommend it from the standpoint of low initial cost, simplicity (hence low maintenance), adaptability to a wide range of metals and melting temperatures, and safety for the operator. Figure 1 shows a high-frequency coil and crucible assembly. Between the coil and the crucible is a heat-insulating layer of refractory powder which need be only about one-half inch thick. Just inside the coil, however, is an electrically insulating layer of mica that prevents arcing between the coil and crucible and helps contain the powder. The top of the heat insulating powder is covered with some refractory cement to hold the powder in place, so that the crucible and coil assembly may be tipped over to pour the heat without spilling the insulation. A pouring lip may be molded in the cement topping if a crucible with projecting lip is not used.

The crucibles used for high-frequency melting may be electrically conducting such as clay-graphite, graphite, silicon carbide–graphite (Tercod), or they may be non-conducting like magnesia or alumina. Because the crucible is closer to the high-frequency coil than the charge itself, more efficient heating is likely if the crucible is conducting. In this case, the crucible is heated by eddy currents generated by the high-frequency field, but the charge is mainly heated by radiation and conduction from the hot crucible. Conducting crucibles such as clay-graphite are particularly useful when melting metals of high electrical conductivity, like copper, as such metals do not heat well by high-frequency induction. Conducting crucibles are of course necessary if it is desired to heat electrical non-conductors. With rather low frequencies, up to about 10,000 cycles per second, some eddy currents are set up directly in the melt even with a conducting crucible, depending upon its thickness and conductivity. However, if maximum stirring of the melt by the induced circulating currents is desired, a

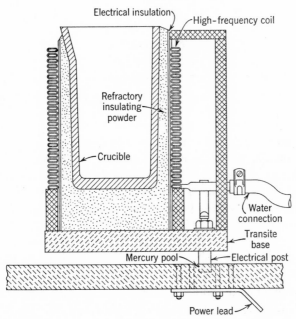

Figure 1. High-Frequency Coil and Crucible Assembly. (Ajax Electrothermic Corp.)

conducting crucible should be avoided. With spark gap equipment of about 30,000 cycles frequency or over, the amount of stirring is not large. A great deal of stirring of the melt, however, does occur at 3000 cycles and to a lesser extent at 10,000 cycles. Such stirring is of course desirable from the standpoint of getting good mixing when adding alloying metals.

It is possible to heat a conducting crucible very rapidly by induction, so rapidly that spalling may be caused by vaporization of absorbed moisture if the crucible had not been dried out thoroughly before use. In using a new clay-graphite crucible, it is advisable to heat up rather slowly the first time it is used, particularly when high temperatures are required, since the dangerous low temperature region may be traversed quite rapidly in this case. This precaution is not necessary for Tercod (silicon carbide–graphite) crucibles as they do not absorb appreciable amounts of water.

In any melting operation, it is desirable to put a lid over the melt to cut down radiation losses. A lid is naturally required when a protective cover of the gas type is used (see below).

High-frequency melting is particularly adaptable to vacuum melting or inert gas atmosphere melting, as will be discussed later.

Gas-furnace melting has the advantage that it is fast, and requires very inexpensive equipment for small-scale work. A disadvantage of gas furnaces where the crucible is exposed to the products of combustion is the absorption of undesirable gases, such as hydrogen, by the metal being melted. Also, provision must be made to vent the furnace so that the products of combustion are removed from the work area. In addition, as commonly used, gas melting is not capable of producing as high temperatures as high-frequency induction melting, nor is it as conveniently adaptable to inert atmosphere or vacuum melting. Although under special conditions, such as using air enriched with oxygen, temperatures up to about 2000°C are possible in a gas furnace, such temperatures are not attainable with a gas-air mixture. A temperature of about 1200°C is the practical upper limit for the simple type of furnace about to be described.

In Figure 2 is shown an easily made gas pot furnace whose combustion chamber is about 8 inches in diameter and about the same in height. The outside of the furnace may be a discarded can about a foot in diameter and about one foot high. The bottom of the can is lined with broken scraps of lightweight brick or Sil-O-Cel, etc., to a depth of about 2 to 3 inches. To hold such a lining in place and to provide a solid working surface, an inch or somewhat less of Sillimanite Wet Patch is rammed over the bottom. The sides are built up by ramming the same mix around a slightly tapered wooden form of size equal to the desired combustion chamber. When the mix has been firmly tamped up to the top of the can, the core plug is removed. A hole through the furnace wall about 1 to 1½ inches in diameter must be provided for the blast burner. This hole should be close to the furnace bottom and pointed nearly tangentially to the furnace wall. It may be bored out while the mix is still damp, or it can be cored-in with a cylinder of the right diameter before ramming. After a few hours' drying, the furnace may be ignited and the drying hastened by burning the gas at a slow rate. After a little experience one learns how to adjust the gas burner for maximum heating; the tangential flame wraps around the crucible on the inside, and the heating is surprisingly uniform. The color of the gas flame at the top of the furnace changes from blue to yellow as the conditions inside change from oxidizing to reducing. A space of at least an inch between the furnace walls and the crucible should be left to allow space for the burning gas.

An air-gas torch suitable for firing the furnace may be obtained from any of the laboratory-equipment supply houses. The air required need be supplied at only a few ounces pressure, but higher pressure air may be used if throttled by a valve.

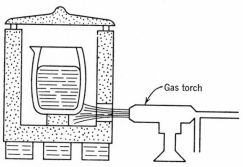

Figure 2.   Gas Pot Furnace.

Commercial installations are usually much more elaborate than the simple furnace just described. In such furnaces, the air and gas are premixed before they enter the burning chamber, and special blowers are incorporated in the unit to insure correct pressure and rate of gas flow for maximum efficiency. Also, the combustible mixture is usually introduced at several points around the periphery of the chamber.

Electric resistance furnaces are frequently used for melting low-melting alloys of lead, zinc, tin, etc., but less often for high-melting metals, as high-frequency induction heating is ordinarily more convenient for this purpose. At temperatures above a red heat, the most important mode of heat transfer is by radiation. Since heat radiated is proportional to $T_1^4 - T_2^4$, where T_1 is the temperature of the furnace walls and T_2 is the temperature of the crucible, it may be seen that the rate of heating is a sensitive function of this temperature difference.

Since there are no burning gases in the atmosphere of an electric resistance furnace, the melting atmosphere is likely to be better than that of an open muffle gas furnace where the products of combustion sweep around the crucible. However, moisture in the air may cause trouble in some cases even if no other gases are present.

Figure 3 shows a furnace suitable for electric resistance melting. Resistance wire of 80% nickel and 20% chromium is the most common heating element used, but, as pointed out earlier, other higher temperature elements are available. In general, however, high-frequency induction is used for higher melting metals. The more refractory heating elements such as platinum, Alloy No. 10, Kanthal, and Globars are usually employed in heat-treating (non-melting) applications.

Electric arc melting, except for a few isolated experiments in melting metals of extremely high melting point, had rarely been used as a

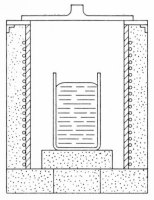

laboratory tool until interest developed in the metallurgy of titanium. Zirconium and titanium have not been successfully melted in ceramic (oxide) crucibles because of their extreme chemical reactivity, particularly toward oxygen. They may be melted in graphite but only at the cost of picking up about 0.2 weight per cent carbon or more. W. J. Kroll [1] in 1930 successfully melted titanium by arc melting in a water-cooled copper crucible, and this method has been much used since for refractory alloy melting. The metal forms its own crucible, the cold copper serving the function of keeping at least a thin

Figure 3. Electric Resistance Pot Furnace.

layer of titanium or zirconium, etc., frozen on the bottom and sides of the copper. Hence in striking an arc between a tungsten electrode above, and pieces of the charge below, only the top layer of the charge melts, while that in contact with the cold copper remains solid. In order to melt the charge completely, it must be inverted, and what was formerly the bottom melted in a second operation. However, by adding more charge during operation of the arc, more and more metal may be melted layer by layer until a sizable ingot is obtained.

Ordinarily an argon atmosphere is maintained inside the chamber to avoid oxygen or nitrogen contamination, as both titanium and zirconium are very susceptible to embrittlement from these gases. The upper electrode is a water-cooled copper or steel rod, tipped with tungsten, to allow arcing without damage to the copper rod. The tungsten-tipped electrode is often mounted through a rubber sleeve to allow freedom of movement over the crucible area; hence by rotating or swinging the electrode slowly over the charge or by manipulation of the arc path by a magnet, all parts of the upper surface of the charge can be melted.   Although some tungsten is picked up by the molten metal, it is usually not enough to affect the properties of the metal, at least when the furnace is operating properly.   A direct current of the order of several hundred amperes is used for rather small

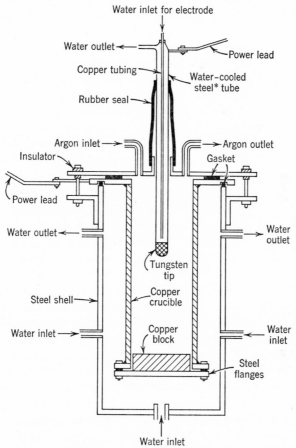

Figure 4.   Inert Arc Melting Furnace.   (Allegheny Ludlum Steel Co.)

furnaces capable of melting a pound or so of metal, the charge being positive as this is the hotter of the two electrodes.   Figure 4 shows an arc furnace of this type.   Other metals may be melted in such a furnace, but there is not much point in using this method except where ordinary crucible materials react with the charge, or where the melting point is in the vicinity of 2000°C or over.   Another example of such a metal is vanadium, which has been successfully melted in this manner (and which cannot be melted in graphite).   Obviously, casting in the usual sense is out of the question. One disadvantage of this method of melting is very poor control over homogeneity in making alloys. As one would expect, in melting only a little of the charge at once there is a very marked tendency for alloying additions to segregate in the ingot being built up. Repeated remelting helps considerably in reducing severe segregation, but segregation is still a problem. If it is feasible to prepare rods of the metal to be arc-melted, the metal may be melted by making the electrode a consumable one, hence dispensing with the water-cooled tungsten-tipped copper electrode. In this case, an arc is struck between the consumable electrode and pieces of the same material in the water-cooled copper crucible.

Melting Procedures

Addition of Alloying Metals. There is no set practice governing the sequence of making alloying additions, but the procedure is governed by the melting point, reactivity, volatility, and quantity of the alloying constituents. When preparing an alloy rich in one constituent, as copper in a copper-base alloy, the copper is melted first and the minor constituent is added later. If the added metal has quite a high melting point, solution will be hastened by superheating the solvent, particularly if the solvent can be heated to a point above the melting point of the solute. When iron is added to copper, however, heating the copper above the melting point of iron is not feasible, since superheating copper to such high temperatures would greatly increase its volatilization, oxidation, and the amount of hydrogen solution. Some intermediate temperature in the vicinity of 1200°C might be chosen as high enough to secure reasonably rapid solution of the iron, but not so high as to affect the copper seriously. Naturally, the more finely divided the iron, the greater the rate of solution since the solution rate is a function of the surface area of the iron. However, it does not follow that iron powder is the best form for the addition since there is too much opportunity for oxidation of the iron to iron oxide unless excellent atmosphere control is maintained. The use of a molten flux over the copper would tend to reduce oxidation of both the copper and iron, but thin iron sheets or wire would be a better form than powder. If powder is used because of availability or purity, it should be compacted into briquettes in a steel die before addition.

If the alloying metal has a low melting point compared to copper, such as tin, the copper should be heated to just above its melting point; or the tin can be added even before the copper has completely melted, since, as the tin dissolves, the melting point of the alloy is lowered, and the temperature of the melt can thus be held low to prevent excessive oxidation or loss of alloying constituent. Alloying at as low a temperature as possible is particularly important when the addition is volatile, as is zinc. In general, the temperature should be kept as low as possible to avoid reaction with the atmosphere, loss of volatile constituents, and possible reaction with the crucible.

After the alloying metal has been added, the rate of solution can be considerably hastened by vigorous stirring. In high-frequency induction melting, some stirring occurs from induced eddy currents as mentioned previously; otherwise a rod of a suitable refractory can be used to stir. Graphite is good for most non-ferrous metals.

If an alloy which contains approximately equal parts of two metals is to be made, it would usually be best if the lower melting metal were melted first in order to avoid superheating. Although adding the second metal might raise the melting point, as in adding nickel to copper to make a 50–50 copper-nickel alloy, the temperature required for making the alloy is nevertheless considerably lower than the temperature required for the reverse procedure. An exception to this rule would occur if the low-melting metal were rather reactive and corrosive to the crucible; then the best scheme would probably be first to melt the less reactive but higher melting metal. An example would be a copper-magnesium alloy containing approximately equal volumes of both metals.

If several additions are to be made, the foregoing considerations would apply. The most reactive metal would be added last, however, so that it would have least opportunity to combine with dissolved oxygen or to react with other components of the environment.

Master Alloys. It is often difficult to add high-melting metals or very reactive metals to a melt and secure good recovery of the added metal. A case in point was the example of adding iron to copper, cited above. Also, reactive substances such as phosphorus, cerium, calcium, and lithium are so readily oxidized and inconvenient to handle that adding them in elementary form is unsatisfactory. To overcome these difficulties master alloys are used. A master alloy is one containing a fairly high percentage of the desired element alloyed with the same base metal as is required in the final alloy. For example, in deoxidizing copper-base alloys with phosphorus, a master alloy is often used which contains about 12% phosphorus and the remainder copper. Since the active constituent is already alloyed with the desired metal, mixing in the final melt is rapid, and losses are usually negligible.

Many master alloys are commercially available, but in experimental work it is often necessary to make one's own. If the constitution of the alloy allows it, a composition near a eutectic is desirable because it has a lower melting point, and this permits more rapid solution in the final alloy. It is generally desirable for a master alloy to be brittle, so that it may readily be crushed into fragments for making up the desired weight, and for taking a representative sample for chemical analysis. For crushing brittle alloys, a diamond mortar is commonly used. It consists of a steel block bored with a cylindrical hole into which a steel sleeve fits. A loose-fitting steel punch heat-treated to a

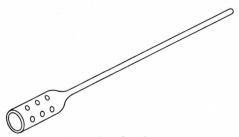

Figure 5.   Phosphorizer.

medium hardness is placed on top of the material to be crushed inside the sleeve. By hammering the punch, the brittle material is crushed into smaller pieces without loss or danger from flying fragments.

Very reactive elements such as phosphorus, calcium, and magnesium are often added to a melt, as in making a master alloy, by means of a "phosphorizer" (see Figure 5). This is a rod, best made of graphite, with a perforated expanded opening or chamber at one end. The active material is tamped into the perforated chamber so that it will not fall out, and, when the liquid metal to which the material is to be added is somewhat superheated, the chamber end of the phosphorizer is thrust under the surface of the liquid and held there for a few minutes until it is certain that the addition has melted and alloyed with the base metal. While held under the melt, the phosphorizer should be moved about to stir the melt and aid rapid solution. Care should be taken to see that additions are dry, so that explosions due to generation of steam cannot occur.

Gases in Metals. Most metals react with the gases oxygen, nitrogen, and hydrogen, the three gases of main importance in melting operations since all three occur in the air, hydrogen mainly in the form of water vapor. However, water vapor is readily broken down into hydrogen and oxygen by contact with hot metals which act as catalytic agents for this reaction.   In addition, hydrogen is frequently used as a furnace atmosphere as mentioned previously.

Nitrogen is generally of little consequence compared to the other two gases because of its comparatively inert nature, reacting much more slowly with most metals than oxygen or hydrogen.   However, with some reactive metals, nitrogen can play a prominent role, by going into solid solution or forming nitrides; examples are zirconium, titanium, vanadium, tantalum, and niobium.   Iron is also capable of forming nitrides, but only very slowly if at all by combining with molecular nitrogen.

In order to dissolve in metals, molecular gases as O_2 must break down into atomic form.   Hence Henry's law, which states that the solubility of a gas is proportioned to pressure, must be modified for diatomic gases to state that the solubility is proportional to the square root of pressure, or

$$S = k\sqrt{p} \tag{1}$$

This modified law is generally known as Sievert's law.   The operation of this relationship is illustrated for a series of copper-tin alloys [2] in Figure 6, which also shows that hydrogen is less soluble in molten copper the greater the amount of tin it contains.

For many metals, gas solubility increases with temperature, with a discontinuity at the melting point where the solubility is much greater than in the solid state.   This behavior is illustrated for hydrogen in iron and nickel [3] in Figure 7.   It will further be noted that there is also a discontinuity in the gas solubility in iron at the alpha-gamma solid transformation, where iron changes from body-centered cubic to face-centered cubic.   An exception to the usual case (where gas solubility increases with temperature) occurs in certain hydrogen-metal systems where hydrides are formed.   In these cases, the hydrogen solubility is much greater at lower temperatures.   The decrease in solubility at high temperatures is caused by decomposition of the hydrides.

The gas solubility decreases abruptly when a metal solidifies and the gas is thus suddenly expelled.   The gas thus expelled forms bubbles and unsoundness if the gas content is high enough.   The elemental gas generally responsible for this behavior is hydrogen, as oxygen forms stable oxides in nearly every case (silver is one exception) and hence can cause no gas pressure since the decomposition pressure of most oxides is quite low.   It should be noted that no gas can cause gas bubbles, and hence gas porosity, unless its pressure is

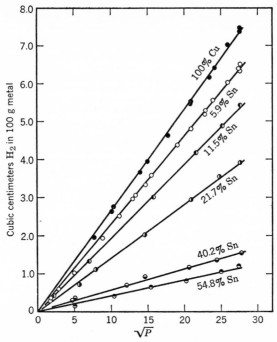

Figure 6. Solubility of Hydrogen in Copper and Copper-Tin Alloys at 1200°C as a Function of Pressure (Mm Hg). (Bever and Floe.[2])

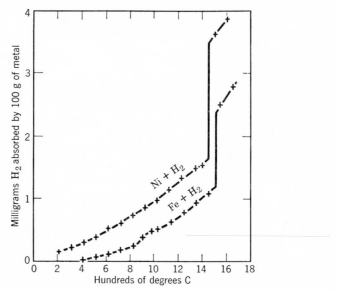

Figure 7. Isobars for Ni + H₂ and Fe + H₂ at One Atmosphere. (Sieverts.[3])

greater than atmospheric pressure plus the hydrostatic head of the freezing metal.

Very often gas unsoundness or porosity in frozen metals is not caused by hydrogen or by any other elemental gas, but rather by the formation of a gaseous compound such as H_2O, SO_2, or CO. The first two are particularly important in copper castings; the third plays a prominent role in steel castings. It should not be supposed, however, that gas porosity due to compound gases is limited to alloys of copper or iron, because other metals capable of dissolving both hydrogen and oxygen or carbon and oxygen are equally capable of causing trouble.

Certain grades of commercial copper contain about 0.035% oxygen, and this amount of oxygen can easily be raised by air melting, particularly if no protective cover is used and if heated to high temperatures for alloying purposes. Various investigations have shown that minute amounts of hydrogen which may be introduced by moisture from the air, the order of $10^{-5}\%$, can cause serious porosity by combining with the oxygen present, thus forming steam during solidification of the melt, when the metal can no longer hold large quantities of hydrogen in solution. Phillips [4] has given a complete treatment of this subject. The porosity of copper or its alloys due to this cause is in general related to the hydrogen content (in the absence of deoxidation) since there is ordinarily plenty of oxygen present to react with the hydrogen. An analogous situation arises in the case of oxygen and carbon dissolved in liquid iron, but here it is the formation of CO which causes porosity. Commercial coppers ordinarily contain so little sulphur that the corresponding reaction to form SO_2 is of little concern to those making copper alloys, but it is an important matter in copper refining.

Deoxidation. If one of the gaseous constituents is reduced to a very low level in the liquid, not enough compound gas will be formed to cause trouble. Since the oxygen content is easily reduced to very low levels by deoxidation accomplished by added elements with a high affinity for oxygen, nearly complete removal of oxygen is of considerable importance when melting in air. Deoxidation does not solve the gas porosity problem when porosity is due to hydrogen alone, as in aluminum alloys. The removal of hydrogen will be considered later.

The term *deoxidation* is something of a misnomer, as it implies removal of oxygen from a melt. In practice, it usually means that an addition is made to the melt to tie up the dissolved oxygen in the form of a highly stable oxide as Al_2O_3 or MgO rather than actual removal from the melt. Phosphorus, however, does not leave an oxide in the melt as the P_2O_5 which forms melts and rises to the top. Most higher melting metals melted in the air must be deoxidized (1) to avoid compound gas porosity or (2) to prevent oxygen remaining combined with the base metal because of deleterious effects on the properties. An outstanding example of the difficulties which can occur with un-deoxidized metal is the hydrogen embrittlement of copper. Copper containing appreciable amounts of oxygen as Cu_2O can be seriously embrittled if heated in a reducing atmosphere containing hydrogen because of the formation of steam, which, being unable to diffuse out, builds up high pressure and causes fissures along the grain boundaries.

Table 1 lists the free energies of formation of the oxides of many metals, including those commonly used for deoxidation purposes. The data were compiled from Kelley,[5] Thompson,[6] and other literature. Note that the figures given are *per atom of oxygen* so that direct comparison of "deoxidation power" may be made. The larger the negative value of ΔF at any temperature level, the greater is the tendency for that oxide to form. However, the actual total free energy for the formation of Al_2O_3, for example, is three times the value given since this oxide contains three atoms of oxygen. The uncertainty in the free energy values given in Table 1 is about 5 kilocalories.

In choosing a suitable deoxidizing element, attention must be paid to the effect of trace amounts of the deoxidizer upon the properties of the base metal. More than a stoichiometric amount of deoxidizer is usually added to insure complete deoxidation; hence a residual amount of the deoxidizing element generally remains in the melt. As an example, phosphorus otherwise a satisfactory deoxidizer for pure copper raises the electrical resistivity considerably above the value for pure copper; thus, if maximum electrical conductivity is important, phosphorus is ruled out as a deoxidizer.

The amount of deoxidizer used is difficult to specify exactly since the amount of oxygen in the melt is in general unknown. However, a deoxidizing addition, usually of the order of 0.1% by weight, is more than adequate to take care of normal amounts of oxygen encountered in good melting practice. Generally more than enough deoxidizer is added for the oxygen but not enough to affect appreciably the properties of the metal or alloy being prepared. The cessation of gas evolution just prior to pouring is in some cases an indication of the state of deoxidation. For example, if a heat of steel is somewhat "wild" or "active" due to CO being generated, it is obvious that it is not well deoxidized. On the other hand, if enough deoxidizer is added to "kill" the heat, deoxidation may be adequate, but not necessarily so since the amount of oxygen dissolved in the metal may not be enough to cause bubbles of CO. However, blowholes in the casting could

TABLE 1

FREE ENERGY OF FORMATION OF OXIDES PER ATOM OF OXYGEN IN KILO-
CALORIES AT THREE TEMPERATURES

Element	Oxide	ΔF at 25°C	ΔF at 500°C	ΔF at 1000°C
Aluminum	Al_2O_3	−122	−110	−99
Antimony	Sb_2O_3	−50	−40 *	−31
Arsenic	As_2O_3	−45	−35	−24
Barium	BaO	−126	−115	−104
Beryllium	BeO	−132	−121	−109
Bismuth	Bi_2O_3	−39	−28	−13
Cadmium	CdO	−60	−43	−23
Calcium	CaO	−144	−133	−121
Carbon	CO	−33	−43	−54
Cerium	CeO_2	−110	−99	−88
Cesium	Cs_2O	−79	−74	−69
Chromium	Cr_2O_3	−83	−72	−60
Cobalt	CoO	−51	−43	−34
Columbium	Cb_2O_5	−85	−80	−75
Copper	Cu_2O	−35	−28	−21
Gallium	Ga_2O	−75	−64	−53
Germanium	GeO_2	−71	−105	−99
Gold	Au_2O_3	+6	+10	+15
Hafnium	HfO_2	−129	−119	−107
Hydrogen	H_2O	−55	−49	−42
Indium	In_2O_3	−73	−61	−49
Iridium	IrO_2	−14	−5	+26
Iron	FeO	−59	−51	−43
Lanthanum	La_2O_3	−145	−134	−122
Lead	PbO	−45	−34	−23
Lithium	Li_2O	−138	−130	−123
Magnesium	MgO	−138	−127	−114
Manganese	MnO	−89	−82	−75
Mercury	HgO	−14	+2	+25
Molybdenum	MoO_2	−61	−50	−40
Neodymium	Nd_2O_3	−140	−134	−129
Nickel	NiO	−52	−43	−32
Osmium	OsO_4 (white)	−18	−5	+4
Palladium	PdO	−20	−18	−15
Potassium	K_2O	−82	−75	−68
Praseodymium	Pr_2O_3	−143	−139	−133
Rhenium	Re_2O_7	−39	−32	−26
Rhodium	Rh_2O	−17	−12	−6
Rubidium	Rb_2O	−79	−74	−68
Ruthenium	RuO_2	−20	−11	−0.6

TABLE 1 (*Continued*)

FREE ENERGY OF FORMATION OF OXIDES PER ATOM OF OXYGEN IN KILO-CALORIES AT THREE TEMPERATURES

Element	Oxide	ΔF at 25°C	ΔF at 500°C	ΔF at 1000°C
Samarium	Sm_2O_3	−142	−139	−135
Scandium	Sc_2O_3	−130	−120	−109
Silicon	SiO_2	−95	−85	−74
Silver	Ag_2O	−2	+5	+12
Sodium	Na_2O	−90	−75	−54
Strontium	SrO	−133	−122	−109
Tantalum	Ta_2O_5	−90	−78	−65
Tellurium	TeO_2	−33	−22	−13
Thallium	Tl_2O	−43	−45	−39
Thorium	ThO_2	−140	−130	−119
Tin	SnO	−61	−49	−36
Titanium	TiO_2	−102	−93	−82
Tungsten	WO_2	−60	−52	−43
Uranium †	UO_2	−141	−110	−99
Vanadium	V_2O_3	−97	−91	−83
Yttrium	Y_2O_3	−140	−130	−119
Zinc	ZnO	−77	−66	−49
Zirconium	ZrO_2	−123	−114	−104

* Orthorhombic.

† Moore and Kelley, *J. Am. Chem. Soc.*, **69**, 2105 (September 1947).

still occur due to gas evolution during freezing because of the discontinuity in gas solubility at the freezing point. Metals which when melted in air generally require deoxidation include copper, silver, iron, nickel, cobalt, manganese, and palladium. Low-melting metals such as lead, zinc, and tin appear to dissolve very little oxygen and hence need no such treatment. Aluminum and magnesium alloys require no deoxidation; they form oxides, but they dissolve no oxygen.

Deoxidizing additions should be made just prior to casting the metal in a mold so that the melt will not have an opportunity to reoxidize on standing. They should be thoroughly stirred in to obtain adequate contact with the melt.

Removal of Hydrogen. As mentioned above, hydrogen alone can cause gas porosity in metals, aluminum and magnesium being examples. It is very unusual for hydrogen to be the sole cause of unsoundness in copper alloys. Aside from oxygen, hydrogen is the only other gas that needs to be removed from melts as a consequence of melting in air. Where nitrogen is a serious problem, resort should be had to vacuum melting or to melting in a completely inert atmosphere.

If possible, it is far better to avoid dissolving hydrogen in liquid metals than to attempt to remove it after it has already dissolved. Removal of hydrogen is not as straightforward and simple as deoxidation since hydrogen does not form compounds (hydrides) comparable in stability to oxides. The most stable hydride is probably that of lithium, and the use of lithium as an agent for the removal of hydrogen from copper melts and others of lower melting point has been proposed.[7] However, as far as the authors are aware, no reliable quantitative results relating to this procedure have been published.

A second procedure for reducing the hydrogen content of liquid metals is to allow the melt to freeze in the crucible prior to casting, thus expelling the hydrogen in excess of the solid solubility limit. According to Eastwood,[8] the solid solubility of hydrogen in magnesium is higher than in aluminum. Magnesium, therefore, is less susceptible to hydrogen porosity since not as much hydrogen is expelled during the freezing of magnesium.

The hydrogen content may be lowered considerably in aluminum alloys by bubbling dry gases such as chlorine or nitrogen through the melt. This upsets the normal $Al-H_2$ equilibrium causing displacement of hydrogen from the melt, and causes mechanical disturbance of hydrogen bubbles. It is important to get good contact between the gas sweep and the metal by stirring; the operation may require a few minutes of gas sweeping to lower the hydrogen to a low level. Naturally, care must be taken to use a very dry nitrogen as water vapor in the air (or in burning gases in a gas furnace) is the prime source of hydrogen in aluminum or magnesium alloys. Chlorine cylinder gas, if used, is very dry and requires no further drying. The use of chlorine tends to result in cleaner aluminum castings, but it is not recommended in alloys containing magnesium as it results in excessive loss of magnesium as $MgCl_2$. Chlorine is also a toxic gas, but in a well-ventilated room of considerable size it is not too objectionable; the use of a local hood or exhaust air duct is recommended.

The hydrogen content of metals which can dissolve both oxygen and hydrogen (like copper) may be reduced considerably by drastic oxidation of the melt, since from the law of mass action for a given moisture content over the melt the product of dissolved oxygen and hydrogen is a constant (assuming equilibrium) at a given temperature. However, except in special cases (an example of which is cited in the next section), this procedure is rarely used since usually lowering the oxygen content to a very low level is sufficient to avoid porosity.

Protective Covers in Melting. There are several types of protective covers which may be used in air melting to avoid excessive oxidation of the melt. They include crushed charcoal, glass, and inert gas flushing.

Charcoal is frequently used in making copper alloys and in holding lower melting metals such as lead for long periods of time, as in the lead pot heat treating of steel. With copper and its alloys, care must be taken to see that the charcoal used is quite dry; otherwise the bath may become highly charged with oxygen and hydrogen from the water absorbed on the charcoal. There are few ways of making a more unsound casting of a high copper alloy than by the use of damp charcoal, followed by inadequate deoxidation. Actually, charcoal is not to be recommended very highly as a cover for molten metals which are to be cast into a mold as it is difficult to clean the surface of the melt well enough so that no bits of charcoal are mixed in with the casting. Also, except for copper and its alloys, charcoal has very limited application. It cannot be used with metals which form carbides, and there is no reason for using it with lower melting metals except in heat-treating baths where, because of long holding times, oxidation can be a serious matter.

Glass covers, either of bottle glass or of fused sodium tetraborate (borax glass), have been much used for protecting copper alloys during melting. Borax glass is very reactive with clay-graphite crucibles, and Tercod (silicon carbide–graphite) crucibles should be used instead. Bottle glass is very viscous at the temperatures ordinarily used with copper alloys, and is messy to remove just prior to pouring. Dry sand may be added to either of the two glasses to thicken them enough for removal by winding up on the end of a length of strap iron; sand or some other thickening agent is particularly necessary for borax glass, which at 1100°C is extremely fluid.

Borax glass with dissolved cupric oxide has been successfully used as a cover to oxidize tin bronzes,[9] and hence reduce hydrogen content to a low level. After this controlled oxidation step, the glass is removed as described above, and the melt is deoxidized and cast.

Glass covers have an advantage over charcoal covers in that they seal better the surface of the melt from the atmosphere and tend to keep in volatile constituents like zinc and cadmium, but, like charcoal, they are troublesome to remove. It should be noted that glass covers are generally only useful on melts made at temperatures in the range of copper-base alloys, 1000 to 1200°C. At lower temperatures the glasses are insufficiently fluid, and at much higher temperatures they are too unstable and reactive.

Salt Covers. The only metal regularly melted under a salt cover is magnesium. By the use of a salt mixture based on $MgCl_2$, oxidation of the metal is kept to a negligibly low level. Because of the low specific gravity of molten magnesium, the salt is more dense than the metal, and hence tends to sink to the bottom of the iron crucible; but enough salt remains at the sides and top to prevent the metal from burning. Entrainment of salt in the casting is minimized by the use of a special bottom pouring or skimmer ladle used to dip out metal from the holding pot.[10]

In many cases there is little tendency for a salt cover to react with a metal, but, if the metal is quite electropositive and the salt comparatively unstable, rather complete reaction may occur, resulting in adding considerable amounts of the salt cation to the melt. Small amounts of sodium are added to aluminum-silicon alloys for the purpose of refining their structure, by means of melting under a salt cover. In this case, the sodium salt is sufficiently stable so that only trace amounts are dissolved in the aluminum. Zinc-chromium alloys [11] have been made by melting zinc under a cover of chromium chloride.

Gas Covers. Flushing the surface of a melt with an inert gas such as argon or helium avoids most of the difficulties cited for the previous covers. The general procedure with an inert gas is to keep a lid or ceramic cover over the crucible so that the gas is confined in a space just above the melt surface. A small hole may be bored in the crucible cover for insertion of a fused silica tube carrying a slow stream of gas, or the tube may be introduced through a notch cut in the edge of the lid. When a gas is used there is no mess to clean off the surface of the melt, and the heat may be poured at any moment desired, as it requires only a few seconds to remove the gas tube. The inert gas may require drying, but most grades of noble gases are sufficiently dry already.

Dry nitrogen would be satisfactory in nearly every instance where air melting produces satisfactory results, with the possible exceptions of alloys containing alloying elements with a high affinity for nitrogen. Another advantage of gas covers in air melting is that one is not limited to any temperature range, nor is there a crucible reaction problem as in using glass (or salt) covers.

Vacuum Melting

Because of the great progress made in recent years in vacuum engineering, vacuum melting is no longer the dubious operation it used to be in the 1930's or before. Although vacuum melting has found little application in commercial melting, its use in the laboratory is now so commonplace that it is regarded as a standard procedure for the preparation of pure metals or alloys where the best possible compositional control must be obtained, and especially to avoid reaction with the gases of the atmosphere. As mentioned in the discussion on deoxidation, the use of deoxidizers entails leaving some residual material in the melt, with the possibility of significant change in the properties of the metal. Where such residual elements cannot be tolerated, vacuum melting provides a way to melt and cast alloys without the necessity of such contamination.

In addition, purification of certain metals may be possible during vacuum melting, especially the removal of volatile impurities such as magnesium, sulphur, manganese, and calcium. Not only are gases prevented from dissolving in the melt, but gases which may have been originally present in the melting stock are in some cases removed. For example, the partial pressure of oxygen over molten copper is so high that oxygen is practically quantitatively removed from pure copper (but not if present in the form of stable oxides, such as Al_2O_3). Hydrogen in metals is removed, at least to so low a level that it has no effect on the properties.

Oxygen is removed from low-carbon steel as CO until either all the carbon or oxygen is removed. Since usually carbon is present in excess, the oxygen is removed to a very low level. Hydrogen refining may be useful in connection with the vacuum melting of metals such as copper, nickel or iron, whose oxides are readily reduced by hydrogen. After vacuum melting, and while still at temperature, hydrogen is substituted for the vacuum. After a sufficient holding period of several minutes to allow complete reduction of the oxides, the hydrogen is turned off and a vacuum obtained again. The water vapor and residual hydrogen are then removed, and a deoxidized and degassed melt results. Removal of water vapor is aided if a "cold finger" is used to freeze out the water as ice at $-196°C$ with liquid nitrogen. (See Chapter 5.) Gas porosity in castings made by vacuum melting is naturally completely eliminated. The fact that certain volatile metal impurities can be removed during vacuum melting means that these same metals cannot be satisfactorily melted in a vacuum, for such melting would amount to a distillation process. However, metals of high vapor pressure and alloys containing them can be melted in vacuum equipment if a sufficiently high partial pressure of a noble gas is introduced to hold down the metal vapors. The maximum feasible vapor pressure of liquid metals during vacuum melts probably lies between 500 and 1000 microns (0.05 to 0.1 mm of mercury). Even at 500 microns, however, considerable amounts of metal will be condensed on cooler parts of the system, but not so much that vacuum melting becomes impracticable. Since the rate of distillation of a liquid metal at a given temperature is proportional to the surface exposed, a tall, narrow crucible is to be preferred to keep down evaporation losses. Naturally, time is an important factor, and rapid melting and casting will also minimize loss. Evaporation losses are in general negligible, however, if the metal vapor pressure is not greater than a few microns.

Vacuum Melting Equipment. Although vacuum melting equipment may be built around any of the four types of general melting furnaces described earlier in this chapter, the flexibility in design permitted by high-frequency induction melting is so important that it appears desirable to confine the discussion of vacuum melting to apparatus of this type.

Vacuum induction melting furnaces may be conveniently divided into two principal types: first, those in which the high-frequency coil is in the air and, second, those where the coil is inside the vacuum chamber. The first type is more common, particularly among furnaces of smaller size, and hence is more frequently encountered in the laboratory. Furnaces of this type also are very much cheaper and easier to build. They will be discussed first.

Generally the vacuum chamber consists of a fused silica tube, or sometimes a Vycor tube. The coil is wrapped around the silica tube, and some thermal insulation is ordinarily required inside the silica tube to prevent excessive heat loss and too much heating of the tube. The silica tube may be open at both ends or closed at one end. If the tube can be opened from both ends, it allows a little more flexibility in loading and unloading. For very small furnaces, however, a tube closed at the bottom end is very satisfactory, and has the advantage that a bottom metal to silica seal is avoided.

The tube is ordinarily mounted vertically, with the pumping system attached to the upper end, as illustrated in Figure 8. For a more complete discussion of a furnace of this type, see Seybolt.[12] It will be noted that the vacuum "head" or metal top of the furnace makes a vacuum-tight seal to the top end of the silica tube, with a similar seal of the flat rubber flange type at the bottom. Such a sealing technique requires that the silica tube be purchased with square, ground ends. The assembly is held together by mounting in an angle iron (or aluminum) frame. The entire weight of the assembly is taken by the wide-bottom flange, and the assembly is compressed by drawing down on the screws in the flange at the top, thus applying force on both the top and the bottom rubber gaskets.

It is suggested that if the silica tube is 4 inches in diameter or under, the metal parts be made of brass for ease of cleaning and avoiding of rust. However, for a furnace about 6 inches in diameter or over, steel parts are more practical from the standpoint of cost. The top should be water cooled to prevent overheating the rubber gaskets; the bottom may or may not require water cooling, but it is usually desirable.

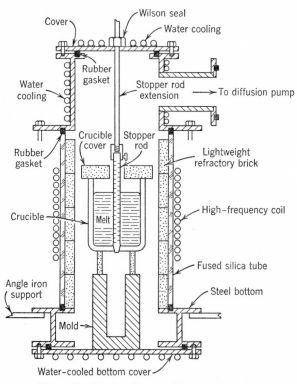

Figure 8.   Bottom-Pouring Vacuum Furnace.

The insulation shown inside the silica tube could be a series of half rings sawed out of K-30 brick unless the temperature will exceed 1650°C at the outside of the crucible, when a more refractory insulation should be used. A stopper rod is shown stopping a small (¼ to ⅜ inch diameter) hole in the bottom of the crucible so that the melt may be poured into the mold below by pulling up the stopper rod extension, preferably stainless steel, which emerges from the Wilson seal. The stopper rod itself may be made of several materials such as alumina, magnesia, or zircon.

In a furnace of this type, it is not important what type of high-frequency power is used for melting except that lower frequencies will induce more stirring of the charge unless it is shielded by a conducting crucible or a heater crucible, in which case very little stirring is likely. A heater crucible may be made of graphite, into which the ceramic crucible fits so that better coupling with the coil is obtained, allowing an increase in attainable temperature of perhaps 200 to 400°C. However, graphite heater crucibles are not generally satisfactory because of a tendency to react with oxide crucibles, yielding a small amount of carbon monoxide, which prevents obtaining a good vacuum. A better choice is a molybdenum or tantalum can about 50 mils thick, with a hole left in the bottom through which the metal may be poured if it is planned to use bottom pouring (see Figure 9).

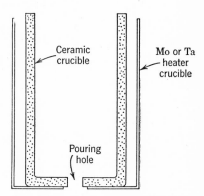

Figure 9.   Heater Crucible.

It is not necessary to precision-grind the end of the stopper rod and to taper the hole in the crucible into which it fits. As long as the stopper-rod point is reasonably conical in shape (no flat spots), a short operation of hand-grinding the stopper into the crucible hole will make a seat adequate to hold the metal.

For furnaces in which the silica tube is closed at the bottom end, it may not be desirable to use the method indicated above to seal the silica tube to the metal vacuum head. Figure 10 shows a technique for getting a grip on a rough-surfaced silica tube without any danger of breaking the tube. This method will also work satisfactorily on Vycor, which is quite smooth, if it is first sand-blasted to roughen it slightly. The heart of the device is a circular rubber gasket cut to a wedge-shaped section, as shown in the figure; it is clear that as the brass ring fitting around the rubber is pulled up, radial compression occurs on the soft rubber gasket. Alternatively, a brass ring may be slipped over the end of the rough-surfaced silica tube and cemented in place. The ring may be gripped by various devices to a rubber-gasketed lid. At the bottom end of the silica tube a small amount of refractory powder may be poured to form a base on which the crucible mold assembly may be placed (see Figure 11). It is customary

to place a short length of a refractory tube between the crucible and
the mold to prevent too much conduction heat loss to the mold.

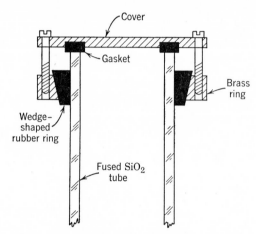

Figure 10.   Method of Silica Tube Closure.

A disadvantage of most vacuum melting furnaces, particularly small
ones of the type just described, is that additions to the charge cannot
readily be made after once pumping down.   The metal pieces in the
crucible take up much more space
than after melting.   Hence if the
crucible is to be filled to its capacity
with molten metal, it is often necessary to freeze the melt, allow it to
cool, and then add more charge after
opening the furnace.   One way of
adding more charge is to place a
tube on top of the crucible of about
the same diameter and place some
of the charge in it.   This procedure
works well in some cases, but frequently, owing to the fact that the
charge above is usually comparatively cold, the lumps reach a point
where they stick together, but do
not get hot enough to melt and run
down into the crucible.   The most

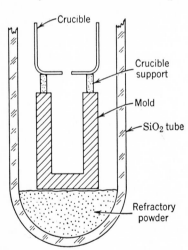

Figure 11.   Crucible and Mold in
Round Bottom Fused Silica Tube.

satisfactory method, without building a rather complex furnace to allow for direct additions to the molten metal, is to plan matters so that

the total capacity of the crucible is not utilized but is large enough so that enough metal can be charged at the outset for the job at hand.

Another design which is planned for tilt pouring rather than bottom pouring is shown schematically in Figure 12. Like the furnaces just discussed, the coil is outside the vacuum envelope. Mechanically, such a furnace is more complex than the bottom pouring type.

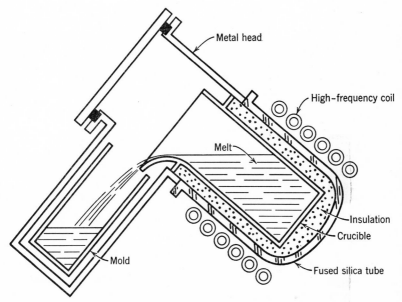

Figure 12.   Tilt-Pouring Vacuum Furnace.

It is possible to allow the metal to freeze in the crucible without a pipe (freezing-contraction cavity) by arranging for the high-frequency coil to move slowly upwards toward the top of the crucible so that the freezing starts at the bottom and gradually progresses upwards. (See discussion in Part II of this chapter on the casting of metals.) This technique is limited to securing ingots identical in diameter with the inside of the crucible used, but in general not as long. Hence, if a long thin rod is desired, it cannot be readily produced by this method.

The amount of refractory material used in a vacuum furnace should be kept to a minimum, as refractories with their large surface area are an important source of gas during melting. The first time a new crucible or a new furnace lining is used, the vacuum will be rather poor. It is good practice to keep a vacuum chamber of any type constantly evacuated if it is used frequently, to prevent adsorption of atmospheric gases on the various interior parts. Another method which has proved quite useful is to break the vacuum with helium, and put in an atmosphere of this gas. The vacuum chamber may be left for long periods filled with helium and still be pumped down readily.

Vacuum furnaces have been built with Pyrex glass as the vacuum chamber. This usually requires a double-walled glass container with water cooling between the two walls. Such furnaces are excessively fragile and in the authors' experience are not very satisfactory. In fact, sand-surface fused silica tubes are preferable to the thin-walled, but more fragile Vycor. Vycor is only preferable when it is necessary to be able to see through the chamber wall.

One defect inherent in the vacuum furnace using a coil outside a gas-tight tube is that the distance between the coil and the melt is rather great, making for poor electrical coupling and hence failure to secure the maximum temperature of which the high-frequency generating unit is capable. Another limitation of the gas-tight silica tube type of equipment is that, although the tube should be as small in diameter as is consistent with the amount of metal to be melted, such limitation in tube diameter naturally limits the over-all space available in the vacuum chamber, making it very difficult to use auxiliary equipment, such as a means of adding more metal to the charge as discussed previously. However, once the concept of requiring the high-frequency coil to operate in air is eliminated, and the coil placed inside the vacuum chamber, many of the former limitations disappear. Now the coil can be placed within a quarter inch of the crucible if desired, as no longer must a gas-tight tube intervene between the coil and the crucible; this makes a tremendous difference in heating efficiency.

The vacuum chamber may be made as large as desired with plenty of room for manipulation of all kinds of mechanisms such as charging devices, arrangements for centrifugal casting, and for tilt pouring since now there is room to mount trunnions about which the crucible can rotate into pouring position. Obviously, however, such a universal furnace of ample space for manipulative operations is a much more costly piece of equipment.

A schematic drawing of a vacuum furnace of this type is shown in Figure 13. One does not have the former freedom in choice of high-frequency power, however, as the use of higher voltages than 220 is attended by a pronounced tendency to cause arcing between parts of the coil. This in practice eliminates from serious consideration all types of high-frequency converters except the motor-generator type.

High-frequency motor-generator equipment is available at 220 volts output at the coil up to a capacity of 100 kw. If voltages higher than 220 must be used inside a vacuum system, electrical insulation of the coil and leads may be necessary to avoid the arcing difficulties. Even

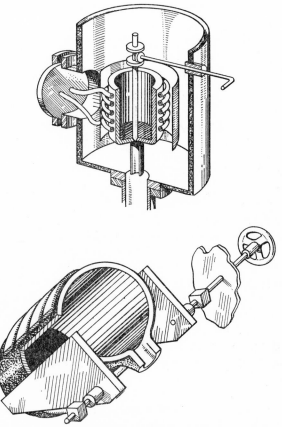

Figure 13.   Vacuum Furnace with High-Frequency Induction Coil inside Chamber.   *Top:* Furnace arranged for bottom pouring.   *Bottom:* Tilt-pouring arrangement.   (National Research Corp.)

with insulation, however, it is doubtful if voltages appreciably higher than 500 are practical. Arcing is eliminated if the vacuum is very good, as there is then not enough gas present to conduct an electrical discharge. Similarly, if the pressure is quite high, no gaseous discharge occurs. Unfortunately, pressures frequently encountered in vacuum melting when considerable degassing is occurring are such (the order of 100 microns) as favor a gaseous discharge. Such gaseous discharges are quite common in vacuum melting with the coil outside the vacuum system, but in this case no damage is done, except that with vacuum tube high-frequency generators the tubes may stop oscillating, necessitating shutting off the power until the vacuum improves.

It is desirable, although not necessary, to water-cool the walls of a vacuum furnace of the type shown in Figure 13 to keep down gas evolution from the furnace wall, to eliminate overheating of the rubber seals, and, last, to avoid possible melting of the walls if a high-temperature melt is accidentally spilled. It is also desirable to make the

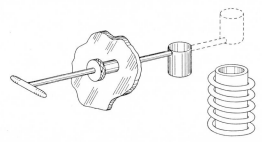

Figure 14. Charging Bucket, Using Wilson Seal. (National Research Corp.)

walls of stainless steel to avoid rusting and hence gassing due to slow volatilizing of moisture from rust. The best construction is probably the use of double walls with stainless steel on the inside, and ordinary steel on the outside for economy. Two major ports to the furnace are required, one for the pumping system and the second for bringing the high-frequency power through a Mycalex or plastic cover. Additional seals of smaller size may be required for the various manipulations required, and for vacuum measuring, as outlined in Chapter 6.

As mentioned above, one of the advantages of the coil within the vacuum chamber is the relative ease with which additions may be made during the melting operation. Several devices of more or less complexity have been used for this purpose, but one of the simpler methods is shown in Figure 14. A metal bucket mounted on a smooth stainless steel rod is passed through a Wilson seal, allowing motion of translation and rotation. By previously filling one or more such buckets mounted on shafts pointing toward the crucible, alloying additions or additional charge may be added at any time by inverting the filled bucket over the crucible. Electromagnetic (Syntron) [13] feeding devices allow gradual additions of a granular charge and hence avoid the excessive splashing which is hard to avoid in inverting charging buckets. Syntron feeders require considerable space, however, and would need a special vacuum housing except in very large furnace shells. They have proved very satisfactory for moderate-to-large-scale vacuum or inert-gas melting operations.

It should be emphasized before leaving the subject of vacuum melting that in order to have proper control one must know not only the pressure inside the vacuum chamber but also the leak rate. Very fast pumps can maintain a low pressure in a leaky container, but the metal being melted can become oxidized if a large volume of gas passes through the furnace at a low pressure. A leak rate of a few micron liters per hour is usually satisfactory.

Inert-Gas Melting

In order to have adequate control over the atmosphere in inert-gas melting, it is necessary to conduct such melting in vacuum-tight equipment. Such an operation is not to be confused with the protective cover technique described above as a variant of air melting; in the latter case all that is attempted is to reduce contact with the atmosphere. However, in true inert-gas melting, the objective is to avoid completely any contamination from the air. Inert-gas melting is used in melting metals which are too reactive to be melted in air, or are too volatile to be vacuum-melted.

The usual procedure is to evacuate the melting chamber as in vacuum melting, but to introduce purified argon or helium before melting occurs. The pressure of inert gas introduced depends upon how much reduction in volatilization is desired and how much degassing of the melt is wanted. These two aims are mutually exclusive, and some practical compromise must be sought. If no gas removal from the metal is necessary, a full atmosphere of inert gas could be used; but the objection to this is excessive heat loss by conduction and convection. This heat loss may be important if a temperature near the limit of that attainable in the vacuum melting equipment is desired; the maximum temperature which can be obtained with an atmosphere of noble gas will be considerably lower than in a vacuum where the only heat losses are due to radiation. In this case argon is preferable to helium because of the lower thermal conductivity of argon.

A distinction must be made between melting in a stagnant noble-gas atmosphere as contrasted to melting in an atmosphere of flowing gas, as mentioned in Chapter 5. As pointed out there, it is much better to heat metals in a stagnant atmosphere if the system is tight. In the discussion in this section it is assumed that a stagnant inert-gas atmosphere is used.

The amount of metal lost by evaporation during vacuum melting may be approximately computed from the relation [14]

$$ G = \frac{P}{17.14\sqrt{T/M}} \tag{2} $$

where G is the amount of metal evaporated in grams/cm^2-sec,
   M is the atomic weight of the metal,
   P is the vapor pressure of the metal in millimeters,
   T is the absolute temperature in °K.

This equation was first used by I. R. Langmuir [15] to determine vapor pressures from rates of evaporation in high vacua.

Note that the area involved in calculating G is the area of the crucible; hence the rate of loss by evaporation is proportional to the surface exposed to the vacuum system. Equation 2 assumes that atoms of metal vapor immediately are lost to the system as soon as they are formed.

The situation is much more complex when attempting to calculate the amount of metal evaporated in an inert-gas atmosphere.*

It is interesting to compare the metal loss by evaporation in vacuum and in an inert gas by the use of equation 3 (see footnote). In the case of magnesium at 650°C (the melting point), the evaporation rate in vacuum is 11 mg per cm^2-sec, but with only 1 mm of argon the rate is reduced to 0.07 mg per cm^2-sec. Since the evaporation rate in an inert gas is inversely proportional to pressure, it is clear that the

* Epstein [16] has calculated that when an inert gas is used in a melting operation, the ratio of the amount of metal evaporated to that evaporated in vacuum is given to a first approximation by

$$ \frac{M_{(g)}}{M_{(v)}} = \frac{2.736T}{\lambda P} \cdot \left[\frac{1}{b}\right]^{2/3} \cdot \frac{\left[1 + \frac{W_m}{W_g}\right]^{1/2}}{\left[1 + \left(\frac{\rho_g}{\rho_m}\right)^{1/3}\right]^2} \tag{3} $$

where $M_{(g)}$ = grams of metal/cm^2-sec evaporated in the gaseous atmosphere,
   $M_{(v)}$ = grams of metal/cm^2-sec evaporated in vacuum,
   T = absolute temperature,
   P = pressure, in dynes/cm^2,
   λ = to a first approximation the length of the heated section of the system above the metal surface in centimeters,
   W_g = molecular weight of gas,
   W_m = molecular weight of metal,
   ρ_g = density of gas in grams/cm^3,
   ρ_m = density of metal in grams/cm^3,
   b = van der Waals' b for the gas (cm^3/mole).

evaporation rate could be reduced to $0.07 \cdot (\frac{1}{760})$ mg per cm^2-sec if one atmosphere of argon were used.

Less important than pressure is the molecular weight of the gas and its density. But because it helps to use a gas of high density argon is preferable to helium. If the length of the hot zone over the crucible is comparatively large, this also aids in reducing evaporation since the concentration gradient of metal atoms over the crucible is reduced.

Equation 3 given in the footnote was derived on the basis that the evaporation of metal atoms from the surface of a melt occurs, in the presence of an inert gas, by diffusion of metal atoms through the gas. There is some question about the accuracy of this equation, particularly in the vagueness in the value of numerical coefficients. Also, no convective mixing of gas and metal atoms is assumed; this is probably true only for relatively low evaporation rates. It is possible that values derived from the equation may be in error as much as by a factor of 100, but it is at least of value in pointing out the pertinent variables and their relative importance.

Melting Alkali and Alkaline Earth Metals. When melting metals such as sodium, potassium, or calcium, ordinary ceramic crucibles may not be used because of excessive crucible reaction. Metals of this type are, like magnesium, satisfactorily melted in iron. Potassium and sodium may be melted in stainless steel crucibles, but calcium is best melted in iron since it alloys with nickel. Vacuum melting is not feasible because of the high vapor pressure of these metals. However, melting in an atmosphere of argon or helium is quite satisfactory.

II. CASTING

It has been pointed out in the introduction that there are two kinds of castings, ingots and finished shapes. Since in the laboratory ingots are much more frequently made, most of the discussion will center about the casting of ingots. Many of the considerations pertinent to the preparation of satisfactory ingots apply equally well to other castings.

Since most metals contract the order of 4% in volume in passing from the liquid to the solid state at the melting point, care must be taken to cause this contraction to occur at the top of the ingot where it does no harm. Uncontrolled freezing usually results in a shrinkage cavity occurring somewhere below the surface of the ingot, thus requiring excessive removal of unsound metal from the ingot. Such uncontrolled freezing occurs if the metal is allowed to freeze in the crucible without provision to make the top hotter than elsewhere. As pointed out

above, freezing in the crucible is satisfactory if arrangements are made
to insure freezing from the bottom upward, as by slowly moving up
the high-frequency heating coil.   Ideally, an ingot should freeze entirely from the bottom up, in layers parallel to the bottom, with no
heat loss to the sides.   If this were done, then there would be no
shrinkage (pipe) even at the top, which would be perfectly flat, and
no metal would have to be cropped.   This is ordinarily not practicable,
as it would entail heating the mold walls to the liquidus temperature,
and water-cooling the bottom, a cumbersome procedure.   Some side

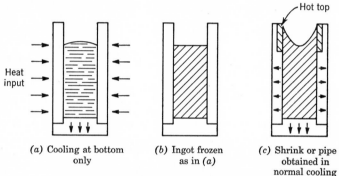

<table>
<tr><td>(a) Cooling at bottom
only</td><td>(b) Ingot frozen
as in (a)</td><td>(c) Shrink or pipe
obtained in
normal cooling</td></tr>
</table>

Figure 15.   Freezing of Ingots.

freezing is inevitable in ingots not handled as suggested above, entail-
ing the removal of some pipe at the top (see Figure 15).

However, in order to insure that the top of the ingot remains hotter
than the rest of the metal, it is customary to place a low thermal conductivity insert at the top of the mold.   In this way enough metal remains liquid at the top to feed a shrinkage cavity which otherwise
would develop near the top.   If the metal is poured rather slowly,
such a hot top can be eliminated since then new hot metal is being
constantly added at the top, thus constituting a moving hot top.

Mold Materials and Shapes

Laboratory ingots are commonly either cylindrical or rectangular.
Rod or cylindrical shapes are cast when no further fabrication is to
be done, or when rod or wire is to be prepared by rolling or swaging,
and by drawing through wire dies.   Rectangular molds are more difficult to make and are generally used only where the casting is to be
rolled to strip.   As regards dimensions of the molds, rectangular molds
with a quarter-inch-wide opening are about as small as is practicable,
whereas in cylindrical molds, an inside diameter less than one-half

inch is not recommended. In addition, the ratio of the smallest dimension (thickness or diameter) to the longest dimension (length) should not be greater than about 1 to 20, but a smaller ratio will give better results.

Cylindrical molds are much more readily made in the shop than rectangular ones, are easier to use, and require less space than rectangular molds, which usually have to be held together with clamps of

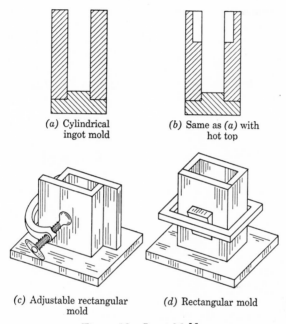

(a) Cylindrical   (b) Same as (a) with
ingot mold   hot top

(c) Adjustable rectangular   (d) Rectangular mold
mold

Figure 16. Ingot Molds.

some variety. Figure 16 shows a few molds of both types, which have been found useful in the laboratory. The bottom plug of the cylindrical mold should be recessed somewhat into the tube part of the mold, as this aids in preventing liquid metal from running out, and also positions the tube and holds it in place. For the rectangular molds, it is more customary to rely upon the chilling of the first metal cast to prevent running out at the bottom, and the only provision usually made is to see that the bottom surfaces of the mold are smooth and flat and are placed on a similarly flat bottom plate. A rectangular plug could be used in the rectangular molds, but this would necessitate a series of bottom plugs for the adjustable mold shown in Figure 16c. The molds need not be built with tapered sides, as the shrinkage contraction of the metal allows ready removal except where the molten metal attacks the mold and hence becomes welded to it. This sometimes happens, particularly in casting high-melting metals into metallic molds, but generally can be prevented by the use of mold dressings.

Graphite is probably the most generally used mold material, as it is not attacked by many molten metals, is relatively cheap, and readily machinable. It also has a high thermal conductivity which is usually an advantage in an ingot mold. Carbide-forming metals attack graphite, dissolving it, and in so doing form carbides at the graphite-metal interface. This can be prevented to a large extent by pouring at low temperatures, and by painting the surface of the graphite with a water suspension of clay, bone ash, etc. Such coatings will usually result in some loss in smoothness of surface compared to an as-machined graphite surface where no mold reaction occurs. Graphite molds, however, are satisfactory without any dressing for nearly all low-melting alloys up to and including copper, with the exception of the alkali and alkaline earth metals.

Copper is often used for ingot molds in the laboratory, but care should be taken to insure that the copper is massive enough so that it is not heated very hot by the metal cast into it; otherwise serious alloying may result. Experimental steel heats have been poured into copper molds with a refractory hot top. To be certain that alloying is prevented, a layer of soot is sometimes deposited on the copper surface with a smoking acetylene flame. If the metal is chilled quickly, very little if any carbon is dissolved at the surface, and it can be removed by machining. Such a soot layer, however, is not generally necessary.

Other metallic molds which have been used are Armco iron, mild steel, and cast iron. These ferrous materials must be coated with an oxidized or graphited surface to prevent sticking unless the mass of the mold is large enough to prevent reaching a sticking temperature. However, since a high temperature is probably reached instantaneously at the interface, the use of some kind of mold dressing on all metallic molds except copper is generally required.

Mold dressings are many, and no attempt will be made to give a complete list here. In addition to those already mentioned are volatile ones such as lard oil, or lard oil-tallow mixtures sometimes used in the brass industry, finely divided ceramic suspensions in water or alcohol, such as MgO, Al_2O_3, and aquadag (colloidal graphite in water). Volatile or oil types of mold dressings are usually painted on metal molds heated to 100 to 200°C so that most of the volatile material is driven off prior to casting. Also, the material sticks on the molds much better when the metal is hot. Water suspensions should likewise be painted on hot metal or an even coating will not result.

Ceramic molds or ceramic-lined molds have been used to some extent, but have the disadvantage that the ceramic cracks when hit by the molten metal and generally can be used only once. Since the thermal conductivity of ceramic molds is low, there can be no hot-top effect (except by increasing the section at the top) since the rate of heat extraction is nearly the same from top to bottom. However, as pointed out previously, a ceramic hot top is not necessarily a prerequisite for a sound casting if the rate of pouring is fairly slow or if other means are available to keep the top hot. One type of ceramic insert which can readily be used is an alundum tube slid into a cylindrical graphite mold. Even if the alundum cracks due to thermal shock, the pieces may remain in place long enough to make several castings, if carefully handled. However, since the bore of alundum tubes tends to vary slightly from point to point, there is a possibility of locking in the casting, which would necessitate breaking the alundum tube in order to withdraw the casting.

Casting Methods

In high-frequency melting in air it is customary to mount the crucible in place inside the coil, ramming a dry ceramic insulating mixture between the crucible and the electrically insulating layer of mica or glass cloth next to the coil, as illustrated in Figure 1. Hence in order to pour a heat made in this apparatus, it is necessary to pick up the crucible and coil mounting as a unit, carry it to the mold, and pour the metal. An alternative method is to rock the crucible forward on its stand on special pouring trunnions and pour the heat into the mold, carefully located with respect to the trunnions. This second technique is not as desirable as the first because it does not allow enough flexibility in pouring. Although the fixed-position pour is necessary in vacuum melting when using tilt pouring with the coil inside the vacuum chamber, it is not necessary when pouring in air, and advantage should be taken of the better control possible by carrying the heat to the mold. One operator can easily handle a 10-pound heat with the coil assembly by grasping handles on either side of the coil mounting, standing back of the furnace, and pouring the heat directly in front of him. In a 20-to-30-pound heat, pouring handles of iron pipe can be screwed into either side of coil frame, a single pipe on one side and a double-handled arrangement on the other, requiring two men to pour the heat. Still larger heats made in the high-frequency furnace are ordinarily poured over trunnions, with a power lift to raise the furnace. However, in larger castings, accuracy in pouring is ordinarily not so important, as the mold opening is rather large.

In making small heats in the gas furnace or electric resistance furnace it is customary to remove the crucible from the furnace, grasp it with tongs, and pour it. Two types of tongs are used for larger cru-

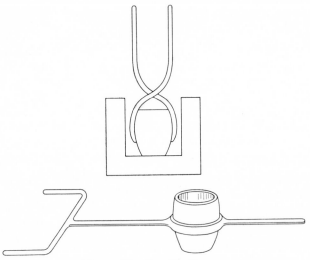

Figure 17. Crucible Tongs.

cibles over about 4 inches in diameter, as shown in Figure 17, one for lifting the crucible, and another type for pouring. The reason for the characteristic pot-bellied shape of most commercial crucibles becomes apparent; it is necessary for proper gripping in both types of tongs. In the pouring tongs, the double handles at one end are for the operator who controls the pouring, and the single-grip end is for an operator who has no control over pouring. Small crucibles may be lifted out of the furnace by laboratory forceps or small tongs grasping the edge of the crucible, but in larger crucibles this method would put too large a torque on the crucible wall, causing it to crumble. Beaker tongs make a very convenient tool for pouring small crucibles up to about 4 inches in diameter, whereas for very small crucibles about 1 inch in diameter, laboratory forceps are useful. The temperature to which a melt is heated above its melting point (liquidus) is in general about 100 to 200°C, and depends upon the following factors:

1. Amount of chilling (rate of heat abstraction) in the mold.
2. Rate of pouring.
3. Mold geometry.
4. Susceptibility of the melt to absorption of gas.
5. Metallurgical considerations such as nuclei effects.

The general aim is to avoid heating the metal any higher than necessary in order to secure a good casting. Unnecessarily high temperatures lead to excessive gas absorption, possible loss of volatile or
readily oxidized constituents, and to excessive pipe in the ingot. On
the other hand, too low a temperature causes "cold shuts," insufficient
filling of the mold, and may not allow complete emptying of the
crucible.

It is usually desirable to secure rapid freezing of the melt, as this
tends to prevent segregation of alloying constituents, and makes a
finer grain size; low pouring temperature promotes these desirable
features. Because of the high thermal conductivity of metal or graphite ingot molds, the heat is extracted rather rapidly from the cast
metal, and by definition a casting made in such molds are "chill castings" unless special provision is made to increase the freezing time,
as by heating the mold, prior to casting. In certain cases, where alloys
may be unusually subject to inverse segregation or gravity segregation, the pouring rate may be made slow enough so that the rate of
pouring is just fast enough to keep apace of freezing. This means
that the metal freezes in layers, and the amount of molten metal in the
mold at any instant is very small. It can readily be seen that this is
not easy to accomplish in practice, which explains why this method
is not more widely used.

Some metals like aluminum alloys, which tend to form tough oxide
films, should preferably be handled in such a way so that turbulence
of the molten metal during casting is avoided, hence minimizing entrainment of such films in the casting. A technique sometimes used
to minimize turbulence is illustrated in Figure 18. The rectangular
"book mold" is mounted on trunnions so that it may be rotated as
indicated. In starting the pour, the mold is rotated so that one edge
is nearly horizontal and the melt is quietly run down this edge. As
the metal nears the point of running back out of the mold, the mold is
slowly tilted toward a vertical position. In essence, the cast metal
is slid into the mold without disturbing the surface at any time. With
aluminum alloys, once the pouring is started it should not be inter-
rupted so that the surface of the pouring stream or the surface of the
cast metal loses its continuity. Because of the presence of this film

of Al_2O_3 over the molten metal, one is really pouring the metal through a tube of Al_2O_3.

A very similar technique, but one which causes less turbulence than the one just described, is the *Durville* casting method or process in

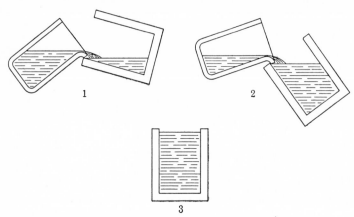

Figure 18. Non-turbulent Pouring.

which the melting crucible is fixed in position with respect to the mold as shown in Figure 19. It can readily be seen by reference to the figure that the metal slowly slides out of the crucible and quietly runs into the mold without at any time breaking the surface of the

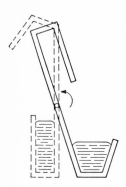

Figure 19. Durville Casting.

metal, if the rotation is accomplished slowly and smoothly.[17,18] This method was developed primarily for aluminum bronzes, which are notorious for their tendency to entrain alumina, hence causing poor mechanical properties and inferior machinability.

For the casting of small ingots in the laboratory, there is ordinarily no need for the various pouring basins and strainers which are often used in commercial operations. A *pouring basin*[19-21] is a cavity adjacent to the mold entrance into which the metal is cast instead of directly into the mold, with the objective of maintaining better control over pouring rate. As long as the basin is kept filled up beyond a certain point, the rate of overflow into the mold remains substantially constant; hence irregularities in pouring rate into the basin do not affect the rate of mold filling, which is the same at all times. *Strainers*[19-21] are usually perforated disks made out of core sand, with many small holes in the bottom to strain out foreign bodies such as bits of refractory from the crucible, pieces of charcoal from the cover, and particles of slag. Generally, however, such auxiliary equipment is not necessary in laboratory work, where better control of pouring rate and greater cleanliness of the melt are possible than in industrial foundries.

The use of water-cooled molds in making chill castings is rather unusual, but may be justified in certain instances where very fast freezing is important. If water cooling is used, it is customary to water-cool the stool only (the mold bottom piece) which should preferably be made of copper in this case. The cooling of the stool makes for better unidirectional freezing and for minimum pipe. If the sides of the mold were also water-cooled, the pipe formed would be very extensive and might even go most of the way to the bottom. A water-cooled copper stool would probably not require any dressing since it would remain cold enough to prevent any sticking to the metal being cast. The combination of a water-cooled copper stool with a ceramic insert in the mold sides would make for minimum pipe because of the predominance in this case of heat flow to the bottom (see Figure 15).

There is a considerable body of literature dealing with the solidification of ingots, particularly steel ingots, in which investigators have calculated and experimentally verified the rate of freezing as a function of mold geometry, pouring temperature, thermal properties of mold and metal, etc. This literature was summarized by Ruddle [22] in 1950.

Special Casting Techniques

Sand Casting. The most common method of casting metal into a finished shape is sand casting. The name is derived from the molds which are prepared by ramming "green" (damp) sand around a pattern of wood or metal. After removing the pattern, the sand forms a hollow cavity which, when filled with metal, reproduces the shape of the pattern. After making the casting, the sand is broken away from the casting and may be used over again after cleaning. An adequate description of the technique of preparing sand molds and the factors involved in the design of sand castings would be too lengthy and detailed to be included here. Others have written satisfactory accounts of the problems of sand casting [19-21] if the reader should be interested in this subject. The main problem is the proper location and size of *gates* (points at which the metal enters the mold) and *risers* (reservoirs of molten metal to make up for the solidification shrink-age). It is not enough, however, to assume a shape and decide the location and size and shape of gates and risers; it is desirable for best results to design the shape itself so that it can be successfully cast. The objective, as in ingot casting, is to secure as far as possible uni-directional freezing, so that freezing starts at some point in the casting and progresses toward the risers, and ends at the risers. This is not always readily done.

For the proper preparation of sand castings, a rather considerable amount of specialized equipment is almost necessary. The sand itself should be screened to remove foreign matter, such as bits of wood, and it should be mixed thoroughly and uniformly with water (the order of 5% by weight) in a sand muller. Foundry sand for green sand molds must be of a certain quality in regard to the silica content and clay content. Too high a silica content results in a sand which will not adhere on ramming, but if the clay content is too high the mold is not sufficiently permeable to the gases, such as steam, which are formed during casting, and the casting will be damaged by gas accumulation. Sand handling is a rather dirty space-consuming operation, and if much sand casting is to be done, a special area should be available for this work.

Lost Wax Casting. In principle, the lost wax process is similar to sand casting, except that the pattern used is wax, which must be melted out of the mold before each casting. The lost wax process produces one type of so-called precision castings since very close dimensional tolerances may be held, and the surface finish is very smooth. Generally, objects made by the lost wax process are fairly small, but pieces as large as several pounds can be made if desired.

The procedure is as follows. The shape to be duplicated is machined out of brass, and a tin-bismuth alloy mold "negative" is made by cast-ing around the brass piece. The tin-bismuth alloy is used because it has no solidification shrinkage; hence the dimensions of the brass master part are precisely duplicated. The tin-bismuth alloy mold is used as a master mold to produce many wax "positives" by injecting a certain grade of wax (made for this purpose) into the mold. Hence the brass master pattern is now duplicated in wax. The wax pattern is coated with a smooth ceramic *investment* coating, and is sus-pended, with suitable wax gates and risers, into an asbestos tube, which is now filled with a slip of investment material, often high in silica. The composition of the slip is such that it sets to a hard ceramic body, out of which emerges the wax gates and risers. When the in-vestment material has aged enough, the wax may be melted out over a steam bath, and the investment mold fired to about 800°C to remove all traces of wax and to further cure the investment mold. The mold is now ready for use.

It will be seen that since the pattern is melted out rather than pulled out in one piece like a wooden pattern in sand casting, the shape can be very complex without causing any trouble in removal. If the desired shape is such that it cannot be withdrawn from either half of the bismuth alloy master mold, the mold can be made of more than two pieces. Multiple castings are frequently made by joining several wax patterns together with connectors also made of the same wax.

As in sand casting, a considerable quantity of specialized equipment is necessary if much work of this type is contemplated. It is essentially a production technique rather than a laboratory one, and considerable art and "know-how" are involved if high-quality work is to be expected.

Investment materials, waxes, etc., are available from several suppliers, including dental supply houses, as this technique is used in making gold inlays and dentures.

Centrifugal Casting. There are two types of centrifugal casting: (1) where the axis of rotation is an axis of symmetry of the part, such as the center line or axis of a pipe, and (2) where the axis of rotation is outside the casting. Type 1 is more common, and generally the centrifugally cast object is a pipe or disk of circular symmetry. The objective in centrifugal casting a pipe or disk is to allow lighter impurities such as bits of slag and oxides to segregate to the inside surface where they may be subsequently machined out, and to secure good mold-filling qualities and sound structure. The force pushing the metal against the wall is high enough to eliminate slight tendencies toward gas unsoundness or shrinkage porosity.

In the second type of centrifugal castings, the object is entirely to insure close reproduction of fine detail in the mold by forcing the molten metal against the mold wall by a force several times that of gravity. An example of this type of casting is the making of gold inlays, which must fill exactly a cavity in a tooth.

In casting pipe, it is customary to rotate the mold about the horizontal axis with a speed which generates a centrifugal force equivalent to a few "g's." When the mold is up to maximum speed, the metal is cast into the inside of the rotating mold by means of a runner or gate which projects into the inside of the mold. If the speed of the mold is fast enough, it would be possible to rotate it in a vertical position; but, since the surface of the metal assumes the shape of a parabola of revolution, the bottom of the casting would be thicker than the top, depending upon the speed.

A flat disk is most conveniently made with the axis of rotation per-pendicular. The mold material should preferably be such that chilling is avoided in order to get the liquid up to speed before it starts to solidify.

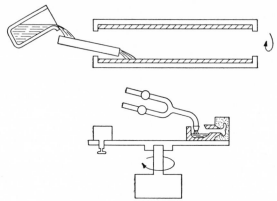

Figure 20.   Centrifugal Casting.

Figure 20 shows schematically the two types of centrifugal casting, taking the horizontal pipe and the dental technique as representative.

Continuous Casting.   Continuous casting is ordinarily an industrial process rather than a laboratory technique; hence it will be mentioned only briefly here.   In the usual process, continuous casting involves pouring a heat into a water-cooled mold or die which chills the metal enough so that it is completely solidified before it emerges from the mold.   The bottom of the mold is open, so that the rod being cast can be continuously withdrawn downward in a vertical direction. Naturally, the rate of withdrawal must be equal to or somewhat less than the rate of solidification.   The rod is ordinarily withdrawn by a pair of opposed rollers on each side of the cast rod.   There have been several articles written on this subject to which the reader is referred for more details.[18, 23]

REFERENCES

1. W. J. Kroll, *Metallwirtschaft*, **9**, 1043 (1930).
2. Michael B. Bever and Carl F. Floe, "Solubility of Hydrogen in Molten Copper-Tin Alloys," *Trans. Am. Inst. Mining Met. Engrs., Inst. Metals Div.*, **156**, 149–158 (1944).
3. A. Sieverts, "Absorption of Gases by Metals," *Z. Metallkunde*, **21**, 37–46 (1929).

4. A. J. Phillips, "The Separation of Gases from Molten Metals," *Trans. Am. Inst. Mining Met. Engrs., Inst. Metals Div.,* **171**, 17–46 (1947).
5. R. K. Kelley, *Contributions to the Data on Theoretical Metallurgy:*
   I. *U.S. Bureau Mines Bull.* 350 (Washington, 1932)

II.	371	1934
III.	383	1935
IV.	384	1935
V.	393	1936
VI.	394	1936
VII.	406	1937
VIII.	407	1937
IX.	434	1941
X.	476	1941

6. M. DeK. Thompson, "The Total and Free Energies of Formation of Oxides of Thirty-two Metals," The Electrochemical Soc., New York, 1942.
7. W. P. Sykes, "Rare and Precious Metals," *Mining and Metallurgy,* **24**, 66 (1943).
8. L. W. Eastwood, *Gas in Light Alloys,* John Wiley and Sons, New York (1946).
9. W. T. Pell Walpole, "Development of a Flux Degassing Process for Chill Cast Tin Bronzes," *J. Inst. Metals,* **70**, Pt. 4, pp. 127–147 (1944).
10. *Non-Ferrous Melting Practice,* A.I.M.E., New York, 1946.
11. H. Hanemann, "Zinc Chromium System," *Z. Metallkunde,* **32**, 91–92 (1940).
12. A. U. Seybolt, "A Practical Vacuum Melting Furnace," *Metal Progress,* **50**, 1102–1106 (1946).
13. The Syntron Co., Homer City, Pa.
14. Saul Dushman, *Scientific Foundations of Vacuum Technique,* John Wiley and Sons, New York, 1949.
15. I. R. Langmuir, *Phys. Rev.,* **2**, 329 (1913).
16. L. F. Epstein, Private communication, Knolls Atomic Power Laboratory, Schenectady, N. Y.
17. Reginald Genders and G. L. Bailey, "Casting of Brass Ingots," Research Monograph 3, British Non-Ferrous Metals Research Assoc., London, 1934.
18. E. Schever, "Modern Billett Casting with Special Reference to the Solidification Process," *J. Inst. Metals,* **76**, Pt. 2, pp. 103–120 (1949).
19. "Melting and Moulding of Ferrous and Non-ferrous Metals and Alloys," *Foundry Manual,* U.S. Navy Bureau of Ships, 250–0034.
20. Pat Dwyer, *Gates and Risers for Castings,* Penton Publishing Co., Cleveland, Ohio, 1949.
21. *Recommended Practices for Sand Casting of Nonferrous Alloys,* American Foundrymen's Assoc., Chicago, 1944.
22. R. W. Ruddle, "The Solidification of Castings," The Institute of Metals (Monograph and Report Series 7), London, 1950.
23. J. S. Smart, Jr., and A. A. Smith, Jr., "Continuous Casting: The Asarco Process," *Iron Age,* **162**, 72–80 (August 26, 1948).

CHAPTER EIGHT

Heat-Treating Techniques

The term heat treating implies that a metal is heated to an elevated temperature to cause some solid-state reaction such as recrystallization, precipitation, or a phase transformation to occur. Since the rate of these solid-state reactions increases exponentially with temperature, both the absolute value and the uniformity of the temperature must be accurately controlled. In some cases only the high temperature need be controlled, and the specimen may be cooled in any convenient way; in other cases it is necessary to control the cooling rate either to retain a high-temperature product or to control a transformation which occurs upon cooling.

In this chapter we shall concern ourselves primarily with the characteristics of various heat-transfer media such as fused salts and molten metals, and with the quenching of metals from elevated temperatures.

HEAT-TREATING MEDIA

Gases

The most commonly used equipment for the heat treating of metals in the laboratory is a tube furnace or a muffle furnace in which the heating medium is a gas, often air. Heat is transferred to the metal primarily by gas *convection* at temperatures below about 500 to 600°C. *Conduction* of heat via gases is ordinarily insignificant.

However, as the temperature is raised to a red heat and above, convective air heating is replaced in importance by radiation from the hot furnace walls. Hence, although the actual medium surrounding the sample may be a gas, it plays very little part in heat transfer at high temperatures.

Since convective heating at temperatures below a red heat is very effective, it is used widely in industrial ovens and low-temperature furnaces as *forced air convection*. Forced air convection furnaces are those in which hot air is rapidly circulated by means of a powerful fan around the samples or work being heated. There are two main types in use: one in which the hot air is heated in a separate compartment from the work, and one where the heating coils surround the work but at sufficient distance to allow forced air passage between the heating coils and the work. In the latter type the fan is mounted at the bottom of the furnace, and the air path is around the heating coils to the top, where it is deflected down through the work and back to the fan. In the other, the hot air generated in the heating chamber is swept out through a channel to the work area, through the work, and back through a different channel to the fan and the heating zone. There is in practice very little difference in operating characteristics between these types. The main characteristic of such furnaces is quite rapid heating and particularly very uniform heating of even a rather dense charge, such as a basket of nuts or bolts. The temperature uniformity is in the neighborhood of $\pm 2°C$.

Forced air convection furnaces are mainly used commercially, but small models are available which are suitable for laboratory operation. They are mostly used in the tempering of steel and for heat-treating age-hardening aluminum alloys and similar relatively low-temperature operations which can be conducted in air and where accurate temperature control is important.

Vacuum Annealing Furnaces

In recent years vacuum furnaces for annealing, degassing, and sintering of metals are coming into wide use because almost any kind of metal specimen may be annealed in them without danger of atmospheric attack. Since relatively few vacuum annealing furnaces are available commercially, several types will be described in this section.

A simple type of vacuum annealing furnace is illustrated in Figure 1. One end of a fused silica tube is capped by a metal disk fitted with a rubber gasket, which is held in place by hinged bolts fastened to a brass collar cemented to the silica tube; the other end is sealed in the same manner to the metal diffusion pump through a 90-degree elbow. The tube is heated with an ordinary tube furnace. For operation between 1200 and 1400°C, a tube of mullite or zircon porcelain may be substituted for fused silica. In this case a resistance furnace would be equipped with platinum or globar heating elements. It is frequently convenient to equip the tube with a water-cooled metal jacket on the end opposite the pumping system so that the specimen may be pushed into this region for more rapid cooling (Figure 2). If a

high-vacuum valve of large conductance is provided between the furnace and the diffusion pump, the furnace may be opened up while
hot for changing samples in this cold zone. The new sample is placed
in the cold zone, furnace sealed again, and pumped down with an

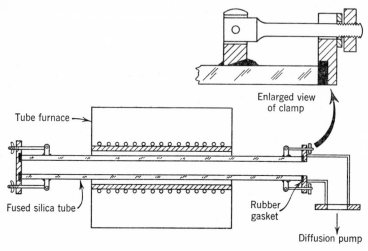

Figure 1.   Fused Silica Tube Vacuum Resistance Furnace.

auxiliary pump.   After the pressure has been brought down to the
operating value, the sample may be pushed into the hot zone with a
rod passing through a Wilson or similar seal.   If no cooling zone is

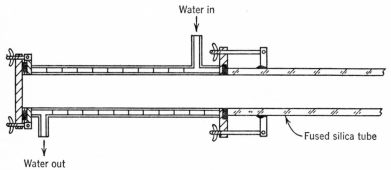

Figure 2.   Water-Cooled Metal Chamber Attached to Fused Silica Tube.

supplied in the furnace, the furnace must be cooled to room temperature for changing specimens.   In this case it is convenient to use a
split-tube furnace so that it may be opened to permit more rapid
cooling.

Metallic Tube Vacuum Furnace

If temperatures up to about 800°C are satisfactory, a metal tube of Inconel or 25% chromium, 12% nickel stainless steel may be substituted for the porcelain. A metal tube has the advantage of smoothing the temperature distribution somewhat, but the strength of the steel falls off so rapidly above 800°C that it cannot be used at high temperatures. If the tube itself is contained in a vacuum chamber the

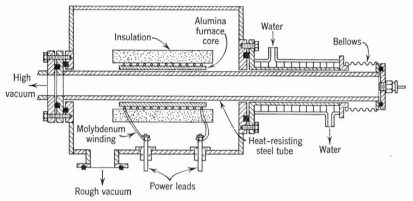

Figure 3. Vacuum Resistance Furnace, Using Metal Tube with Vacuum on Both Sides.

useful temperature range may be raised to about 1100°C, since it is no longer subjected to atmospheric pressure. Such a furnace is shown in Figure 3. The heating wire support and the insulation are located in the outer vacuum chamber, which is pumped down to about 100 microns by an auxiliary mechanical pump. This design is useful also for rather large furnaces where temperatures in the neighborhood of 800°C would cause gradual collapse if the alloy steel tube were subjected to atmospheric pressure. This general design has been used for the construction of a box-type vacuum muffle furnace by one of the vacuum equipment supply houses.[1]

Molybdenum or Tungsten Resistance Vacuum Furnace

High-temperature vacuum annealing furnaces may be made by winding a high-purity alumina tube with molybdenum or tungsten wire and operating the whole assembly in the vacuum chamber. The alumina core limits the maximum temperature to about 1900°C; hence for higher temperatures, an all-metal resistor must be resorted to (see p. 208). Also, at temperatures in excess of 2000°C, the volatilization of molybdenum may be appreciable; therefore, tungsten is generally used as a metallic resistor for such ultra-high temperatures.

A typical wire-wound ceramic (Al_2O_3) core type of vacuum resistance furnace is shown in Figure 4. The refractory tube is grooved to prevent sagging of the wire, but no refractory cement is used so that quick replacement of the heating element is possible. The vacuum container is a brass or copper cylinder fitted with ¼-inch

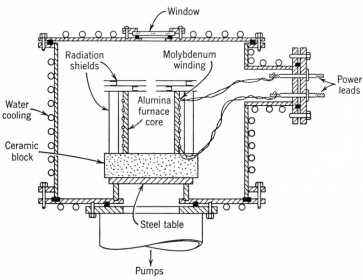

Figure 4. Vacuum Resistance Furnace with Molybdenum Winding.

copper water-cooling coils, and gasketed to the end plates with rubber. The power is brought in through leads in a plate of Mycalex or a laminated plastic as described in Chapter 6. Two or three concentric molybdenum cylinders are used as radiation shields. The furnace core is laid on top of an alumina or zircon brick which rests on a steel plate supported by three pegs. The steel plate is raised sufficiently high by the pegs to allow adequate pumping space for the diffusion pump directly below. A series of 3-4 molybdenum disks with small central holes is riveted together for a top radiation shield.

For temperatures near 2000°C or above, it is necessary to dispense with a ceramic furnace core and to use an all-metal system such as has been devised by Sowman and Andrews.[2] In their furnace the tungsten resistor is in the form of a cylinder. Figure 5 is a somewhat schematic drawing of their furnace. McRitchie and Ault[3] have also

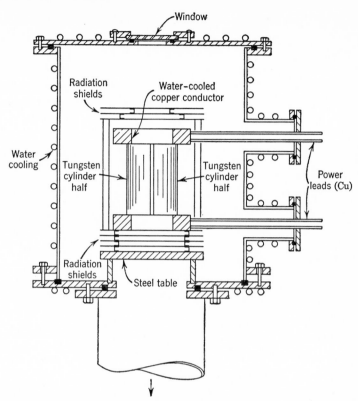

Figure 5.   High-Temperature Vacuum Resistance Furnace.   (After Sowman and Andrews.[2])

described a tungsten resistance vacuum furnace.   Kroll[4] has suggested a number of designs.

Heat Treating by Induction Heating

A great deal of industrial heat treating, particularly for the hardening of steel, for the heating of other metals, for forging, and for brazing and soldering operations, is carried out by high-frequency induction. In these cases no attempt is made to control the temperature directly; rather the amount of power supplied to the specimen is carefully controlled in a reproducible fashion by using specimens of the same size and using the same kind of induction coil.   Although this is excellent for production operations, it finds little use in the laboratory because of the small number of specimens of any given size or shape that are usually treated.   Induction heating is sometimes used for annealing in the laboratory in special cases. It permits very rapid heating and cooling and is advantageous where very high temperatures are needed. Figure 6 shows a furnace which can be used for vacuum annealing up to about 800°C. An alloy steel tube of 25% chromium, 12% nickel, or of Inconel is heated with a high-frequency

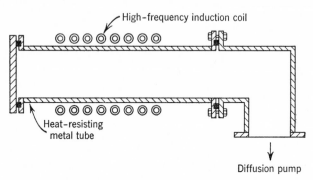

Figure 6. Metal Tube Vacuum Furnace Heated by High-Frequency Induction.

induction coil. Such a furnace as this is useful only for short-time heat treatments and does not readily permit a very accurate temperature control. For very high heat-treating temperatures a furnace similar to that used for induction melting could be used, with a molyb-

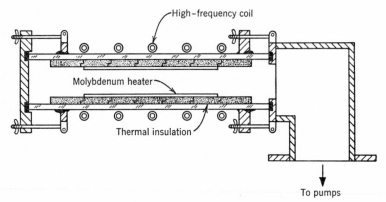

Figure 7. High-Frequency Induction Vacuum Furnace.

denum heater inside an evacuated fused silica tube and with the induction coil outside the tube (Figure 7). To protect the vacuum envelope some insulation should be supplied between the heater and the fused silica tube. Again it is very difficult to control the temperatures in furnaces of this type. The chief reason for using them is that these temperatures are readily achieved by high-frequency heating.

Salt Baths

Molten salts, usually mixtures of such salts as KCl, NaCl, $BaCl_2$, $CaCl_2$, K_2CO_3, and others, comprise important heat-treating media, much used in commercial operations and to a considerable extent in the laboratory because they provide rapid heat transfer and uniform specimen temperature. Although primarily useful in the temperature range of about 600 to 1000°C, this range can be considerably broadened to 163 to 1340°C if one is willing to use a mixture of $NaNO_2$-KNO_3 at the low range and $BaCl_2$ at the high range. At high temperatures, considerable fuming occurs, accompanied by rapid pot scaling and danger of attack on metal specimens, whereas at the low range the use of nitrate or nitrite-nitrate mixtures can be dangerous because violent reactions may occur with reducing agents such as carbonaceous materials or electropositive metals like aluminum and particularly magnesium. Nitrate baths are used for heat-treating aluminum and its alloys, but the temperature should be below 590°C, and aluminum alloys containing more than a few per cent magnesium should be avoided.

A list of practical salt mixtures for use at various temperature ranges is given in Table 1. Fused chlorides tend to form oxychlorides, which oxidize some metals such as iron and steel. Oxychloride attack is overcome in heat-treating steel by the use of "rectifiers," which reduce the oxychlorides or otherwise tie up oxygen in a harmless form. Graphite, ferrosilicon, and borax are used for this purpose.

Although the most satisfactory commercial method of heating salt baths is the immersed electrode method, in which a low-voltage heavy current is passed between two adjacent metal electrodes or between one electrode and the metal salt bath pot, this technique is rarely used in the laboratory because of the special and expensive equipment required. For small-scale use an electric pot furnace with a steel container, as shown in Figure 8, can be made in the laboratory and gives satisfactory service. Such a pot may be fabricated from either mild steel or preferably stainless steel by welding a plate to one end of a steel tube of appropriate diameter and a flange to the other end. The flange is necessary to keep the salt from creeping around the edge of the pot down into the furnace between the pot and furnace walls, where it will attack the furnace core. It is customary to support the flange on a circular piece of asbestos rope, which acts as a seal to prevent salt migration. Mild steel (plain carbon steel) is only satis-

TABLE 1

COMPOSITIONS AND HEAT-TREATING TEMPERATURES FOR SOME SALT BATHS [5]

NaCl	KCl	BaCl₂	NaNO₃	NaNO₂	KNO₃	K₂CO₃	LiCO₃	Approximate Melting Point, °C	Recommended Heating Range, °C
				High-Temperature Salt Baths					
4-6		98 min 92-96						980 870	1035–1340 950–1260
				Medium-Temperature Salt Baths					
15-25		25-35				45-55		480	510–760
						CaCl₂ 65	35	475	535– 815
15-25	20-30	50-60						590	675– 925
45-55	45-55							675	730– 900
20-30		70-80						700	760– 925
10-20		80-90						760	815–1090
				Low-Temperature Salt Baths					
			40-50	40-50	50-60			140	165– 650
					50-60			225	260– 590
				96 min				370	400– 590

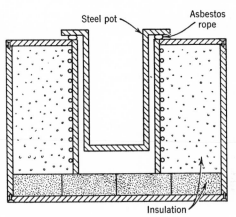

Figure 8.   Salt Bath or Lead Pot Furnace.

factory for a rather short life, particularly at temperatures above a red heat, but will give good service if it is at least ⅜ inch thick and the temperature is not higher than 600°C. The furnace itself is similar to those described briefly in Chapter 1 and in Chapter 7.

If more than occasional use is expected, it would be desirable to buy a laboratory pot furnace especially designed for salt pot work from one of the regular electric-furnace manufacturers. These furnaces are available in a variety of sizes, with either circular or rectangular pots.

A salt bath operated near its upper useful temperature limit may volatilize enough to be troublesome and may require an exhaust system to carry away the fumes. In general, however, fuming is not noticeable. If excessive fumes are encountered, it means that the temperature is too high for the type of bath employed. In particular, barium salts are poisonous, and ventilation should be provided if they are used.

Great care must be taken to see that all articles placed in the salt bath are dry so that sudden generation of steam and consequent splattering of hot salt are avoided.

The size of the bath should be large enough so that the temperature of the bath is not appreciably lowered by placing in it a sample to be heated. If excessively large pieces are put in the bath, a considerable thickness of salt solidifies around the object, and heat transfer to the metal is greatly reduced; hence an excessive heating-up time is required. Usually a salt bath is used in preference to other heating methods because it is possible to secure nearly isothermal heat treatment; this advantage is lost with overloading.

Another advantage of salt-bath heating is the degree of cleanliness maintained during heating; scale in heat treating iron and steel is completely avoided. It is customary to quench salt-heated articles in a large bath of water after the heat treatment to get rid of the salt clinging to the work.

Molten Metals

Because of the high cost or reactivity of molten metals other than lead, lead is the most generally used metallic heat-treating medium in the laboratory. Lead may be used over a wider range of temperature than individual salt baths. Where temperatures below 327°C (the melting point of lead) are required, such metals as eutectic lead-tin and Wood's metal are occasionally used. Lead is relatively inert to iron and steels and other high-melting metals, but reacts (alloys) with many non-ferrous metals. Its high density requires that most

samples being heat-treated be forcibly submerged to prevent floating. Molten lead also oxidizes rapidly and must be protected by a
heavy cover of finely divided charcoal, which only actively protects
the lead if heated above the ignition point of charcoal, about 425 to
480°C. Below this temperature range, charcoal acts like an inert
blanket. The temperature range suitable for lead pot operation is
about 340 to 925°C.[5]

Because lead is toxic a lead pot used at temperatures near the upper
end of the indicated temperature scale, or for prolonged periods at
lower temperatures, should be adequately vented with a hood to prevent the possibility of lead poisoning.

Lead pots may be made of iron or heat-resisting steels, and the
technique of heating the pot is the same as described for a laboratory
salt bath. It is not necessary, however, to use a pot flange over the
top of the resistance furnace core since there is no tendency to creep
over the lip of the pot as with molten salts.

The characteristics of salt heating versus molten lead heating are
summarized in Table 2.

TABLE 2

COMPARISON OF MOLTEN LEAD AND FUSED SALTS

Molten Lead	Fused Salts
1. Most rapid heating	1. Rapid heating
2. Requires charcoal cover	2. No protective cover necessary
3. May be used with limited number of metals	3. May be used with a very wide range of metals
4. Temperature range 340 to 925°C	4. Temperature range 165 to 1230°C (but requires several salts)
5. Is toxic	5. Mostly non-toxic
6. No protection for hot samples removed from pot	6. Coating of salt protects samples removed from pot
7. Little or no "drag-out"	7. Appreciable "drag-out"
8. Samples tend to float	8. Samples sink

It would appear that, except for the extra heating rate possible by
the use of molten lead, the main advantages lie with the fused salts.

Direct-Resistance Heating

For special investigations such as kinetic studies, it may be necessary to heat a sample very rapidly to some desired temperature level,
hold for a specified period of time, and to cool quickly. Dienes[6] describes a technique he terms "pulse" annealing in which a 0.005-inch
thick strip of gold-copper alloy is nearly instantaneously heated to a
desired temperature by the passage of a heavy current through the

sample in order to follow a solid phase (ordering) reaction. By turning off the current, the sample may be quenched to some lower temperature. In this way the heating and cooling times become a small fraction of the reaction time. The reaction in this case was followed by electrical resistivity measurements at temperature, but other properties could be measured if desired either at temperature or after cooling to room temperature. Before swaging and drawing tungsten into wire, a sintering operation must be carried out at nearly the melting point of the metal. This high temperature is attained by direct resistance heating in a special treating enclosure or "bottle." The upper end of the bar is held in a water-cooled copper clamp while the lower end dips into a water-cooled mercury bath; hence electrical contact is maintained while the bar is shrinking in length. Tantalum is handled in an analogous manner.

Certain metal strip products are "flash-annealed" by the passage of a heavy current during mill processing. The problem of temperature control of the sample during direct-resistance heating is considerable, and the method is generally restricted to long slender shapes of regular section such as wire, strip, or rod. Because of its lack of flexibility, resistance heating is usually used only in special cases: (1) where very high temperatures are required as in sintering tungsten or (2) where rapid heating or cooling is necessary.

QUENCHING MEDIA, SPECIAL QUENCHING TECHNIQUES

It is often necessary to cool (quench) rapidly a sample in order to retain a desired high-temperature structure or to create a new structure obtainable only by quenching, such as martensite in steels. Because of the importance of the heat treatment of steels, most of the techniques for quenching have been developed for use with them. However, the same procedures can usually be applied to other materials. Quenching media are either liquids or gases; liquids are generally used for samples of usual size when the most rapid quenching rates are desired. Gases are used for slower rates with most samples, but very rapid cooling rates are possible with gases such as helium or hydrogen if the specimens are small. The commonly used quenching liquids are water solutions, water, and oil in descending order of quenching power (ability to extract heat). Mercury has sometimes been used as a quenching medium apparently in the mistaken assumption that it provides a more rapid quench than water. Actually it provides an appreciably slower quench than water, although it is better than oils (see Table 3).

TABLE 3

COOLING RATE AT THE CENTER OF A 4-MM-DIAMETER NICHROME BALL
THROUGH THE TEMPERATURE RANGE OF 720 TO 550°C DURING
QUENCHING IN VARIOUS MEDIA FROM 860°C [5]

	Cooling Rate Relative to That for Water at 18°C *	
Quenching Medium	720 to 550°C	At 200°C
Aqueous solution 10% LiCl	2.07	1.04
Aqueous solution 10% NaOH	2.06	1.36
Aqueous solution 10% NaCl	1.96	0.98
Aqueous solution 10% Na_2CO_3	1.38	1.09
Aqueous solution 10% H_2SO_4	1.22	1.49
Water at 0°C	1.06	1.02
Water at 18°C	1.00	1.00
Aqueous solution 10% H_3PO_4	0.99	1.07
Mercury	0.78	0.62
70 Cd–30 Sn alloy at 180°C	0.77	0.009
Water at 25°C	0.72	1.11
Rapeseed oil	0.30	0.055
Trial oil No. 6	0.27	0.045
Oil P20	0.23	0.055
Oil 12455	0.22	0.022
Glycerin	0.20	0.89
Oil 20204	0.20	0.13
Oil, Lupex light	0.18	0.20
Water at 50°C	0.17	0.95
Oil 25441	0.16	0.18
Oil 14530	0.14	0.022
Emulsion of 10% oil in water	0.11	1.33
Copper plates	0.10	0.067
Soap water	0.077	1.16
Iron plates	0.061	0.011
Carbon tetrachloride	0.055	0.34
Hydrogen	0.050	0.011
Water at 76°C	0.047	1.31
Water at 100°C	0.044	0.71
Liquid air	0.039	0.033
Air	0.028	0.007
Vacuum	0.011	0.004

* Cooling rate for water at 18°C is 1795°C per sec through the range from
720 to 550°C, and 430°C per sec at 200°C.

Pilling and Lynch [7] demonstrated that there are three stages during
the quenching of steel in liquids (water or oil):

1. Vapor blanket cooling.
2. Vapor transport.
3. Liquid cooling.

The first stage occurs when the hot body loses heat by conduction and radiation through the gaseous envelope which first completely surrounds the sample. This stage is characterized by relatively slow cooling. The second stage, the fast stage, is reached when the sample is wet by the liquid which becomes vaporized, since heat is rapidly lost by converting liquid to gas. Bubbles of gas collapse slowly in the first stage, but collapse rapidly in the second stage. In the third stage, the body is cold enough so that no vaporization oc-

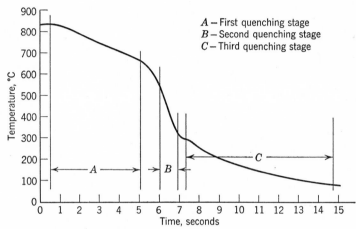

Figure 9. Cooling Curve for Center of a Small Steel Cylinder Indicating the Three Stages of Water Quenching. (Scott.[9])

curs; hence heat is lost by liquid conduction and convection. This stage, like the first, is characterized by slow cooling. French[8] showed that the cooling velocity at various points on the surface of a quenched body may vary appreciably from point to point; this he attributed to variation in the amount of the gas envelope (steam in the case of water) which is alternately attached and wiped away from the surface.

The more rapid heat extraction due to the use of salt solutions (see Table 3) is caused by a shortening of the time in stage 1, that is, the time during which the sample is enveloped in vapor is reduced. A typical cooling curve obtained in quenching a small sample of steel in water is shown in Figure 9, taken from Scott.[9]

For maximum cooling rates, the liquid bath should be agitated to prevent excessive vapor building up around the specimen, and aid in carrying away heat from the vicinity of the sample. However, agitation is probably of no value with very small specimens which are quenched to room temperature within a few seconds; with massive samples which require minutes, agitation may be of considerable value in securing the maximum cooling rate. Obviously, the size of the quenching bath should be sufficiently large so that the temperature of the bath is not appreciably raised by the quenching operation.

It is clear from Table 3 that there is a vast difference between the quenching power of water, oils, and air. It should be noted that in spite of its low temperature, liquid air is a very poor quenching medium because of the persistence of the vapor blanket stage.

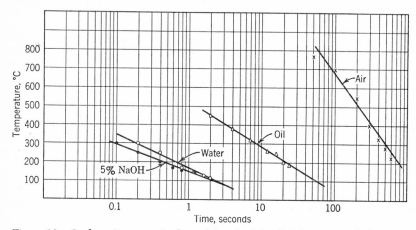

Figure 10. Cooling Curves at Surface of One-Inch Steel Sphere Quenched in Various Media from 875°C. (After French.[8])

For most laboratory work, water represents the best choice for rapid quenching of ordinary samples, but aqueous salt solutions may be used if a still more rapid quench should be required. Oil and air are mainly used for certain classes of steel when very rapid cooling rates are not necessary or desirable. Depending upon the shape of the steel, too rapid quenching often leads to serious distortion or cracking due to differential volume changes, with accompanying internal stresses. A complete discussion of this subject is outside the scope of this book, and reference may be made to standard metallurgical textbooks covering the heat treatment of steel.

Figure 10 presents some of French's [8] data for the surface cooling of a 1-inch-diameter steel sphere quenched into various liquids at room temperature from 875°C. A logarithmic plot was used in order to get all the data on one graph. Quenching speed varies markedly with time. Since the temperature is reduced from 875 to 300°C in 0.1 second in the case of the 5% NaOH solution, evidently the average cooling rate during this interval was about 5700°C per second, but in the next 0.1-second interval, the quenching rate was reduced to 500°C per second. The relative displacement of the data for different quenching media is an indication of relative quenching power.

French [8] developed an empirical relation for calculating the cooling velocity of steel as a function of specimen surface area, specimen volume, and quenching medium:

$$V = \left[\frac{S}{W}\right]^n C_2 \qquad (1)$$

where V = cooling velocity in °C/sec,
 S = surface area in in.^{2},
 W = volume in in.^{3},
 n varies from 1.15 for air to 1.84 for 5% NaOH in water,
 C_2 varies from about 3 to 4 for oil and water respectively.

For more accurate constants, reference should be made to the original paper. The constants n and C_2 are considered to be independent of sample geometry, but depend only upon the coolant used.

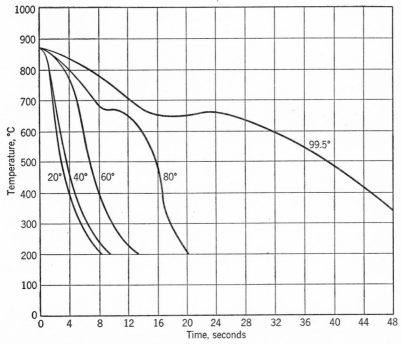

Figure 11.   Center Cooling Curves of One-Half-Inch Diameter Steel Cylinders Quenched from 875°C into Water at Different Temperatures.   (French.[8])

Another factor which has a marked effect in liquid quenching, particularly if the liquid is water, is the temperature of the quenching bath (see Figure 11 taken from French,[8] and Table 3).

Gaseous Quenching—Small Samples

When very rapid cooling rates of the order of thousands of degrees centigrade per second are required over a wide temperature range,

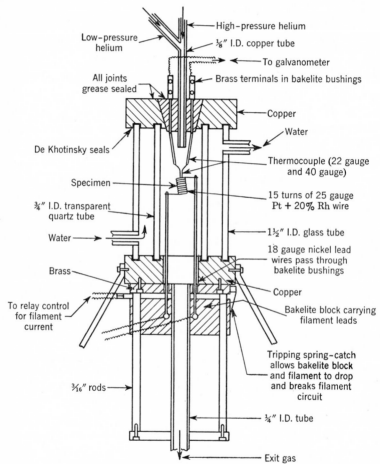

Figure 12.   Gas Quenching Apparatus.   (Greninger.[10])

samples not over about 0.010 to 0.020 inch thick must be used.   With samples of this kind, helium gas cooling has proved to be very effective.   Helium has a very high thermal conductivity, and, being chemically inert, does not react with samples.   Greninger [10] used the apparatus shown in Figure 12 to study the martensite reaction in steels, in which cooling rates up to 4000°C per second were obtained. The sample was 0.010 inch thick by 0.039 inch square, and was held inside a molybdenum coil in which the sample could be heated to the desired temperature level. Helium at one atmosphere pressure was used as the atmosphere until it was desired to quench the steel sample. Quenching was accomplished by quickly moving down the heating coil away from the sample and at the same time introducing a blast of helium gas at 2 pounds pressure in such a way that the specimen was directly under the blast. The fall in temperature was recorded photographically on a revolving drum by means of a torsion galvanometer which provided a deflection of 12 mm for 4 mv, and required 0.017 second to reach 12 mm deflection. Chromel-alumel thermocouples 0.003 inch to 0.008 inch diameter were attached to the specimen.

More recently, Duwez [11] has used Greninger's method to determine the effect of cooling speeds up to 15,000°C per second upon the transformation temperature of several metals which have allotropic forms. The temperature-recording apparatus was an oscillograph consisting of a rotating drum, a galvanometer with a period of $\frac{1}{65}$ second, and a resistance of 45 ohms, where one inch deflection corresponded to 25 microamperes. Chart speeds were varied from 4.5 inch per second to 8 inches per second. Chromel-alumel thermocouples 0.005 inch in diameter were spot-welded to specimens 0.020 inch thick and about 0.063 inch square. Instead of a flowing helium atmosphere, Duwez [11] employed a vacuum of 10^{-5} mm until ready to quench with the helium blast.

Quenching Samples from Vacuum

Small samples such as are used in X-ray diffraction work may be sealed off in evacuated Pyrex glass or fused silica tubes, depending upon temperature level, and quenched from the heat-treating temperature in water in the apparatus shown in Figure 13. This is an electric resistance element tube furnace with a bundle of 3 to 4 Inconel tubes mounted in the center of the heated tube. The vertical arrangement allows more convenient quenching. Samples are suspended, from the top of the Inconel tubes by means of a small 80 Ni–20 Cr wire, in the center of the uniform hot zone. When it is desired to quench the sample, a steel rod is thrust down through the metal tube containing the appropriate specimen capsule, crushing it under water, thus insuring a rapid quench. The Inconel tube bundle is held in place at either end of the vertical furnace by asbestos cement or by a tight-fitting transite plate cut out to conform to the metal tube bundle. During the heating cycle, the ends of the metal tubes are capped with plugs molded of asbestos cement or the like to prevent a chimney effect.

Another similar method is to support specimens in an evacuated fused silica tube furnace as indicated in Figure 14. A neutral gas

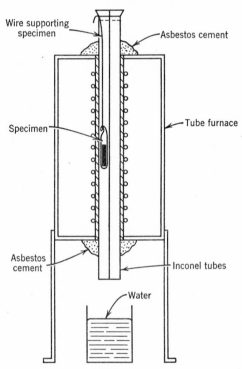

Figure 13.   Inconel Tube Quenching Furnace.

such as argon can be used if desired. The sample is hung by a fuse wire such as 10 mil 80 Cr–20 Ni, which may be quickly melted when quenching is desired by passing a heavy current through it. If the atmosphere used during the heating cycle is vacuum, it is convenient to fill the tube with a neutral gas just prior to quenching to allow the use of a quenching medium situated just below the end of the fused silica tube. Alternately, a non-volatile quenching medium may be placed in a steel cup inside the vacuum chamber. Quenching media which have been used for this purpose include mercury and diffusion pump oil. If mercury is used, it must be recalled that mercury has a vapor pressure of about 3 microns at 25°C; this may be undesirable as an atmosphere in many cases. Diffusion pump oil or silicone oil is more desirable since its vapor pressure at room temperature is negligible, but its quenching power is also considerably less than that of

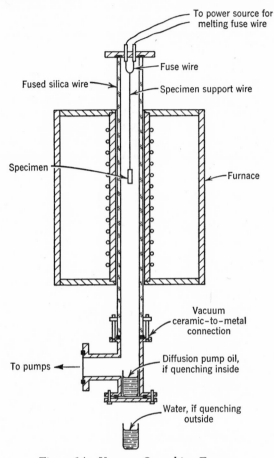

Figure 14.   Vacuum Quenching Furnace.

mercury. Nevertheless, the rate of cooling obtained by the use of such oils may be adequate for the investigation at hand.

REFERENCES

1. The National Research Corp., Cambridge, Mass.
2. H. G. Sowman and A. I. Andrews, "A Quenching Furnace for High Temperature Studies of Small Specimens," *J. Am. Ceramic Soc.*, **33**, 365–366 (1950).
3. F. H. McRitchie and N. N. Ault, "Design of a High Temperature Resistance Furnace," *J. Am. Ceramic Soc.*, **33**, 25–26 (1950).

4. W. Kroll, "High Temperature Metallic Resistor Furnaces," *Trans. Electrochem. Soc.*, **79**, 199–212 (1941).
5. *The Metals Handbook*, 1948 Edition, The American Society for Metals, Cleveland, Ohio, 1948.
6. G. J. Dienes, "Kinetics of Ordering in the Alloy Gold-Copper," *J. Appl. Phys.*, **22**, 1020–1026 (1951).
7. N. B. Pilling and T. D. Lynch, "Cooling Properties of Technical Quenching Liquids," *Trans. Am. Inst. Mining Met. Engrs.*, **62**, 665 (1920).
8. H. J. French, *Quenching of Steels*, The American Society for Metals, Cleveland, Ohio, 1930.
9. Howard Scott, "The Problem of Quenching Media for the Hardening of Steel," *Trans. A.S.M.*, **22**, 577–603 (1934).
10. Alden B. Greninger, "The Martensite Thermal Arrest in Iron Carbon Alloys and Plain Carbon Steels," *Trans. A.S.M.*, **30**, 1–24 (1942).
11. Pol Duwez, "Effect of Rate of Cooling on the Alpha-Beta Transformation in Titanium and Titanium Molybdenum Alloys," *J. Metals*, **3**, 765–771 (1951).

CHAPTER NINE

Fabrication of Metals

Metals may be worked in the laboratory to study the effect of deformation on the properties of the metal, to produce a desired structure such as fine-grain size, or to prepare specimens of appropriate size and shape. Occasionally, the desired deformation can be produced with equipment commonly at hand in most laboratories. For example, small controlled deformations can be produced by slightly stretching specimens in a tensile machine, by bending sheet around a mandrel, or by indenting with a Rockwell or Brinell hardness tester. Useful forging operations can be satisfactorily performed either hot or cold with a blacksmith's anvil and a hammer. More elaborate equipment, however, is needed for most fabrication operations.

In this chapter we shall discuss the equipment for several primary metal-working operations—rolling, swaging, wire drawing, and extrusion. With these processes a wide variety of desired shape changes and amounts of working can be produced. Secondary forming operations such as deep drawing, spinning, and stretching will not be considered since they are principally used for manufacturing finished articles. No attempt will be made to analyze these deformation processes in a theoretical way. The reader interested in this aspect of forming operations may consult the works of Siebel,[1] Underwood,[2] or Sachs and Van Horn.[3]

ROLLING

The most common and generally useful working process is rolling. It includes both the rolling of flat strip and of round rod. Sheet metal is fabricated by means of smooth cylindrical rolls, sometimes called "flat" rolls, to differentiate them from grooved rolls used for rod. Of these two processes, flat rolling is much more widely practiced in the laboratory because sheet or strip finds more use as a test material than rod, and rod may often be more conveniently made by swaging.

225

Rolling of Sheet

In commercial parlance, sheet is rolled metal sold in definite lengths and widths, whereas strip is coiled sheet metal of indefinite length. However, the two terms are used more or less interchangeably in the laboratory.

In order to roll sheet from a small casting, the casting should be rectangular in shape (a parallelopiped) of approximately the same width as the desired sheet, and reasonably thin in order to reduce the amount of rolling required.

Because most cast ingots have a somewhat rough surface due to such factors as rough mold walls, cold shuts, or other irregularities in the freezing process, it is often desirable to "scalp" the flat surfaces of the ingot by shaping or milling, removing about $\frac{1}{16}$ to $\frac{1}{8}$ inch on each side. Scalping the ingot makes a better surface on the rolled sheet, eliminating slivers, rolled-in surface oxide, etc. If a rather heavy oxide layer is formed during intermediate anneals between rolling operations, it is good practice to pickle the metal in dilute strong acids, or to sand-blast or shot-blast the surface before continuing with the rolling.

As pointed out in Chapter 7, castings thinner than $\frac{1}{4}$ inch thick are generally not practicable. However, the casting should be at least four times thicker than the required sheet in order to obtain sufficient breakdown of the cast structure. While there is some sideways spreading of the strip during rolling, it is usually not enough to be important, and may generally be neglected.

Kinds of Rolling Mills

Most laboratory mills are two-high mills, that is, only two rolls are used (Figure 1). Where very thin stock must be rolled, particularly in rather hard or strong material, a four-high mill is preferable. A four-high mill consists of two relatively small power-driven work rolls backed up by two much larger backing rolls (Figure 2). This arrangement allows one to take advantage of the more favorable roll diameter to stock thickness ratio, which permits rolling to thinner sizes than with larger rolls. The function of the backing rolls is to stiffen the work rolls so that they do not bend under the tremendous pressures necessary in rolling to very thin sizes. The four-high mill is a special-purpose mill, and is not good for general rolling as the strip thickness range is quite narrow.

In laboratory-size mills, the rolls may vary in diameter from about 2 inches for hand-operated jeweler's rolls to about 12 inches for larger power-operated equipment. Jeweler's rolls are limited to small samples about one inch wide and are not satisfactory for tough materials like stainless steel; on soft metals like copper and brass they may serve in

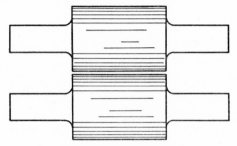

Figure 1. Two-High Rolls.

the thickness range from about 0.250 to 0.005 inch. In order to roll larger samples satisfactorily, power-operated equipment is necessary. The roll diameter of such mills is sometimes as small as 3 inches, but is more often 6 inches or even more. Rolls as large as 12 inches in diameter are rarely used in the laboratory, as the size and cost of the equipment increase rapidly with roll diameter. According to Sachs

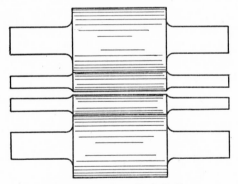

Figure 2. Four-High Rolls.

and Van Horn,[3] in cold rolling in two-high mills the length of the rolls should be not more than 1½ times the diameter, or excessive roll bending will be encountered.

It has been established [3] that the roll diameter should be not more than approximately 500 times the sheet thickness for practical reductions. If larger roll diameter to thickness ratios are used, the reduction per pass becomes exceedingly small. In thin sheet, surface friction becomes increasingly important; hence very high roll pressures are necessary to force the metal to flow. Very high roll pressures are only practicable by the use of small diameter rolls where the area of contact between roll and sheet is small. Some rolling mills especially designed for producing very thin foil have working rolls in the neighborhood of 0.5-inch diameter, and are able to roll foil as thin as 0.0005 inch, somewhat thinner than indicated by the 500/1 ratio. On the other hand, with 6-inch-diameter rolls, it is not easy to roll to much less than the 0.012-inch sheet predicted. After the practical lower thickness limit is reached, no further reduction occurs because the rolls spring apart elastically.

The best rolls for cold rolling are made of a low-alloy tool steel, and those for hot rolling are generally made of chilled cast iron or cast low-alloy steel. Some roll manufacturers supply hardened high-speed tool steel rolls for hot rolling, but these are comparatively expensive. However, they have the advantage that even if the roll temperature rises quite high, no softening occurs, and the roll surface remains unmarred after considerable use. In addition, they may be used for cold rolling. The high cost of such rolls prevents their use except on rather small mills. The somewhat rougher surface of the cast iron is adequate for hot rolling, and such rolls are considerably cheaper than steel ones. For the higher stresses encountered in cold rolling, chilled iron may not be adequate, and the generally poorer surface is often objectionable.

The amount of reduction achievable per pass depends upon the roll diameter, roughness of rolls, flow stress of the metal being rolled, power available, lubrication, and method of feeding stock into the mill. For simple cold rolling of most metals in a two-high mill, a reduction of about 10 to 20% per pass is common. The total reduction between annealing operations depends upon the characteristics of the metal. Very ductile metals such as pure copper, silver, gold, aluminum, and a few others may be rolled indefinitely without cracking. Apparently working heats these metals enough to produce stress relief during rolling, so that they maintain their plasticity. However, even with these metals it is generally desirable to use some intermediate anneals to allow more rapid reduction in thickness. Most metals and alloys are annealed after about 40 to 80% reduction in thickness.

The work expended during rolling is given by the equation

$$W = VS \ln t_0/t \qquad (1)$$

where W is the work expended to deform the metal,
  V is the volume of metal rolled,
  S is the average flow stress (average of yield strength before and after rolling),
  t_0 is the original strip thickness,
  t is the final strip thickness.

Since the formula above neglects friction, attempting to calculate actual power required to form a sample by its use will result in too low a value, possibly by a factor of about 3 or even higher if the strip is very thin.

Pack Rolling

If it is necessary to roll thinner sheet than can be made by regular rolling, it is possible to employ pack rolling, in which the sheet is

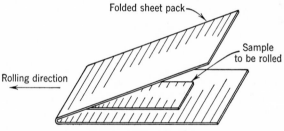

Figure 3. Method of Assembly for Pack Rolling.

sandwiched between a folded steel envelope, where the envelope steel is conveniently about 0.030 inch thick (see Figure 3). Sheet about 0.001 inch thick may be rolled in this manner, using a regular two-high mill, but the surface is usually not as smooth as when the rolls contact the surface.

Cross Rolling

The width of strip may be increased by "cross rolling" or rolling in a direction perpendicular to the original direction. In this way pieces may be prepared nearly equal in width to the length of the rolls, even when the starting strip is considerably narrower than this. It is generally recommended that the specimen be annealed before cross rolling as occasionally brittleness in the transverse direction may result from a pronounced rolling texture or from inclusions. This difficulty is not so likely to be encountered, however, in very soft and ductile materials. Cross rolling is often used as a means of preparing samples with a minimum of directional properties due to rolling textures.

Compression Rolling

C. S. Barrett [4] used a technique he called "compression rolling" for studies of the nature of the compressional deformation of metals and to further reduce preferred orientation. This technique involves rolling a disk, using very small reductions per pass. By rotating the disk a few degrees before each pass, the rolling direction is continually varied. Thus no preferred orientation develops in the rolling plane, but the piece will have a fiber texture similar to that developed in wires. It can be readily seen that this amounts to a pure compression of the disk, but, since no frictional forces develop to any significant extent, compressional deformations can be produced that are much larger than those possible when the sample is pressed between lubricated polished plates in a compression jig.

Effective Deformation

One can compare the strain developed by different processes such as tensile strain and rolling strain on the basis of percentage reduction in area of the sample, but strains measured by such a scale are not linear. That is, a reduction in area of 40% is not half the strain developed during an 80% reduction in area in terms of fundamental or true deformation.

Consider the case of the plastic stretching of a tensile specimen of length l by an increment dl. One may then define the increment of strain by $d\delta = dl/l$. Thus

$$\delta = \int_{l_0}^{l} d\delta = \int_{l_0}^{l} \frac{dl}{l} = \ln \frac{l}{l_0} \tag{2}$$

The natural or logarithmic strain δ is essentially the same as $\Delta l/l$ for small strains, but for large strains this is not true. Hence, the true strain or effective strain is given by $\ln l/l_0$ or $\ln (A/A_0)$, etc., where A is the final area and A_0 the original area of the specimen, before and after deformation, respectively. Thus a natural reduction of 1 indicates that a specimen has been reduced in area to $1/e$ or to about 0.37 of its original cross-sectional area. This corresponds to a reduction of 63%. A natural reduction of 2 indicates a reduction to $1/2e$ or to 0.19 of the original area, or a percentage reduction based on the original area of 81%. The advantage of the natural method of expressing reductions is that it clearly indicates the relative amounts of working given by two different reductions without extensive auxiliary calculations.

Hot Rolling

Hot metals are softer than cold metals; hence much larger reductions can be made per pass in hot rolling than in cold rolling. The term hot rolling usually implies that the metal recrystallizes during working; thus no annealing during the course of hot rolling is necessary. Hot rolling may be used as an intermediate process to reduce the metal rapidly to nearly the final thickness. By finishing by cold rolling, a cold-worked structure may be obtained in the final sheet if desired, and at the same time a specimen of better surface is produced than is possible by hot rolling.

Sachs and Van Horn [3] quote the following temperature ranges for the forging of a number of metallic materials. It can be assumed that

TABLE 1

Approximate Temperature Range for Hot Working Various Metals, Degrees Centigrade

(After Sachs and Van Horn)

Carbon steels	
0.1% carbon	1300
1.5% carbon	1050
Low-alloy steel	(25 to 50°C lower than plain carbon steel of same carbon content)
High-speed or stainless steels	1050–1200
Nickel	1250–875
Monel	1175–1000
Inconel	1250–1000
Copper	900–650
Brasses	800–650
Aluminum	500–350
Aluminum alloys	500–400
Magnesium alloys	400–200
Zinc alloys	300–220

the temperature range for other hot-working operations would be essentially the same. As a rough rule, a temperature somewhat above half the melting point is usually satisfactory.

Protection of Reactive Metals

Reactive metals such as zirconium and titanium may pick up objectionable amounts of oxygen and nitrogen from the air in hot rolling, in which case it is possible to protect the metal by temporary cladding in a steel or other metal jacket (see Figure 4). Such a jacket may be readily made for sheet by welding a box of ⅛ to ¼ inch thick plate, or for cylindrical specimens from a tube with welded ends. The side strips shown in Figure 4a are not necessary if the material to be rolled is about 0.030 inch or thinner. Exhaustion of air from inside the jacket is usually not necessary if the jacket fits the sample rather tightly.

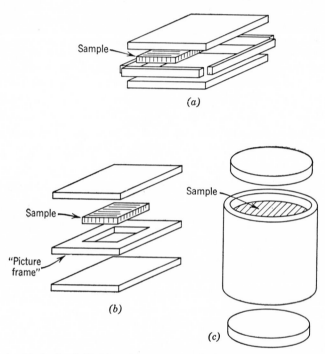

Sample

(a)

Sample

"Picture frame"

(b)

Sample

(c)

Figure 4.   Methods of Cladding Reactive Metals for Rolling or Other Working.

Another technique for preventing excessive atmospheric attack is to heat the material in a fused salt bath, with the salt selected so that its melting point is below the rolling temperature. The salt clinging to the metal affords sufficient protection during rolling in some cases.

Rolling Defects

The most common rolling defect, edge cracking, is encountered in rolling metals when too great a reduction between anneals is attempted, or where the metal has limited ductility. This defect appears as transverse cracks at the edge of the strip, that gradually propagate across it. If the rolling is stopped when edge cracks first appear, the sheet can usually be salvaged by annealing and then cropping the edges to remove the cracks. If the cracked material is not sheared off, the cracks may progress even if very frequent anneals are used. Improper preparation of the ingot is responsible for much of the trouble encountered in rolling. As mentioned above, scalping the ingot by machining flats on both sides is of considerable assistance in securing a good surface, and will also help in avoiding cracks.

An exaggerated form of edge cracks occurs with brittle materials where the first cracks which appear may go all the way across the sheet perpendicular to the rolling direction. In this case, the sample must usually be scrapped or returned to the melting furnace.

Another defect known as "alligatoring" is sometimes observed when a certain type of residual stress pattern is created during the rolling operation. This defect is characterized by a splitting at one end along a central plane parallel to the surface of the sheet. Alligatoring is particularly prevalent in rolling strong alloys, and can generally be avoided by more frequent anneals during cold rolling or by hot rolling. For a more complete description, see Baker [5] et al.

Rod Rolling

There are many forms of grooved rolls (Figure 5) used in rolling rods (which is usually a hot-working process), the most common type in the laboratory being nearly half round oval grooves, although a series of nearly square diamond-shaped passes is good if one wants to end with a square cross section. These types are the simplest to use since no guides are necessary to keep the rod in the proper groove.

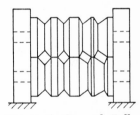

Figure 5. Grooved Rolls. (Trinks, *Roll Pass Design*, Penton Publishing Co.)

Guides are slots of appropriate size and shape to allow the rod just to go through, but not allow it freedom to twist in entering or leaving the rolls. However, nearly round oval grooves have the disadvantage that they allow twisting or turning of the rod through the mill, with consequent lack of control of the process. In addition, if the grooves are not sufficiently oval, the metal will be too constrained except at the opening at either side and will tend to form excessive fin. Roll passes for steel rod rolling are frequently a series of fairly flat ovals and diamond-shaped passes (Figure 6), ending with half round grooves to afford more working of the metal, hence better break-up of the cast structure, or "ingotism." In Figure 6 are shown two similar roll pass designs to go from a square,

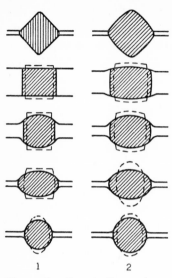

1   2

Figure 6. Two Roll Pass Designs. Dotted lines show entering bar. (Trinks, *Roll Pass Design*, Penton Publishing Co.)

or essentially a square, to a round.
The dotted lines indicate the stock fed
in from the previous pass. Obviously,
considerable planning is required for a
set of grooved rolls, as the various areas
of the openings and changes in shape
must be properly regulated for the
type of material being rolled, as different materials show different tendencies toward lateral spreading. There
is considerable tendency for flash to
form at the space between the rolls,
but this is minimized in good roll design.

The setting-up of a pair of grooved
rolls in the mill is a time-consuming
job, particularly if guides must be used,
hence is not particularly attractive in
the laboratory where flexibility is important. On a small mill, such as a
4 by 6 inch size, the amount of labor
is not great. On the other hand, rotary swaging allows more adaptability, as will be discussed below.

ROTARY SWAGING

Rotary swaging is essentially a forging or hammering operation to
reduce the diameter of round rods or tubes. The term "swaging" is
also applied to a type of forging operation in which a billet is pressed
or hammered between oval dies in a hydraulic press or drop hammer.
In rotary swaging, two opposed dies are rotated rapidly, and simultaneously open and close several times in one revolution. As the
spindle of the machine is rotated, two steel backing blocks or hammers
push against the steel dies. Centrifugal force causes the dies to open,
and the hammers striking the fixed rolls cause the dies to close (see
Figure 7). Since the speed of the machine is several hundred rpm,
several thousand blows a minute are struck on the rod being swaged.
Insertion of shims between the dies and the hammer is usually necessary for control of the closing stroke, thus determining the die pressure
upon the stock. The distance that the dies open between hammering
strokes is controlled by mechanical adjustments provided in the swaging machine. Both the amount of the die opening and the length of

the die stroke must be carefully adjusted to secure satisfactory operation of the process, dimensional control of the work piece, and surface
finish.   If the dies open too wide, they allow the rod to move laterally
to the plane portion of the die face, which can then pinch the metal
being swaged, thus cutting and spoiling the surface.   This is particularly likely to happen in the smaller die sizes, and eventually places
a lower limit on the practical swaging diameter.

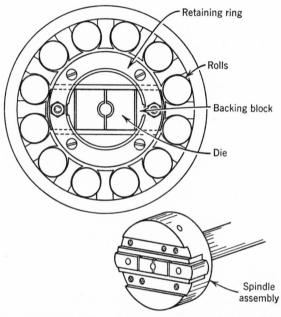

Figure 7.   Arrangement of Rolls and Dies in a Rotary Swaging Machine.   (The
Torrington Co. and *American Machinist*.)

There are many die designs used, but they can be divided into the
two main classes of short bearing dies and long bearing dies.   Figure
8 shows examples of both types.   Short bearing dies are normally
used for hot swaging, whereas long bearing dies are used for cold
swaging.   The length of the blade in hot-working dies should be about
equal to the diameter.   Dies for swaging rod are never exactly circular
in section, but are somewhat oval.   Harder materials require more
oval dies than softer metals.   Tube swaging, on the other hand, may
be performed using round dies.   The amount of reduction feasible in
one die is of the order of 20%, depending upon the ductility and hardness of the material being worked.   A number of dies is required to
cover the range of diameters possible in one machine.   A die line can

be purchased in equal increments of diameter in inches or in equal percentage reductions, such as Brown and Sharpe gauge numbers, where about 20% reduction between successive dies is obtained. The normal range of swaging sizes for solid stock is about 1 inch to perhaps 0.030 inch. The swaging of larger rounds than 1 inch diameter becomes a rather difficult operation without provision for mechanically feeding the stock into the machine. At about this size, rod rolling becomes more attractive than swaging. Also at the lower range, below

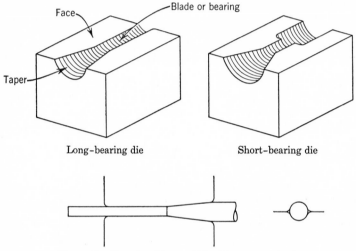

Face— Blade or bearing

Taper—

Long-bearing die   Short-bearing die

Figure 8.   Swaging Dies.   (The Torrington Co.)

about 0.040 inch diameter, wire drawing produces a better product than swaging since the surface produced by swaging at very small diameters is rather poor. It is difficult to control the wire, and the creation of fins or flash is very likely.

Machines of many different sizes are available. To cover the range between 1 inch diameter down to the smallest sizes three to four machines are required. Probably the most useful range for the average laboratory is between one-half inch and 0.040 inch (between nearly the smallest feasible casting and the wire-drawing sizes). This range requires two different machines.

A machine of given size will handle tubing of much larger size than solid rod because of the much lower stresses required to sink tubing. Similarly, a given machine will handle soft metals in larger sizes than hard metals.

Unlike rod rolling, it is not necessary to follow a definite series of roll passes in order to finish with a round of desired size. Dies may be skipped if larger reductions are feasible or desirable. In most grooved roll designs, where ovals or diamond passes predominate, only the last pass or two yields a round, whereas in swaging, a round section is obtained at every pass.

In the range of diameters where swaging is competitive with rod rolling (approximately between 1.0 and 0.250 inch), swaging is generally to be preferred because of much superior surface finish and freedom from flash. Swaging also has the advantage that the tedious roll changing from flat rolls to grooved and setting up roll guides are eliminated; changing swaging dies requires only a few moments.

Die materials are usually tool steels of various types. The requirements for cold-swaging dies are not severe, and almost any good-quality oil-hardening tool steel is satisfactory if properly heat-treated to about 60 Rockwell C. Hot-swaging dies are frequently made of high-speed steel because of its resistance to tempering at elevated temperatures, but for extreme temperature service, as in the swaging of tungsten, Stellite dies or the equivalent give better service. It should be emphasized that the surface finish of cold-swaging dies is important if good surface is desired in the finished rod. Such dies should be polished or lapped. It will be found much better generally to purchase swaging dies from the principal manufacturers [6,7] rather than attempt to make them oneself. There is considerable art involved in making swaging dies.

It is quite feasible in swaging to start with a bar of square cross section and finish with a satisfactory round if considerable total reduction is made. In the early stages of working a square bar, most of the work is confined to the corners; but, after a series of anneals and swaging passes, the round bar becomes uniformly worked. For such an operation hot swaging allows more rapid approach to the desired shape. Additional details on swaging equipment and techniques are available in references 8 and 9.

Making Tubing by Swaging

It is possible to make tubing by swaging. If a seam is not objectionable, a strip of metal may be wrapped around a hard steel mandrel to form a crude tube. If the width of the strip is equal to the circumference of the mandrel, it is readily swaged to fit the mandrel snugly, without making a lap at the seam. The seam when the edges of the wrapped strip meet will not generally remain straight, but will assume a twist, owing to the rotation of the swaging dies. By the use of successively smaller dies, the wall thickness of the tube may be reduced as desired, keeping the inside diameter constant since this is fixed by the diameter of the hard mandrel. Naturally, the tubing must be considerably weaker than the mandrel, which should be subject only to elastic stresses.

Seamless tubing may be fabricated in the same way, except that a drilled-out rod is used as starting material instead of wrapped sheet.

WIRE DRAWING

Dies and Lubricants

In wire drawing, a pointed rod or wire is drawn through a specially shaped hole or die so that the diameter of the wire is reduced and the length of the wire correspondingly increased. Figure 9 shows a cross section through a typical wire drawing die which may be made of hardened steel, cemented tungsten carbide, or diamond. The die consists of a die holder which supports the carbide or diamond while the die proper consists of four parts: (1) the bell or cone, (2) the entry angle, (3) the bearing, and (4) the back relief. The bell is the large radius at the die entrance which merely serves to guide the pointed wire into the entry angle (the included die angle), which may vary from about 12 degrees for harder metals to about 30 degrees for soft materials. It is in the conical portion of the die that the actual reduction takes place. This area is followed by a short straight or cylindrical section called the bearing, which sizes the wire and tends to give it a smooth surface. The relief at the exit side of the die is to relieve the die pressure at the outside surface of the die, and thus prevent surface spalling of the brittle die materials. The design of wire drawing dies is an art, and there are apparently no well-recognized rules for choice of optimum entry angle, length of bearing, etc.

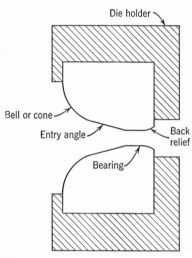

Figure 9. Wire-Drawing Die (Section).

Steel dies are not much used because of the high frictional forces they develop. Cemented tungsten carbide (such as Carboloy) dies are generally used for sizes down to about 0.020 inch in diameter. For smaller sizes, diamond dies are usually preferable. Excessive wire breakage (tensile failures) occurs when tungsten carbide dies are used in the smaller sizes, owing to excessive friction. On the other hand, diamond dies have minimum tendency to seize during drawing because of their extremely high hardness. It is characteristic of diamond dies that if one plots die cost versus size, the curve goes through a minimum in the neighborhood of 0.005 inch in diameter. The reason for this is that with larger sizes the cost of the diamond is the determining factor whereas for smaller sizes the cost rises because of the difficulty of piercing and grinding accurate holes in very small dies.

Die lubricants are of considerable importance in wire drawing and are required in nearly every case to prevent die seizing, tensile failures, and to produce good surface. Various soaps, including yellow laundry soap or Ivory soap, have been used successfully by merely rubbing the wire with the solid soap prior to drawing. There are many commercial preparations available, some of which are essentially emulsified oils which can be suspended in water, much like the "soluble" oils used in machining metals. To use such emulsions it is generally desirable to immerse the die and die holder under the liquid or at least to drip the liquid over the die, taking care to drench the bell side of the die where the wire enters.

It has been found necessary in drawing rather hard steels, such as those of high carbon content, to use a hydrated lime coating [10] which is held on the steel wire by a somewhat rough surface developed in acid pickling. The lime-coated steel during drawing is passed through a box of solid lubricant of the soap type, such as aluminum stearate or palmitate mounted on the die holder. This combination lime-soap film is so adherent and protective that several drawing operations may be made without need for additional lubrication.

Some metals, such as tungsten and molybdenum, must be drawn hot. In such cases it is general practice to coat the wire with "Aquadag," a colloidal suspension of graphite in water. By first passing the wire through Aquadag, followed by heating with a gas flame, the water is driven off, leaving a thin coating of graphite on the wire which serves as a lubricant.

As mentioned above in the discussion on swaging, it is generally desirable in laboratory work to swage to about 0.040 inch diameter before wire drawing. Swaging is a somewhat simpler and faster operation than wire drawing, particularly when dealing with lengths of 3 feet or less.

Wire-Drawing Equipment

Short lengths of the softer metals in small sizes can be drawn by hand through a die or a steel draw plate available from a jewelry equipment manufacturer.[11] Either of these may be held in a vise, however. Generally more elaborate equipment is needed.

There are two types of wire-drawing equipment suitable for laboratory work: (1) the draw bench and (2) the reel-type drawing machine. In investigating the market for wire-drawing equipment for the laboratory one finds very little which is both available and suitable. If wire drawing is only an occasional operation in the laboratory, one can make use of a tensile testing machine. By mounting a die in a suitable adapter in the lower jaws of the machine, and by grasping the wire by the upper jaws, very satisfactory wire drawing can be accomplished if one wants only rather short lengths. The wide range of speeds available in a tensile testing machine makes possible the slow starting so necessary in wire drawing. However, if there is frequent occasion for drawing wire, and if it is desirable to make a good many feet of one kind for an investigation, a special wire-drawing machine better serves the purpose. Nearly all commercial wire-drawing machines are intended for the production of large quantities of wire and are usually too big, too expensive, and not flexible enough. However, small draw benches, 6 feet long or slightly larger, can occasionally be obtained from jewelry equipment manufacturers. A draw bench has certain advantages over a reel-type machine in that it is easier to use on larger sizes of wire and on short lengths. On the other hand, a draw bench can handle only lengths as long as the bench, and many cuts and pulls are required as the wire is drawn to smaller and smaller sizes. With the reel-type machine the wire can increase in length almost indefinitely without cutting, the operation being essentially continuous except for changing dies. Figure 10 shows schematically each type of wire-drawing equipment.

The reel- or spool-type drawing machine can very readily be made in the laboratory. All that is required is a $\frac{1}{4}$ to $\frac{1}{2}$ horsepower motor, with a variable speed drive fitted with reels (preferably made of wood) mounted on axles in such a way that the spools or the spool rims holding the wire can be interchanged as the drawing progresses (Figure 10). The power-driven spool becomes the supply spool every time a die is changed. The supply spool should have an adjustable brake so that it is not free to rotate rapidly since it is likely to unwind faster than the power spool winds, with resulting tangling of the wire.

In commercial practice a certain definite back tension is applied between the supply spool and the die, but this is not necessary in laboratory work. All that is required is to prevent the supply spool from overtaking the power spool. The die holder should be arranged for quick die changes, and, if a liquid lubricant is to be used, should

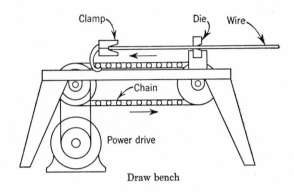

Draw bench

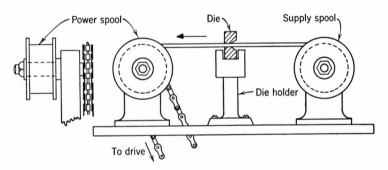

Wire drawing machine (reel type)

Figure 10. Two Types of Wire-Drawing Machines.

be so mounted so as to catch the lubricant being dripped or pumped around the die. It is very important to have a variable speed drive so that the wire may be started through the die very slowly, about 5 feet per minute, to avoid applying an impact load. The speed can then be gradually increased to the order of 100 feet per minute or even greater if desired. There are many methods of securing speed control such as electronic devices for the control of d-c motors, and mechanical devices like the well-known Reeves drive. Often special solutions to the speed-control problem are possible at very little cost. For example, a surplus variable-delivery oil pump has been found very suitable for a variable-speed "fluid drive" for a wire-drawing machine, allowing continuous speed changes from almost zero to the full speed of the electric motor.

Pointing wire to insert it through a die so that the clamping device can grasp it for pulling can be a source of as much exasperation as threading a needle. For wire sizes as small as 0.040, swaging a point using long bearing dies is probably the simplest method. It is below this size where most of the difficulty in threading dies occurs. One method is filing, but this is laborious, and frequently does not produce a sufficiently long point. A method successfully used by one of the authors is to etch away the wire anodically by holding it in a pair of pliers connected to the anode of a storage battery. A 50-50 HCl solution in a beaker with a graphite cathode completes the circuit. Dipping 2 to 3 inches of the wire into the acid for a few seconds is usually sufficient to produce a very long narrow point. The point should not be too thin or it will break off when grasped by the pulling jaws. Roll-type pointing devices with small grooved rolls of varying groove width are not recommended.

Wire Defects and Failures

If the rod from which the wire is made has surface defects such as folds, seams, or laps due to improper swaging, good-quality wire will not be possible. If such defects are present, they should be removed on the rod by centerless grinding, by filing, or by the use of a belt sander, etc.

If the wire breaks with a cup-and-cone fracture, the tensile forces were too high. This can be caused by inadequate lubrication resulting in excessive frictional forces, too much back tension on the supply spool, too high an initial drawing speed (impact load), or improper die design such as die angle.

It is important to have the wire enter and leave the die perpendicularly to the die face or, to put it differently, to have the wire axis and die axis aligned as well as possible. If this is not done, bending forces are superimposed on the drawing forces, with the result that the wire is given a "cast" or twist so that if thrown on the floor it will not lie flat. Instead it will assume a shape resembling a barbed-wire entanglement.

The drawing of wire smaller than 0.005 inch in diameter is not recommended as a laboratory operation. It requires considerable skill and special equipment to draw very fine wire; when wire is 0.001 inch in diameter it is finer than human hair, and it is even difficult to see it.

Annealing Wire

In principle, wire offers no different annealing problems from any other form of metal, but it is well to bear in mind that, if a coil is to be annealed, there is a good chance that adjacent turns will stick together. This is particularly likely when wire is annealed in a hydrogen atmosphere at relatively high temperatures. It is for this reason that "strand annealing" is used so much in the wire industry. Strand annealing as the name implies means annealing the wire one strand at a time. In practice a rather long tube furnace is employed, fitted with reel holders at each end of the furnace. A supply spool containing the hard-drawn wire is mounted at one end of the furnace, and a long stiff iron wire is passed through the hot tube and hooked to the free end of the spool. The iron grab wire is then pulled back, carrying with it the wire to be annealed, which is then fastened to the power spool exactly as in setting up the two-spool drawing machine. A little trial and error determines the optimum speed of drawing the wire through the furnace. It is desirable to have a water-cooled sleeve on the exit end of the furnace so that the wire is cold by the time it is wound on the power spool; this prevents oxidation of the wire as it passes into the air. It is as important to use a variable-speed drive here as in drawing since the wire is generally very weak at the annealing temperature, and any jerks will cause thinning of the wire if not actual failure. Back tension of the supply spool must also be carefully controlled for the same reason.

EXTRUSION

In extrusion, solid metal is forced out of an opening in a chamber by an advancing ram or punch (see Figures 11 and 12). Extrusion is ordinarily "direct," in which case the billet is pushed through the die and is moved with respect to the container. In indirect extrusion, the billet remains stationary with respect to the container, and the die is pushed against the billet. As can be seen in Figure 12, in indirect extrusion no frictional forces are developed between billet and container since no relative motion between the two is involved. Since this is so, the extrusion force is less for indirect extrusion. However, it is little used commercially probably because the tooling is appreciably more complicated, and it does not lend itself as conveniently to the production of tubing. The metal-flow pattern is considerably different in indirect extrusion (see Pearson [12]). The extrusion process

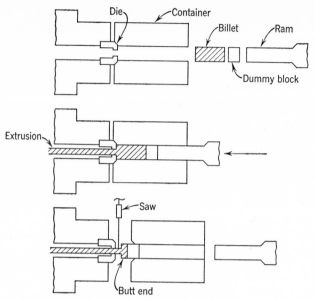

Figure 11.   Direct Extrusion.

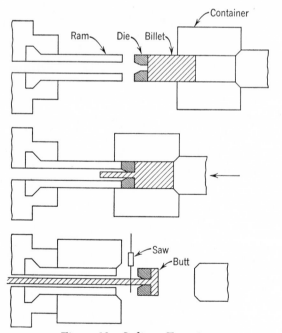

Figure 12.   Indirect Extrusion.

is much used commercially for the production of rod, tubes, and irregular shapes of constant cross section, the last usually being impossible to fabricate in any other way. Although formerly only the softer
non-ferrous metals were fabricated by extrusion, there are few materials today which are considered impracticable for extrusion.

The temperatures used for extrusion are about the same as in hot
rolling, the only requirement generally being operation above the recrystallization temperature. Where extrusion is competitive with other
processes for making shapes such as round rods, it has the advantage
that the forces on the billet are nearly hydrostatic compression, thus
allowing the fabrication of rather brittle materials. In addition, it
allows very large reductions, of the order of 30/1 between original
billet and final shape in one operation; such reductions are not feasible
in any other process.

Although in industrial practice specially designed extrusion presses
are used, some of which have capacities up to 5000 tons, it is readily
possible to fit up a laboratory hydraulic press for the extrusion of
small rods or tubes, depending upon the size of the press available
(see Figure 13). According to Sachs and Van Horn,[3] the forces in
extrusion, neglecting friction, may be approximately calculated from
the relationship

$$p = 2k \ln \frac{A_1}{A_2} \qquad (3)$$

where p is the pressure on the extrusion ram in pounds per square inch,
k is the flow stress (approximately the yield strength) at the extrusion
temperature, and A_1 and A_2 the container area and the die area, respectively, both in square inches. This relation does not take into
account friction of the container.

For aluminum and lower melting metals, extrusion can be carried
out by heating the extrusion chamber to the same temperature as the
billet being extruded. In the case of experimental apparatus, as shown
in Figure 13, the billet can be heated in the chamber. The maximum
feasible temperature for a high-speed steel die is about 600°C for
moderate pressures of about 30 tons per square inch, but temperatures
near 400°C are preferred. However, in industrial practice, the billets
are heated in a furnace adjacent to the extrusion press, and are quickly
transferred to the press container and extruded before too much heat
is lost. In order to minimize loss of heat, the container may be heated
as high as 400°C, particularly in the case of aluminum or magnesium
alloys, which are slowly extruded, and hence remain in the press for
relatively long periods of time. A hot container also aids in preventing

too rapid cooling of billets which must be extruded at high temperatures, such as steels or nickel alloys. These materials must be extruded very rapidly to avoid excessive cooling and hence excessive
extrusion pressures.

In commercial practice extrusion speeds out of the die in the neighborhood of 200 feet per minute are obtained by the use of accumula-

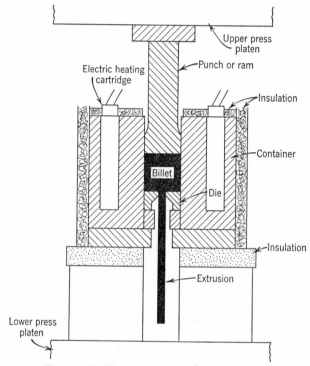

Figure 13.   Extrusion in a Laboratory Press.

tors or high-pressure storage bottles, where a large volume of water
or oil maintained at very high pressures can be quickly discharged
into the hydraulic cylinder actuating the ram.   As regards speeds in
general, it may be said that the only technical objection to very slow
extrusion is excessive cooling of the billet.   On the other hand, excessively fast speeds can cause trouble such as cracking, as pointed out
by Sachs and Van Horn.[3]   Presumably such cracking is due to the excessive temperatures generated, causing some melting and hence hot
shortness.

For extrusion temperatures in the neighborhood of 800 to 1000°C
high tungsten-chromium hot-work steels are used for the container

(chamber) liners and dies, although some experimentation has been done with Stellite-coated dies and other hard facing materials.

Extrusion dies are generally of two types: (1) flat-faced "shear" dies and (2) conical dies (see Figure 14). Shear dies are usually used with metals like aluminum that tend to seize and gall the steel dies. Since less steel is subject to the wiping action of the flowing metal in shear dies, frictional losses and tearing of the surface of both extrusion and die are reduced. On the other hand, conical dies require less pressure where seizure is not a problem, and are necessary when

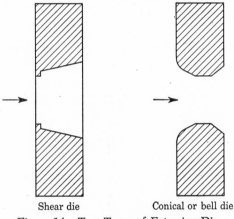

Shear die   Conical or bell die
Figure 14. Two Types of Extrusion Die.

extruding a clad billet, as in the extrusion of reactive materials where contact with the atmosphere is undesirable. The conical die allows the billet cladding metal to enter the die and to extrude along with the billet, thus affording protection during the extrusion process. Conical dies are customarily used in the extrusion of tubing, as they tend to aid metal flow between die and the mandrel which forms the inside diameter of the tube (see Figure 15).

In the commercial extrusion of tubing, the mandrel is actuated by a separate ram which pierces the billet after it has been upset by the main ram, the mandrel end being locked in the approximate position indicated in Figure 15. However, it is quite feasible to prepare tubing in the laboratory by the use of a floating or separate mandrel, the mandrel passing through a central hole already cast in place, or drilled in the billet (Figure 15). In this case the mandrel is pushed through the die along with the billet. Since the pressure of the metal being extruded is equal on all sides, the mandrel remains centered in the die opening, thus producing a tube of quite uniform wall thickness.

Lubrication does not play as vital a role in extrusion as in wire drawing, but it is usually necessary in order to avoid metal-to-metal contact between the billet and the chamber and between the billet and the die. In most work, a mixture of graphite powder and grease is applied to the hot chamber and die to prevent excessive seizing or sticking. A new die and chamber should be blued by heating in air at a low temperature to form an adherent oxide film. As a chamber

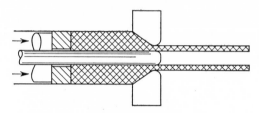

Mandrel pierces billet and remains in fixed
position shown.

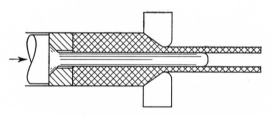

Mandrel inserted in hollow billet, moves
with billet.

Figure 15. Two Methods of Extrusion of Tubing.

and die are continually used, an adherent oxide film builds up which tends to prevent seizure and makes for a better surface on the extruded piece. Aluminum in particular is troublesome in its habit of adhering to the hot tools; fortunately, it may be readily removed with a caustic soda solution which does not affect the steel.

For a further discussion of extrusion the reader is referred to the monograph by Pearson.[12]

REFERENCES

1. Erich Siebel, "The Plastic Forming of Metals," *Steel*, Oct. 16, 1933–May 7, 1934.
2. L. R. Underwood, *The Rolling of Metals*, Chapman & Hall, Ltd., London, 1950.

3. George Sachs and Kent R. Van Horn, *Practical Metallurgy*, American Society for Metals, Cleveland, Ohio, 1940.

4. C. S. Barrett, "Structure of Iron after Compression," *Trans. Am. Inst. Mining Met. Engrs., Iron & Steel Div.*, **135**, 296–322 (1939).

5. R. McC. Baker, R. E. Ricksecker, and W. M. Baldwin, Jr., "Development of Residual Stresses in Strip Rolling," *Trans. Am. Inst. Mining Met. Engrs., Inst. Metals Div.*, **175**, 337–354 (1948).

6. The Torrington Co., Torrington, Conn.

7. The Fenn Manufacturing Co., Providence, R. I.

8. Anon., "How and When to Swage," *American Machinist* (April 22, 1948).

9. Anon., *Service Manual*, The Torrington Company (1940), Torrington, Conn.

10. D. E. Washburn, *Wire and Wire Products*, **12**, 572–575 (1937).

11. William Dixon, Inc., Newark, N. J.

12. C. E. Pearson, *The Extrusion of Metals*, John Wiley and Sons, New York, 1944.

CHAPTER TEN

Powder Metallurgy

The preparation of metal samples by the techniques of powder metallurgy is convenient when working with very high melting metals such as tungsten and molybdenum, in metal–non-metal systems, where alloying by melting techniques is impossible, where non-equilibrium structures are required, and in the preparation of materials of special structure like porous bodies. Powder metallurgy also offers certain manufacturing advantages in precision small parts, since the technique lends itself well to mass-production. This last point will not be expanded since it falls outside the scope of this book.

The principal steps in preparing a metallic part by powder metallurgy are (1) to press the metal powder (usually fine enough to pass a 100-mesh screen or finer) to a desired shape in a steel die and (2) to consolidate or densify (*sinter*) the pressed *compact* at some temperature well above the recrystallization temperature, often approaching the melting point. These two steps can be accomplished simultaneously in some cases, and the process is then called *hot pressing*. Under suitable conditions the resulting pressed part may closely approach the theoretical density of the metal or alloy used. Powder-metallurgy techniques have been used for years for the fabrication of tungsten wire for electric-lamp filaments and for molybdenum wire, although molybdenum in recent years has been successfully cast by means of an arc melting process.[1] However, the melting point of tungsten is so high that as yet no competing commercial melting process has been developed. Platinum was originally consolidated by a powder-metallurgy process due to Wallaston[2] in 1829, in an era when high-temperature melting techniques were poorly developed. This process is of historic interest only as platinum is readily melted and cast today by high-frequency induction heating, or by other methods.

The art of powder metallurgy lies principally in controlling the two steps of pressing and sintering, but each of these operations is affected by a multitude of variables. In the following pages a brief summary of more important considerations and techniques is given, including selection and blending of the powders to be used, choice of suitable dies, pressing techniques, heating atmospheres, times and temperatures of sintering. For a more thorough exposition of this subject the reader is referred to books by Goetzel,[3] Schwarzkopf,[4] Hausner,[5] and Wulff.[6] The work by Goetzel is particularly complete.

POWDER-METALLURGY APPLICATIONS

Incompatible Systems

There are a number of binary metal systems where the two liquid metals are immiscible, or where one metal is very sparingly soluble in the other. Obviously in such cases the preparation of regular alloys by normal melting and casting procedures is impossible. However, such systems may have some practical or scientific interest, and combinations of immiscible metals can usually be prepared by starting with metal powders and pressing and sintering them as mentioned above. For example, the high electrical conductivity of copper and the superior strength of molybdenum can be combined to make electrical contacts that are good conductors and resist pitting. Commercial use [7] is made of similar 20 to 30% copper-tungsten mixtures for spot-welding electrodes. At least three techniques can be employed for this alloy: cold press sinter, hot press, and infiltration of liquid copper into the pores of a cold-pressed tungsten briquette. These techniques will be discussed in detail later on.

Metal–non-metal mixtures are another type of incompatible system. Here again ordinary melting techniques cannot be employed because the resulting structure would not be the one desired or the non-metal is completely insoluble in the liquid metal. A classic example of this is *cemented tungsten carbide* (tungsten carbide bonded by cobalt), where melting is ruled out for structural reasons. A third example of incompatible systems is the metal-oxide mixture or *cermet,* a combination of a *ceramic* material and a *metal* in which the ceramic is bonded by a metal phase. Such a combination has high thermal conductivity and resistance to thermal shock contributed by the metal and elevated temperature strength contributed by the oxide. Ceramic additions of several volume per cent may be made to a ductile metal such as aluminum without destroying its ability to be fabricated by swaging or rolling, and much larger additions may be made if high ductility in the final product is not required. This technique has been found particularly useful in atomic-energy applications, where the form of the required element is not important since the desired properties are those of the nucleus. Certain rare metals are more available as the oxide than as the metal. In addition, this procedure facilitates the handling of pyrophoric metals. If very high density is required (low pore volume) the preparation of such composites is often most conveniently accomplished by hot pressing in graphite dies heated nearly to the melting point of the metal.

Avoiding Segregation

When making alloys of limited mutual liquid solubility where there is a considerable difference in density between the two liquids, gravity segregation is difficult to avoid. An example is the copper-lead system. Even when there is complete liquid solubility, if the solid freezing out during the solidification process is considerably heavier than the liquid, segregation can be a problem. Powder techniques can be useful in these cases. Obviously, if the low melting constituent is in excess, the sintering temperature must be below the melting point of the low melting metal. This restriction does not apply if the high melting metal is in excess, as the small amount of liquid formed is usually retained in place by surface tension forces.

Since metal powders are readily obtained which are smaller than the grains in castings, the time required for complete homogenization of a powder compact may be appreciably shorter than that required for a casting. This is because the diffusion path is shorter in the powder structure.

Avoiding Melting Problems

There are refractory metals in addition to tungsten which sometimes may be handled with advantage by powder metallurgy. Some examples are zirconium, titanium, vanadium, and beryllium.

Although zirconium is available as sponge metal, and may be either vacuum melted in graphite or inert arc melted (see Chapter 7), it is frequently more convenient to use powder techniques for zirconium alloys. This is because it is very difficult to arc-melt refractory alloys without getting considerable segregation, and, in addition, the melted alloy usually requires considerable fabrication to secure a suitable shape. Graphite melting of zirconium allows some carbon pick-up and, like arc melting, is not adaptable to securing a rather small quantity in a desired form. However, by powder techniques it is easy to press a small compact without carbon pick-up or segregation. It is necessary, however, to handle the zirconium powder in a noble-gas atmosphere until the powder is compacted. These same remarks apply to titanium and vanadium, except that the latter cannot be melted in graphite, nor is it as pyrophoric as zirconium. In general, it may be said that the use of powder metallurgy as a method of consolidation allows one to by-pass the crucible problem, that is, reaction with the crucible.

In the case of beryllium, consolidation of metal powder offers the chief advantage (as against cast beryllium) that it is much finer in grain size and hence more ductile and machinable than the cast metal.

Special Structures

The only feasible method of preparing metals and alloys of a definite controlled porosity is by powder techniques, examples of which are metallic filters and oil-less bearings. In the latter technique a porous bronze or steel structure is prepared by driving off a volatile substance in the powder mixture during sintering. The volatile substance leaves behind pores which may later be filled with oil, hence producing a bearing with "built-in" permanent lubrication. The use of volatile substances is not always necessary for producing a porous body as proper choice of particle size and particle shape of the powder and control of the pressing and sintering operation will often produce the desired structure.

In a binary alloy system a certain composition may be desired in which one component (A) constitutes the continuous phase or matrix, whereas the other component (B) consists of islands surrounded by A. On the other hand, the nature of the phase diagram may be such that the reverse structure is obtained by melting and casting. If, however, the volume per cent of A is considerably greater than B, it is possible to obtain the desired structure by pressing and sintering below the solidus, as A will tend to be the matrix since it is present in larger volume.

Two metal powders C and D if melted to form an alloy may produce a very brittle material unfit for the intended use. But by using powders and controlling the sintering conditions, a synthetic, non-equilibrium structure may be obtained in which not enough diffusion has occurred to form much of the brittle phase.

METAL POWDERS

It is outside the scope of this work to describe in detail the various methods used to prepare commercial metal powders. However, brief mention of the more important techniques is probably worth while as powders made by different methods may have quite different particle shapes and other characteristics which should be considered in handling them. For a complete review of this subject, see Goetzel.[3]

Atomization

Some non-ferrous metals and alloys such as aluminum, tin, lead, zinc, cadmium, brass, and copper are reduced to powder by melting in special equipment which provides a blast of air or inert gas against a small stream of metal pouring from a crucible or holding pot. The design of the nozzle from which the metal issues and the mode of gas impingement upon the stream is rather critical as regards production of the desired particle range and shape. Powders are produced by this method in a variety of shapes, including nearly perfect spheroids, tear-drop particles, or irregular or ragged shapes. This is the most common method of preparing the type of aluminum powder used in powder-metallurgy work (as contrasted with the undesirable plate-like shape of aluminum pigment powder).

Oxide Reduction

This method consists of reduction of metal oxides by such reducing gases as hydrogen, cracked ammonia, and CO, and is a widely used technique for metal-powder preparation. It results in the production of powders of a very wide range of characteristics of particle size, shape, porosity, etc. Metals commonly prepared by this technique include tungsten, molybdenum, cobalt, and iron. As would be anticipated, the temperature of hydrogen reduction is quite critical as regards powder characteristics. Rather low temperatures must be employed to avoid excessive sintering. There is danger that if the time of reduction is too short or if the temperature used is too low, the core of the powder particles may remain unreduced.

Electrolysis

By electrodeposition at higher current densities than normal for ordinary electroplating, and by making other adjustments in electrolyte composition and cell geometry, it is possible to deposit spongy metal or actual powder which requires, besides washing and screening for size, very little additional processing. Powders of very high purity may be prepared in this way, including copper, zinc, lead, and tin. Electrolytic powder is dendritic or tree-like in shape, and because of its irregularity tends to hold together well in compacting because of particle interlocking.

A somewhat different electrolytic process is used for iron and nickel whereby a hard brittle mass is deposited requiring mechanical comminution subsequently as well as a degassing and annealing treatment to render the powder plastic enough for good compaction characteristics.

Carbonyl Decomposition

Nickel and iron powder may be made by thermal decomposition of their respective carbonyls prepared by passing CO over heated metal sponge at high pressures. The carbonyl is then subsequently decomposed to a fine spheroidal powder by heating to 150 to 400°C at atmospheric pressures. Carbonyl powder is of high purity, but is relatively expensive. The spherical particle shape is often undesirable because of its generally poor pressing characteristics, although some commercial carbonyl powders are non-spherical. Spherical powders are desirable in making porous structures like filters, as this particle shape does not consolidate as readily during pressing.

Other Methods

There are several other commercial methods which are used for preparing powders, including mechanical comminution, intergranular corrosion, and thermal decomposition of compounds (other than carbonyls). They are described in references 3 and 4.

Grinding Powders in the Laboratory

Frequently it is desirable to prepare powders in the laboratory. Laboratory preparation of metal powders is usually restricted to breaking up brittle alloys in a ball mill or in a hammer mill.[3, 4] Larger particles about $\frac{1}{4}$ inch in diameter or over should first be crushed in the diamond mortar described in Chapter 7 or in a small jaw crusher available from various commercial suppliers.[8]

A ball mill is a cylindrical container which is frequently made of porcelain, steel, or rubber-coated steel that is filled to about one-third of its capacity with balls of similar material. The charge of material to be ground is about 25% of the volume of the balls. The covered cylinder is rolled on rollers or in a cradle for several hours. A ball mill works well only on brittle materials, as ductile pieces flatten out rather than break up into smaller fragments. Wet ball milling is sometimes advocated, but it seems to have little advantage over dry milling except where organic liquids such as carbon tetrachloride are employed to prevent oxidation of pyrophoric powders. However, wet ball milling may produce a different particle-size distribution compared to dry milling.

Where it is applicable [with metals which form hydrides], preparing the hydride often causes pulverization. If not, the hydride is usually readily fragmented mechanically. Vacuum heat treatment removes the hydrogen.

Particle Shape and Size Distribution

Particle shape may control pouring characteristics and as-pressed density. Spherical particles are difficult to press to a strong *green* (unsintered) compact because there is little surface contact between particles. In a powder prepared by comminution of brittle sheets such as electrodeposits, the particles are angular and irregular and present greater opportunity for interlocking or intermeshing during the pressing operation. Flake powder, however, such as aluminum pigment, is very undesirable since the bulk density of such powder is extremely low due to the tendency of neighboring flakes to assume a random orientation instead of lining up with the flat surfaces parallel. Hence aluminum flake or similar products are avoided in the preparation of powder compacts.

In order to secure maximum cold-pressed density, a range of particle size should be used. Obviously, if a box were filled with spheres of the same diameter, more material of smaller size could be added by sifting in between the spheres already present, thus adding to the density of packing. Theoretical studies of the optimum range of particle size have been made, but in practice it is generally advisable to determine this value experimentally as the distribution required for highest density will depend to a considerable extent upon the particular character of the powder employed. Also in practice it is only feasible to work with a rather small number of powder fractions, and certain fractions which might be desired may not be available. Powder bought from suppliers may be purchased in certain screen size ranges such as $-200 + 325$, meaning that all the powder passes a 200-mesh screen but it is all retained on a 325-mesh screen. However, there is a range of particle size in such a sample, and if desired a $-200 + 250$ sample or some other fraction may be separated.

For most cold-press sinter work particles coarser than 100 mesh are not desirable nor are particles finer than -325 mesh usually required. If the range of particle size is in the finer fractions, then some particles considerably finer than just -325 mesh may be desirable in order to secure an adequate size dispersion. Very fine particles sinter more rapidly and shrink more on sintering than coarser particles. They are also somewhat less convenient to handle and grade since screens cannot be used as readily. A suitable blend between these sizes is usually possible. As a rough guide, about half the mix should be relatively coarse, with perhaps 30% in the finer sizes and the remaining 20% of intermediate size. Small variations of the screen analysis generally have little effect upon the as-pressed density; hence one need not be concerned about variations of a few per cent in the various screen fractions blended.

Methods of Powder Classification

For samples as fine as 325 or occasionally even 400 mesh, the use of U.S. Standard or Tyler screens is the common method of analyzing particle size or of actually preparing lots of different particle size. Such screens are available in diameters ranging from about 2 inches to 10 inches. The larger screen sizes are used for handling several hundred grams of powder. Although small or infrequent samples of a few grams can be handled by hand sifting, a mechanical device such as the commonly used Ro-Tap [9] sieve shaker is practically necessary for handling usual laboratory quantities of powder. In this device a stack of the screens required is made, starting with the coarsest screen at the top and ending with the finest screen at the bottom. After a standard period of time, usually about 15 minutes, the machine is stopped and the portions in the various screens may be weighed to compute the *screen analysis.*

For particles in the so-called subsieve sizes, air classification or elutriation is possible as in the Roller Analyzer.[10] Here again this instrument may be used both for preparing fractions of different particle sizes and for analyzing an unknown sample. It is particularly useful in the particle size range from about 40 to 0.1 microns (below the 400-mesh screen range). The powder is fractionated by a stream of air passing through a metal chamber in which the powder is suspended. Particles below a specific size are carried over into an upper collecting cup, and the remaining powder falls into a lower receptacle. By using metal chambers of different diameter the rate of air flow can be altered, thus altering the particle size of the powder which can be carried over into the upper cup.

There are various other techniques for measuring particle sizes or estimating particle-size distribution, including microscopic examination, photometric methods, observing the rate of fall in a gas or liquid medium, and measuring the rate of gas flow through a pressed sample prepared in a standard manner. None of these methods is entirely satisfactory, and some, like the last named, are only semi-quantitative. Probably microscopic examination is most direct, but it is laborious and can be used only with particle sizes larger than a micron, although the electron microscope may be used for measuring particle sizes down to the angstrom range. Fortunately, most powder-metallurgy work can be accomplished satisfactorily using particle sizes in the screen range.

Table 1 gives a list of sieve sizes ("mesh" numbers) and the corresponding openings in millimeters. These sizes apply to either Tyler or U.S. Sieve Series.

TABLE 1
Sieve Numbers and Openings in Millimeters

Sieve No.	Sieve Opening, mm
100	0.149
120	0.125
140	0.105
170	0.088
200	0.074
230	0.062
270	0.053
325	0.044
400	0.037 (seldom used)

Conditioning Metal Powders for Use

To secure satisfactory results in preparing powder compacts of high density and reproducible properties, the powders used should be as free of oxide and other surface contaminants as possible. Generally the main surface contamination is the oxide, which can often be removed by hydrogen reduction. Rather low temperatures must be employed for this operation, or sintering will occur and a spongy mass rather than a loose powder will result. As a rough rule, the temperature used for hydrogen cleaning should not be higher than about one-third to one-half the centigrade melting temperature, but a little trial and error may be necessary to determine the appropriate temperature and time. After the hydrogen treatment (which should be carried out with very dry hydrogen) the powder should preferably be used immediately or, if necessary to store it, it should be kept under inert gas to avoid reoxidation. Goetzel [3] gives the following hydrogen reduction temperatures for four metal powders for reduction without excessive sintering:

Fe	$<900°C$
Cu	$400–600°C$
Co	$<800°C$
W	$650–700°C$

TABLE 2

METAL POWDERS AND THEIR SUPPLIERS (SCHUMACHER AND SOUDEN [11])

Material	How Produced	Purity or Composition	Available Meshes	Suppliers *
Aluminum	Atomized	99.0+%	−10 to −325	Hardy, MD, Reynolds
	Flake-milled	.....	−325	Alcoa, MD
Aluminum alloy	Atomized	96–98%	−100	Hardy, Reynolds
	Hot-milled	Dural	−60 to −300	Unexcelled
Antimony	Milled	99%	−100 to −325	Hardy, MD
Beryllium	Reduced	97+%	−200	Hardy
Beryllium alloys	Milled	2.5% Be–Cu	−60 to −300	Unexcelled
	Hydride	10% Be–Ni	−100	Hydrides
Bismuth	Milled	99.9%	−200	Hardy, MD
Brass	Atomized	60/40 to 90/10	−100 to −325	Hardy, MD, NJ Zinc
	Atomized	60/40	−30	NJ Zinc
	Atomized	70/30	−100 (Spher)	NJ Zinc
Bronze	Flake-milled	Cu-Zn-Al	Various, to −325	Am Bronze
	Reduced	.....	Various	MD
	Hot-milled	77% Cu, 8% Sn, 15% Pb	−60 to −300	Unexcelled
Cadmium	Milled	99.5%	−100, −300	Hardy
	Atomized	.....	−325	MD
Chromium	Milled	98+%	−150 to −325	Hardy, MD
Cobalt	Reduced	97.5–99%	−100 to −300	Hardy
	Reduced	99.9%	−325	R & R
Columbium	Reduced	95.0+%	−50	Fansteel
Copper	Electrolytic	99.5+%	−100 to −325	AM Co, Gen Met, Hardy, MR
	Reduced	99.5+%	−40 to −325	MD, P M & A
	Atomized	.....	−30 to −200	NJ Zinc
	Flake-milled	.....	−325	Am Bronze
Copper-nickel	Hot-milled	70% Cu, 30% Ni	−60 to −300	Unexcelled
Graphite	.....	97–98% C	−200, −325	Dixon
	.....	95+% C	−325	Dixon
	.....	90–92% C	−200	Dixon
	.....	95, 97% C	5 micron	Dixon
	.....	.....	−200 and finer	National Carbon
Iron	Reduced	99+%		MD, P M & A, Hardy
	Reduced	97–98.2%	Many, to −325	MR, Plast Met
	Electrolytic	99.5%	−8 to −325	Plast Met, E & T
	Carbonyl	98–99.9%	−8 to −325	GAW
Lead	Atomized	99.5–99.9%	−180, −400	AM Co, Hardy, MD, MR
			−100 to −325	
Magnesium	Milled	96–99.9%	−15 to −325	Apex, Magna, NS, Nat Mag, NE Mag
Manganese	Milled	99.9%	−100 to −325	Hardy, MD
	Electrolytic	99.75%	−20 to −325	Plast Met
Molybdenum	Reduced	99.90%	−150, −200, −300	Callite, Hardy
	H-reduced	99.7+%	−80	Fansteel, NAP
	Reduced	99+%	−80	Hardy
Nickel	Milled	Ni + Co 99%	−150 to −325	Hardy, MD
	Flake-milled	.....	−325	Am Bronze
	Reduced	99.5%	Various	P M & A
Nickel-copper	Hot-milled	70% Ni, 30% Cu	−60 to −300	Unexcelled
Nickel Silver	Hot-milled	Cu-Ni-Zn	−60 to −300	Unexcelled
Silicon	Milled	96, 97+%	−100 to −325	MD, Plast Met, Hardy
Silver	Electrolytic	99.90%	−200 to −325	AM Co, H & H, Hardy, MD
	Flake-milled	.....	−325	Am Bronze
Solder	Atomized	50/50; 40/60	−40 to −325	MD

TABLE 2 (*Continued*)

METAL POWDERS AND THEIR SUPPLIERS (SCHUMACHER AND SOUDEN)

Material	How Produced	Purity or Composition	Available Meshes	Suppliers
Stainless steel	Corrosion	18/8	−60 to −300	Unexcelled
	Milled and reduced	35/15	−60 to −300	Unexcelled
Steel	Reduced	97–99% Fe	Various	P M & A
Tantalum	Electrolytic	99.8+%	80% −400	Fansteel
Tantalum carbide		TaC	−200	Fansteel
Thorium	Reduced	95+%	−100	Hardy
Tin	Atomized	99.5+%	−40 to −325	MD, MR, Hardy
	Flake-milled	.....	−325	Am Bronze
Titanium	Reduced	99.5%	−250	Hardy
	Hydride	98–99.5%	−100	Hydrides
Titanium hydride	Hydride	98–99.5%	−325	Hydrides
Tungsten	Reduced	99.9+%	−150, 200, 300	Callite, Hardy, R & R, Fansteel, NAP
	Reduced	99.0%	−80 to −300	Callite, Hardy
Tungsten carbide		WC	Various	Carboloy, Fansteel
Vanadium	Milled	90%	−80 and finer	Hardy
Zinc	Atomized	99+%	−24 to −325	MD, Hardy, NJ Zinc
Zirconium	Reduced	99.5%	−250	Hardy
Zirconium hydride	Hydride	99–99.9%	−200	Hydrides

* *General list of powder suppliers:* (Alcoa) Aluminum Co. of America, Pittsburgh. Aluminum Bronze Powder Co., Bedford, O. (Am Bronze) American Bronze Div., Metals Disintegrating Co., Verona, N. J. (AM Co) American Metal Co., Ltd., New York. (Apex) Apex Smelting Co., Chicago. Baer Bros., New York. Belmont Smelting & Refining Co., Brooklyn, N. Y. (Callite) Callite Tungsten Corp., Union City, N. J. (Carboloy) Carboloy Corp., Detroit. (Dixon) Jos. Dixon Crucible Co., Jersey City, N. J. (E & T) Ekstrand & Tholand, Inc., New York. (Fansteel) Fansteel Metallurgical Corp., No. Chicago. (Gen Met) General Metals Powder Co., Akron, O. (GAW) General Aniline Works Div., New York. Goldfield Consolidated Mines Co., San Francisco. (H & H) Handy & Harman, New York. (Hardy) Chas. Hardy, Inc., New York. Harshaw Chemical Co., Cleveland, O. Hommel Co., Pittsburgh. (Magna) Magna Mfg. Co., Inc., New York. McAleer Mfg. Co., Rochester, Mich. (Hydrides) Metal Hydrides, Inc., Beverly, Mass. (MD) Metals Disintegrating Co., Elizabeth, N. J. Metals, Inc., San Francisco. (MR) Metals Refining Co. of Pa., Palmerton, Pa. (NAP) North American Phillips Co., Cleveland. (Nat Mag) National Magnesium Corp., New York. (NS) National Smelting Co., New York. (NE Mag) New England Magnesium Co., Inc., Malden, Mass. (NJ Zinc) New Jersey Zinc Co. of Pa., Palmerton, Pa. (NAP) North American Phillips Co., Inc., New York. (Plast Met) Plastic Metals, Inc., Johnstown, Pa. (P M & A) Powder Metals & Alloys, Inc., New York. Pyron Corp., Niagara Falls, N. Y. (R & R) Reduction & Refining Co., Newark, N. J. (Reynolds) Reynolds Metals Co., Louisville, Ky. (Unexcelled) Unexcelled Mfg. Co., New York. U.S. Metal Powders Co., Closter, N. J. U.S. Magnesium Co., Pleasant Valley, N. Y.

Powders as received from the supplier are often in a more or less cold-worked condition and hence have little plasticity. This is, of course, particularly true of powders prepared by a mechanical comminution process. Annealing such powders will allow higher aspressed densities to be obtained as the softer powder cold-welds better than the more brittle cold-worked powder. The hydrogen cleaning operation also allows some softening to occur; hence the two conditioning operations of cleaning and annealing can often be combined.

An ingenious method of annealing metal powders without sintering has been devised by Von Batchelder and Stauss.[12] These investigators mixed gold, silver, and iron powders with sodium chloride in the ratio of one part of metal to ten parts of salt. The metal-salt mixture is then annealed in the normal fashion, the large excess of salt preventing metal-to-metal contact and hence sintering of the metal powders. The particle size of the salt should be comparable to the metal powder size. The amount of excess salt can be varied, but the ratio noted above was suggested by Batchelder and Stauss. After annealing, the salt is readily removed from the metal powder by washing in water. There seems to be no reason why other salts could not be used, provided they are sufficiently stable, inert, and high melting.

Table 2 lists many metal and alloy powders available commercially, including method of production, purity, sizes available, and suppliers.

Blending Powders

Powder mixtures must be well mixed or blended before pressing to secure uniformity in the pressed compact. Blending may be accomplished in a number of ways. Ball milling with just a few balls, not enough to secure grinding action, has been used for this purpose. Rotating a round jar on its own axis in a roller is not satisfactory as the powder merely slides around without good mixing. Placing the jar in a special cradle or holder and rotating end over end, however, produces good mixing. A square box mounted on an axis along a body diagonal makes a satisfactory blender. Merely hand shaking a jar of powder can do a good mixing job, but is rather tedious.

Mixing powders of widely different densities can be a vexing problem as the heavier powder tends to segregate to the bottom. It has been found that the use of very fine powders alleviates this difficulty. If one has a choice, it is better to have the less dense powder finer than the heavy powder, the opposite to what one might intuitively believe. Wet mixing aids in securing a homogeneous blend, and organic liquids such as benzene, hexane, and acetone have been used for this purpose. The consistency should be that of a heavy slurry or thin mud; the volatile liquid can afterwards be cautiously driven off under a hood by simply air drying or careful heating.

PRESSING

Pressing of the metal powder to the desired shape may be accomplished either hot or cold; the more common cold pressing technique will be described first. For much laboratory experimentation, a cylindrical shape is the simplest one, both from the standpoint of the pressing operation itself and from the standpoint of the die manufacture. A die suitable for pressing a long narrow square rod, for example, will cost much more than one used for pressing short cylinders. A satisfactory cylindrical die is shown in Figure 1. The simplest shape to make is a disk with the thickness somewhat less than or equal to the diameter. As the height of the cylinder is increased, the density of the as-pressed piece falls off because of increased friction at the die wall and within the powder itself. The effect of die-wall friction can be minimized by coating the wall with stearic acid, paraffin, or other lubricants. By pressing the piece, using the double-action plunger principle, a more uniform as-pressed density is possible. Such double action is obtained by allowing the bottom punch to project through the bottom of the die so that the die body is "floating" on the punches, as described in Chapter 4. Since now both bottom and top punch move with respect to the die, the powder becomes as much compacted at the bottom as at the top, and the height of the compact can be as much as twice the diameter. Even with this procedure, however, the central part of the pressing is less dense than the ends.

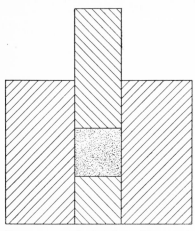

Figure 1.   Cylindrical Steel Pressing Die.

The ratio of the height of fill to the pressed height is called the compression ratio. Obviously, the compression ratio depends upon the bulk density of the powder and the compacting pressure employed. Compression ratios of 2 to 3 are customary in most work.

Details of Die Construction

A cold-pressing die should be made from an oil-hardening non-deforming type of tool steel hardened to 45–60 Rockwell C. However, as mentioned in Chapter 4, it is safer to use die bodies at less than maximum hardness to avoid possible brittle failure. Naturally greater wear will occur with softer dies. The finish of all mating parts should be very smooth; finishing by a lapping operation is desirable. The optimum clearance between punch and die is a function of the punch diameter; larger diameter dies work better with larger clearances. In Table 3 are given clearances which have been found satisfactory with metal powders. Ceramic powders usually require greater clearances because of their tendency to promote galling.

TABLE 3

PUNCH AND DIE CLEARANCES

Die Diameter, inches	Clearance between Punch and Die, inches
0.5	0.0005–0.0015
1.0	0.001 –0.0015
1.5	0.0015–0.002
2.0	0.002 –0.003

The bottom of the die through which the piece is ejected should be slightly tapered for a distance equal to the diameter of the compact, using a taper of about 0.1 inch per foot. This tapering allows

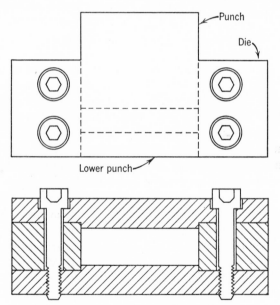

Figure 2.   Rectangular Steel Pressing Die.

gradual release of elastic stress in the piece during ejecting and combats a tendency for the piece to break or laminate during ejection. As described for pressing ceramic shapes, a ring somewhat taller than the height of the pressing is convenient for supporting the die during ejection. A piece of heavy rubber placed directly under the die is often used to lessen shock on the falling weak compact. The parts of the die should be carefully wiped off before making another pressing to avoid jamming loose powder between punch and die. Increased wear resistance and corrosion protection may be obtained by plating the parts of the die with a thin (0.0001 inch thick) hard chromium electroplate. For dies being used with rather abrasive powders, a high carbon–high chromium (2 C–12 Cr type) steel may be used. If there is a chance that the die will be used at moderately elevated temperatures, a high-speed steel such as 18 W–4 Cr–1 V

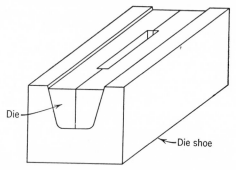

Figure 3. Die Shoe with Die.

may be used. This steel, however, has no advantage over ordinary oil-hardening tool steels at ordinary temperatures.

There are many possible designs for a rectangular die from the simple, readily made die illustrated in Figure 2 to very expensive quickly demountable dies equipped with die "shoes" to hold the parts together. Die shoes are usually made of massive mild steel and tapered so that the hardened die pieces are prevented from spreading apart during pressing (see Figure 3). Rectangular dies are ordinarily used to press bars for subsequent working by rolling or swaging. The bolts in the die of Figure 2 may be loosened if desired before ejecting the pressed part; this is an aid in preventing cracking upon release of elastic stress in brittle materials.

Lubricants

Die-wall lubricants have already been mentioned. Aluminum flake (pigment) has been used as a die-wall lubricant since the flake slips readily over itself, as is readily observed by rubbing it between forefinger and thumb. Other die-wall lubricants which have been used are graphite and Molykote [13] (molybdenum sulphide). Die-wall lubricants may be suspended or dissolved in a volatile organic vehicle and painted on the die surface.

The powder fill itself is often lubricated, particularly in non-plastic or brittle powders such as metal carbides, oxides (see Chapter 4), silicon, and the like, since such materials cannot flow under the ordinary die pressures used. An internal lubricant helps hold the green compact together, protects easily oxidized metal powders, and is used where wall lubrication is not possible or desirable. A partial list of lubricants include stearic acid, aluminum stearate, paraffin, lucite (in acetone), vinyl chloride (in acetone), Ceremul C [14] (emulsified paraffin), and Sterotex [15] (a hydrogenated oil). Usually around 2 to 3% by weight of such lubricants is used, and most of this is burned out during the subsequent sintering operation. A very small residue of carbon usually remains in the compact, particularly if carbide-forming elements are present, but ordinarily this is not objectionable. Slow heating of the compact in the early stages of sintering aids in evaporation of the lubricant and reduces carbon residue.

The usual procedure in adding such lubricants is to take the required weight in a suitable solvent and add enough solvent to wet the powder thoroughly. After hand blending the wet mix with spatula or glass rod, the solvent is driven off under a hood by cautious heating or natural evaporation, occasionally stirring until dry. If caked, the mass can be broken up in a mortar and pestle and is then ready for use.

The Pressing Operation

After the die is filled to the desired level with the powder mix, it may be lightly tapped to settle the powder and to help level the surface. If the powder is not level, uneven pressure results in non-uniform density during pressing. If the die opening is an inch or more in diameter, it may be desirable to level the surface with some type of scraping device (see Figure 4 in Chapter 4). Adhering powder is wiped off the upper wall of the die, and the punch is carefully and slowly inserted to avoid blowing the surface of the powder with trapped air.

Entrapped air may be eliminated during the pressing operation by evacuation of the die through a small hole drilled vertically in the die wall and connecting with a radial hole near the center of the die. The die cavity can thus be evacuated after assembly of the die and powder. Since the hole leading to the die cavity is in the upper section of the cavity, the upper punch moves down, sealing off the hole before high pressure is applied, thus preventing powder from being pushed into the hole. (See Figure 4.) Excessive entrapped air can cause swelling of the compact during sintering.

Pressure is applied by means of a hydraulic press, which may be an inexpensive hand-operated one for rather small parts or a power-operated press. If the latter, it is necessary that good speed control be available. A hydraulic testing machine of the type used for tensile specimens is ideal for such work, but satisfactory and less expensive

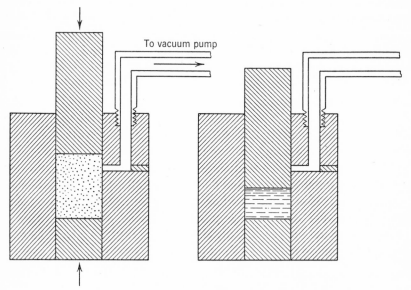

To vacuum pump

Figure 4. Evacuation of a Steel Die to Avoid Air Entrapment.

hydraulic presses are available. It is important that the die be located centrally on the press platens to prevent cocking or die misalignment.

The actual pressure used varies widely with the nature of the powder being pressed. In general, the yield strength of the metal must be exceeded by a fair margin to secure a good green compact since the powder must be plastically deformed to secure the partial cold welding which causes the particles to adhere to their neighbors. Pressures used in cold compaction are generally stated in tons per square inch, and it is usual practice to use pressures in the range of 15 to 50 tons per square inch. The higher pressures lead in general to higher densities, but there are limitations to the upper pressure. One is the strength of the steel die, and another is the formation of laminations or cracks which, in general, traverse the entire compact in a plane perpendicular to the pressing direction. Such laminations are particularly prevalent with brittle powders, and are caused by entrapped air and die-wall friction which causes alternate seizing and releasing of the powder during the pressing operation. Laminations can be avoided partly by better die-wall lubrication, by lowered pressure, by evacuation of air from the die, and by the use of a taper at the ejection end of the die as explained above. In addition, too much pressure during pressing causes excessive entrapped air in the compact and hence swelling during the subsequent sintering operation. The typical graph of density versus pressure in pressing, presented in

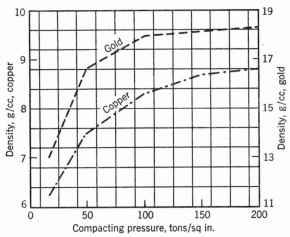

Figure 5. Effect of Compacting Pressure on the Density of Copper and Gold Compacts. (Hausner.[5]) (Reprinted by courtesy Chemical Publishing Co., New York, N. Y.)

Figure 5, shows that the rate of densification falls off rather rapidly above a certain pressure. For example, a compact which has 80% of theoretical density after pressing at 40 tons per square inch may have only 82% of theoretical density after pressing at 50 tons per square inch.

Final sizing to exact dimensions may be carried out after sintering; this operation is usually termed *coining*.

SINTERING

When a cold-pressed compact is heated to a sufficiently high temperature, the nature of the compact changes remarkably. The originally weak, friable compact becomes very much stronger, it increases in density, and adjoining powder particles coalesce with accompanying grain growth. If the temperature is high enough and the time long enough, the compact may closely approach the ultimate density characteristic of the composition. Although in the absence of intermetallic compounds the density of an alloy can be closely approximated by assuming that the density is equivalent to that calculated for a mixture, if an entirely new phase is formed the density may be appreciably different from that calculated. Hence a lower density may result than that expected, without being caused by the presence of pores. Usually, however, sintered compacts have 5 to 15% porosity. In order to densify the compact completely, an additional pressing operation (coining) or other working operation as by rolling or swaging is usually necessary, followed by more sintering. In some instances, compacts expand somewhat rather than contract during sintering. Such behavior has usually been attributed to the expansion of air entrapped during the pressing operation or to other gases formed during sintering.

The actual mechanism by which densification of powder compacts occurs during sintering is not completely clear as different investigators of this phenomenon have not been in agreement. There appears to be rather strong evidence, however, that it is due to diffusion of lattice vacancies to the surface along grain boundaries. Alexander [16] has demonstrated that pore reduction ceases when grain boundaries no longer intersect the pore-particle interface.

Since sintering requires atom movements, the rate of sintering increases exponentially with temperature according to the Arrhenius equation:

$$V = V_0 \exp\left(-Qs/RT\right) \tag{1}$$

where V is the sintering rate at temperature T, R is the gas constant, Qs is the activation energy required for sintering, and V_0 is a constant with the same dimensions as V. Therefore, the rate of sintering is greatly accelerated by only a moderate increase in temperature.

The time required for a certain degree of sintering at some temperature level may be calculated from equation 2 if the temperature and time required to produce this state at a different temperature are known, and Qs is known.

$$\ln\left(\frac{t_1}{t_2}\right) = \frac{Qs}{R}\left(\frac{1}{T_1} - \frac{1}{T_2}\right) \tag{2}$$

where t_1 and t_2 are the times required to produce a given amount of densification at temperature T_1 and T_2, and Qs is the heat of activation for sintering. Qs may be computed by determining the times necessary to produce the same amount of sintering at two temperatures. Empirically, this is observed to be somewhat less than the activation energy for self-diffusion in the metals concerned. As a rough approximation, at temperatures where sintering occurs at appreciable rates, the sintering rate is doubled for every 10°C rise in temperature. Some curves showing the effect of temperature on compact density are given in Figure 6.

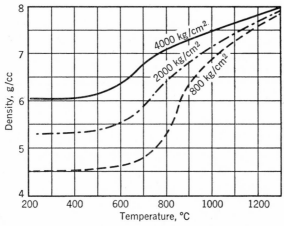

Figure 6. Effect of Sintering Temperature on the Density of Carbonyl Nickel Powder for Three Compacting Pressures. (Hausner.[5]) (Reprinted by courtesy Chemical Publishing Co., New York, N. Y.)

Atmospheres for Sintering

Much sintering of metals whose oxides are readily reduced by hydrogen (for example, iron, copper, nickel) is done in a dry hydrogen or cracked ammonia atmosphere because of its reducing action. Metals which form hydrides must be sintered in very pure noble gas or in vacuum. Naturally, any foreign material such as surface oxides must be eliminated prior to and during the sintering operation in order to preserve the clean surfaces necessary for interdiffusion. Table 4 lists some metals and suggested atmospheres for sintering.

It should be noted that, as suggested in Chapter 5, a noble gas is best used as a stagnant atmosphere; but a reducing gas like hydrogen should be continuously passed over the compact to avoid reversal of the reducing action.

For some reason that is not clear, a cleaner compact often results when the compact is completely embedded in a non-reactive refractory powder such as fused Al_2O_3 grain.

TABLE 4

METALS AND SINTERING ATMOSPHERES

Hydrogen	Dissociated Ammonia	Argon or Helium	Vacuum	Air
W	Fe	Cr	Ti	Pt
Mo	Ni	Mg	Zr	Au
Co–WC	Cu	Any metal	Cb	Ag
Fe		(Used in preference to	Ta	Al
Ni		to vacuum for met-	V	
Cu		als with high vapor	Cr	
Cr		pressure)		

Liquid-Phase Sintering

Liquid-phase sintering is quite a different process from solid-phase sintering discussed above, and quite specific phase relationships must exist at the sintering temperature. It is only feasible when there are two phases of quite widely different melting points, and when the amount of the liquid phase present is small. Also, the liquid phase must thoroughly wet the solid phase. A case in point is the tungsten-copper system mentioned previously. A tungsten-copper compact containing about 80% tungsten and 20% copper may be mixed, pressed, and heated to above the melting point of copper. Since there is enough tungsten to form a skeletal network which is self-supporting, the shape of the compact is not destroyed when the copper is melted. The copper, by means of capillary action penetrates the tungsten network, filling all voids and thus makes a completely dense two-phase structure in which the tungsten is essentially the continuous phase. This procedure would obviously not be possible if the volume per cent of tungsten were less than that of copper because then the tungsten could not form a self-supporting skeletal network, and upon melting the copper the compact would slump. This same technique is used in the case of cemented tungsten carbide, where cobalt ordinarily in amounts of 3 to 9% by weight is the liquid phase which wets the entire tungsten carbide network and acts as a strong, tough glue to hold the carbide particles together. Structures prepared by this technique are usually practically pore-free and hence tend to be quite strong.

Infiltration Methods

Sometimes more satisfactory liquid-phase sintering is obtained by pressing the high-melting network powder first, and in a second operation causing the liquid phase to penetrate the porous structure in the same manner as water is taken up by a sponge. This technique is particularly attractive when rather large amounts of the liquid are required, as cited above for the tungsten-copper case. Such compacts may contain 20 to 30 volume per cent copper in order to secure the desired properties of a combination of high electrical conductivity and high strength. If 30 volume per cent copper were added to the tungsten powder and the two pressed together and sintered in the usual manner, the compact would not reach as high a density as in impregnation. The tungsten powder may be pressed to 70% ultimate density (leaving 30% pores), removed from the cold pressing die, and inserted into a graphite crucible containing an excess of copper. The graphite crucible is flushed by dry hydrogen to keep the two metals clean. After the tungsten compact is at a temperature somewhat in excess of the melting point of copper, the copper flows around the tungsten, soaking into the pores, thus producing the desired structure. It will be noted that one advantage of this technique is that the volume relations can be controlled quite accurately by controlling the tungsten powder pressing conditions.

HOT PRESSING

There is much to be said for hot pressing as a laboratory operation since it allows the making of rather large shapes with small or modest pressing equipment. In addition, it is relatively easy to secure compacts of theoretical density, whereas, as already mentioned, cold-press sinter methods rarely closely approach ultimate densities except in the case of liquid-phase sintering. Hot pressing has not found favor for commercial operations as it is inherently a slow process, a single pressing often requiring several hours to complete. As a laboratory tool it is invaluable for making shapes which would require enormously expensive tooling and huge hydraulic presses if they could be made at all. Hot pressing offers advantages in compacting powders such as aluminum, beryllium, and magnesium, which densify with difficulty in the cold-press-sinter technique. These metals are always coated with a film of oxide, but this is broken down by the hot-pressing operation, and sintering can take place where fresh surfaces are exposed.

Hot pressing also allows the manufacture of non-equilibrium structures with higher densities than can be readily obtained by the normal technique. The phase relationship between the two metals may be such that a brittle compound is inevitably formed in large amount by the sintering time-temperature schedule necessary for sufficient consolidation by the cold-press-sinter technique. Hot pressing, however, may allow sufficient densification at a lower temperature without forming as much of the undesirable equilibrium structure.

Hot pressing may be conducted up to approximately 600°C with high-speed steel dies, or at higher temperatures where in general graphite dies are employed.

Steel-Die Hot Pressing

This type of hot pressing is subject to one of the limitations cited above for cold-press sinter, in that the tooling is expensive if one is interested in large pieces. High-speed steel tools are feasible for compacts with diameters up to 1 or 2 inches. In this range of compact sizes, the outside diameter would be between 4 and 6 inches. Larger dies than this tend to be quite expensive and are difficult to handle. High-speed steel dies may be used for short times up to nearly 600°C, but there is considerable question as to how much stress they will stand for how long at this level. Oxidation becomes a problem. There are very few data available on even the short-time mechanical properties of high-speed steel at elevated temperatures; probably 100,000 pounds per square inch should be considered a maximum stress for periods of a minute or so unless specific information on this point is available. The authors have had experience in using high-speed steel dies at temperatures as high as 600°C and at pressures of about 30 tons per square inch holding pressure for a few minutes. At 450°C, pressures have been maintained for short periods of time as high as 100 tons per square inch.

Such dies can be heated by inserting them in an electric resistance furnace, although the use of heating cartridges as shown in Figure 13 of Chapter 9 has proved to be quite satisfactory at 450°C. Another method which has been used is to heat the assembled die and powder charge to the desired temperature in a muffle furnace, and then quickly transfer to the hydraulic press.

Graphite lubricants such as Aquadag [17] are one of the few materials which can be employed with steel dies operating at somewhat elevated temperatures, and it is, of course, quite important to coat all interior surfaces of the die and punches with some high-temperature lubricant to prevent binding and sticking to the powder being pressed. The Aquadag is best applied when the die parts are fairly hot (about 100 to 200°C) to secure good coating characteristics; a cold application does not coat the steel satisfactorily.

The advantage of a steel die for elevated temperature pressing, as against graphite dies, is, of course, the much higher pressures which can be employed. This is advantageous in pressing low-melting metal powders such as aluminum, magnesium, or perhaps even copper or mixtures containing a preponderance of these metals. By using pressures between 50 tons per square inch and 100 tons per square inch at temperatures near 500°C, it is often possible to press such materials to nearly theoretical density and with better dimensional tolerances and finish than is possible in graphite dies. It amounts to a simultaneous pressing and coining operation, and fine detail such as ridges, grooves, and shallow recesses may be formed so that the finished pressing is equivalent to a machined piece. Like cold pressing, it is possible to remove pieces from the die rather quickly, but it is desirable to maintain pressure until the piece has cooled somewhat, although it is not necessary to wait until the die and contents have cooled to room temperature.

Higher melting powders such as nickel and iron can be handled by this technique as well, but the density attained will generally fall short of ultimate density. Hence in such cases a sintering operation may prove desirable, followed, if high dimensional control is required, by a repressing operation.

Extrusion of Powders

It is quite feasible to extrude metal powders directly to a rod of any desired cross section by mounting a die opening of the appropriate shape at the bottom of the die holder.[18] The powders can be precompacted first to a partially densified "billet" and then extruded as illustrated in Chapter 9, Figure 13, or the powder may be extruded directly without any prior treatment. If the latter technique is used it is necessary to cover the die opening with a disk of some suitable metal, possibly the same (but not necessarily so) as the powder being extruded, to prevent the powder from falling through the orifice before the extrusion operation commences. The sequence of events is as follows. The laboratory set-up can be the same as Figure 13, Chapter 9. The die opening is covered with a metallic disk of similar high-temperature properties as the powder to be extruded. The powder is charged in, the punch placed in position, and the assembly heated to the extrusion temperature. Pressure is then applied, the powder consolidates, and begins to bulge out the disk, which soon ruptures, allowing the powder to extrude out as a wire through the bottom. As pointed out in Chapter 9, this technique is useful only for lower melting metals which can be extruded at temperatures not over 600°C. If higher melting powders are to be extruded, they must first be canned in copper or steel, heated to the desired extrusion temperature in a furnace, quickly transferred to the press, and extruded while still hot.

Reductions of about 10 to 1 (ratio of original to final cross section) or higher are desirable in the extrusion of powder in order to secure maximum density.

Graphite-Die Hot Pressing

Figure 7 shows a typical arrangement for high temperature hot pressing using a graphite die. The die is surrounded by a cylinder

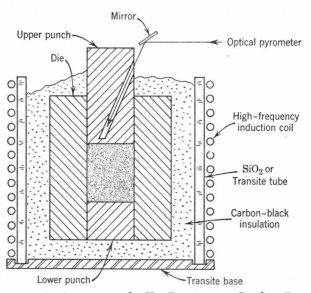

Figure 7.   Arrangement for Hot Pressing in a Graphite Die.

of fused silica, the space between being filled with powdered insulation. For temperatures above 1000°C, carbon black insulation [19] is desirable as explained in Chapter 4. For lower temperatures, many materials can be used. Sil-O-Cel [20] and Vermiculite [21] are satisfactory at temperatures up to about 1000 and 700°C, respectively. Around the fused silica tube (Transite could be employed satisfactorily with adequate thermal insulation) is placed a high-frequency coil of any available frequency for heating the graphite die.

For most work, no atmosphere is required if the die parts fit rather snugly. The only limitations on the size of the die which can be used are the sizes of graphite available (about 36 inches O.D.), the power available, and the size of the press in which the die assembly is placed.

The die is best made from type CS [17] graphite, and should have a wall thickness of the order of 2 to 4 inches, depending upon the size of the die.

With this type of graphite, a pressure of up to about 2000 pounds per square inch is feasible, but this depends also upon die size. For small dies in the neighborhood of 2 inches I.D., 2000 pounds per square inch may be permissible, whereas dies over 6 inches I.D. should probably not be stressed higher than 750 to 1000 pounds per square inch, with a die wall about 2 inches thick. With die walls about 3 to 4 inches thick, pressures somewhat above 1000 pounds per square inch might be permissible.

There is no temperature limit imposed by the graphite die itself, but, unless one is pressing carbides, there is of course the possibility of die reaction with the contents of the die. Pressings of this kind have been made using pure carbides such as WC and TiC at temperatures close to 3000°C. When there is danger of carburization of the powder being pressed, it may be possible to use a metallic liner between the die and the powder. If necessary, the liner may be of composite nature in order to prevent reaction with the powder. For example, one of the authors found it necessary in hot-pressing beryllium powder at 1100°C to coat the steel or Inconel liner with a sprayed glass coating in order to avoid bonding the liner to the beryllium.

Metals like copper which do not react with graphite need no liner, but can be successfully hot-pressed in bare graphite. Similarly, nickel has been pressed to about 95% ultimate density at 1300°C and 1500 pounds per square inch in unlined graphite dies.

It is feasible also to sinter in the liquid phase by hot pressing at appropriate temperatures in one operation instead of using the more customary cold-press sinter technique. Tungsten carbide–cobalt mixtures may be successfully handled by hot pressing at 1500°C, but it is necessary in such cases to avoid excessive pressure for two reasons. One is that there is danger of squeezing out liquid, depending upon how much liquid is formed at the pressing temperature, and, second, when pressing a comparatively fluid mix a higher stress is transmitted to the die walls. This is because one has essentially hydrostatic conditions inside the die in the presence of a liquid phase, whereas in solid-phase hot pressing, only some (unknown) fraction of the applied pressure is transmitted to the die walls since the solid powder has some flow resistance.

Since in hot pressing one is dealing with a viscous material, the effect of time is quite important to the success of the operation. Naturally, the higher the temperature, the lower the viscosity and the shorter the time required for flow. It is usually possible to determine when one has reached ultimate density by calculating the volume which the compact will occupy when the desired density has been attained. By making a mark on the punch, one recognizes the required density by length of travel of the punch.

Although the double-acting die principle may be used in hot pressing, it is not as important as in cold pressing since the frictional forces opposing consolidation are generally so low as to be nearly negligible. The choice of double acting or single acting would depend largely upon how close to the melting point one is operating and also upon the diameter-to-height ratio of the piece being pressed. If one were making a cylinder two or three times its diameter in length, the use of the double-acting principle would probably be worth while.

The sequence of operations is as follows. The silica or Transite tube which holds the insulating powder against the die is placed in the hand-operated hydraulic press with the high-frequency coil around the outside of the tube. The tube should have a Transite bottom which fits fairly snugly into the tube, to prevent the insulation from dropping out. The die and lower punch are lowered into place and the insulation added up to near the top of the die. If this is to be a high-temperature operation (above 1000°C), a carbon black layer about one inch thick or more is added. The die is filled to the desired level, leaving enough space at the top so that the upper punch can be seated without cocking after leveling off the powder. The press is closed, and 100 to 500 pounds per square inch pressure is applied during the early stages of heating. More carbon black is added to cover the top of the die with an inch or so of powder. Optical pyrometer readings are taken by means of a small graphite tube sticking up through the carbon powder, the inside of which looks down into a small (¼ inch) hole drilled into the punch. As the temperature reaches the desired maximum value more and more punch movement will be required to maintain the desired pressure. Upon reaching the maximum temperature and pressure, these conditions are maintained for perhaps 15 to 30 minutes until no further movement of the punch can be noted, and the pressure no longer falls off with time. At this point, the fiducial mark made on the punch should have reached the reference mark, denoting the end point of the operation.

The power is now turned off and the die allowed to cool, but the pressure is maintained at the maximum value until the temperature has fallen to a point at which the compact is no longer plastic. The pressure may now be eased off somewhat, but it is desirable to maintain some pressure until the compact is nearly ready to be removed from the die. It is not necessary to wait until the die and contents have reached room temperature, but it is inconvenient to handle the die and compact until they have cooled to 200 to 300°C. Cooling may be hastened to some extent by blowing air upon the die while it is in the press.

When using a die several inches in diameter, there may be a steep temperature gradient between the inside and outside of the compact during the heating operation. This temperature gradient may impose a limitation upon heating rate, as there may be danger of melting the powder next to the die wall, whereas the material in the center may be 200 to 300°C lower in temperature. Optical pyrometer readings or thermocouple readings at both die wall and at the top punch may be arranged without much trouble.

Ceramic-Die Hot Pressing

As pointed out above, graphite dies are limited to pressures of about 2000 pounds per square inch, and even lower for dies of large size. It would be very desirable for some work if this pressure limitation could be removed, but still allow pressing at very high temperatures. Another limitation of graphite dies is reaction with metals to form a carbide at the die-metal interface.

Ceramic, cermet, or carbide dies would be expected to offer freedom from the disadvantages of graphite noted above. However, as far as the authors are aware, such use of these three high-temperature materials has never been described in the literature.

The high-melting pure carbides such as WC, TiC, ZrC, and possibly others would probably offer the most immediate promise as a substitute for graphite. Carbides of the type MC are electrically conducting and hence may be heated in the same manner as graphite. They have excellent high-temperature strength and are not very chemically reactive. It is unlikely that they would alloy appreciably with most metals as long as liquid-phase sintering were avoided, but non-carbide-forming liquids such as copper would be quite inert. High-melting carbide dies (without metallic binder) can be hot-pressed to shape in graphite at temperatures approaching the melting point of the carbides.

REFERENCES

1. Robert M. Parke and John L. Ham, "The Melting of Molybdenum in the Vacuum Arc," *Trans. Am. Inst. Mining Met. Engrs., Inst. Metals Div.,* **171,** 416–427 (1947).
2. W. H. Wallaston, *Trans. Roy. Soc. (London),* **119,** 1 (1829).
3. C. Goetzel, *Treatise on Powder Metallurgy,* Interscience Publishers, Inc., New York, 1949.
4. Paul Schwarzkopf, *Powder Metallurgy,* The Macmillan Co., New York, 1947.

5. Henry Hausner, *Powder Metallurgy*, Chemical Publishing Co., Brooklyn, N. Y., 1947.
6. J. Wulff (Editor), *Powder Metallurgy*, American Society for Metals, Cleveland, Ohio, 1942.
7. P. R. Mallory Co., Indianapolis, Ind.
8. The Denver Fire Clay Co., Denver, Col.
9. W. S. Tyler Co., Cleveland, Ohio.
10. The American Instrument Co., Silver Spring, Md.
11. Earle E. Schumacher and Alexander G. Souden, *Metals & Alloys* (*Materials and Methods Manual*), **20**, No. 5, 1340 (1944).
12. F. W. Von Batchelder and H. E. Stauss, "A Method of Annealing Metal Powders without Sintering," *Rev. Sci. Instruments*, **22**, 396–397 (June, 1951).
13. The Alpha Corp., Greenwich, Conn.
14. Ceremul C, Socony Vacuum Oil Co., New York, N. Y.
15. Sterotex, Capital City Products Co., Columbus, Ohio.
16. B. H. Alexander and R. Balluffi, "Experiments on the Mechanism of Sintering," *J. Metals*, **188**, 1219 (October, 1950).
17. National Carbon Co., New York, N. Y.
18. R. S. Busk and T. E. Leontis, "Extrusion of Powdered Magnesium Alloys," *J. Metals*, **188**, 297–306 (1950).
19. Ajax Electrothermic Corp., Trenton, N. J.
20. Johns Manville Co., New York, N. Y.
21. International Vermiculite Co., Girard, Ill.

CHAPTER ELEVEN

Preparation of Pure Metals

Minute amounts of impurities may have profound effects upon the properties of metals. Hence, to obtain reliable and significant research data it is necessary to use metals of high purity. The level of purity required depends upon the sensitivity of the property measured to the various impurities present. For example, only about 0.001% carbon is sufficient to cause the phenomena of the yield point in a tensile test in iron, and, in general, mechanical properties are very sensitive to composition. On the other hand, for the determination of a reasonably accurate phase diagram, the purity of the metals used may not be quite so critical.

In most cases, the investigator has a choice of the grade of metal used for his work; some grades may be of equivalent purity but contain different impurities. In estimating the importance of purity it is well to bear in mind that in general the atomic per cent of impurities is more important than weight per cent, since the effect of small amounts of soluble elements is usually proportional to their atomic per cent or mole fraction. Also, the absolute purity of light metals containing heavy-metal impurities becomes much greater than that of a heavy metal containing the same weight per cent of impurities. If 99.99% pure aluminum contains 0.01% by weight of impurities of average atomic weight 50, it contains only about 0.0054 atom per cent impurity. The reverse situation is obtained when dealing with base metals of high atomic weight containing impurities of low atomic weight.

When possible, pure metals should be purchased rather than prepared in the laboratory. It is very difficult to prepare metals on a small scale in the purity possible in large-scale operations if only because of the more favorable surface to mass ratio in large-scale preparation. However, other factors come into play, such as experience, "know-how," and special equipment which metal producers have assembled over a long period of time.

A few years ago there was a general tendency both among users and producers of metals to ignore non-metallic impurities, particularly such impurities as nitrogen, hydrogen, and oxygen for which no satisfactory analytical methods were readily available. Fortunately, this situation no longer exists. With the development of the vacuum fusion gas analysis method and related techniques, analytical information on such impurities is now generally available. It is well to remember, however, that a metal may be quite impure even if spectrographic analysis shows high purity with respect to metallic impurities.

COMMERCIALLY AVAILABLE PURE METALS

Table 1 lists most metals of interest in metals research. It indicates a few of the purer grades available together with some typical analyses, some suppliers and forms in which the metal is sold. Prices are not included as they are too variable. It might be well to point out, however, that frequently the purest grade is available from firms specializing in spectrographic standards. Such standards are normally sold only in lots of a few grams, and naturally a very high price must be charged for such specially purified metals.

In general, the purest grade known to the authors is listed first, with other grades following. When a typical analysis could be obtained it is given, but unfortunately in many grades of metal this information is missing.

The sources indicated are those considered most satisfactory in the experience of the authors, but in many instances, satisfactory suppliers are available which lack of space prevented listing.

REDUCTION TECHNIQUES

Although commercial sources of pure metals should be used where possible, there are occasions when it is necessary for the investigator to prepare his own materials. This preparation may involve actual reduction of metals from their compounds, or it may be simply a matter of increasing the degree of purity of some commercially prepared metal by a suitable chemical or physical treatment.

Hydrogen Reduction

Oxides and halides of many metals may be reduced by hydrogen. The thermodynamic feasibility of such reductions can be ascertained by calculation of the free energy of the reduction reaction. The

TABLE 1

COMMERCIALLY AVAILABLE PURE METALS

Metal	Purity	Principal Impurities (Weight Per Cent)	Form	Suppliers †	Remarks
Aluminum	99.99	0.002 Fe 0.002 Cu 0.002 Si <0.001 Mg 0.000X Na <0.0001 Ca 0.000X Ba 0.000X Ga * 0.000X Zn * 0.000X Pb * 0.000X Sn *	Notched ingot	1	
	99.80–99.85	0.07 Si 0.014 Ga 0.000X Mg 0.000X Ti 0.000X Mn 0.000X Zn 0.000X Cu Mo * V * Pb * Fe (most of remainder)	Notched ingot	1	
Antimony	99.89	0.030 Fe 0.040 S 0.030 As tr Pb 0.010 Cu 0 Zn 0 Bi 0 Se	Lump	2	"Lone Star" brand
	99.84	0.030 Fe 0.040 S 0.020 As 0.010 Pb 0.010 Cu 0 Zn 0 Bi 0 Se		2	"RRM" brand
Arsenic	99.0	None cited	Lump	3	
	99.5	None cited	Crystalline scales	4	Spectrographic standard
Barium	99.0	None cited	Ingot	3	
	98.0	None cited	Rod	3	
	98	0.14 N$_2$ 0.25 Mg 0.20 Ca	20 mm diam. rod, cast billets	5	
	98+	0.05 Al 0.25 Ca 1.0 Sr 0.12 Mg	Billets, extruded rod	12	

* = Sometimes detected.   † See list of suppliers at the end of the table.

TABLE 1 (*Continued*)
COMMERCIALLY AVAILABLE PURE METALS

Metal	Purity	Principal Impurities (Weight Per Cent)	Form	Suppliers	Remarks
Beryllium	~98+	0.10 Al "plus resid- ual Mg" 0.1 Fe 0.03 Si (also ~1% BeO) 0.05 Cu 0.05 Mn	Lump	6	Analysis cited is for as-reduced metal, which is invariably contaminated with 1–2% MgF$_2$-BeF$_2$. These salts are readily removed during vacuum melting (see below). (Metal of similar purity available from 7.)
	~99.3	0.08 Al 0.009 Ca 0.013 Cr 0.005 Cu 0.085 Fe 0.005 Mg 0.024 Mn 0.014 Ni 0.075 Si 0.2 BeO	Ingot		Lit. ref. "The Metallurgy of Beryllium," Albert R. Kaufman, Paul Gordon, and D. W. Lillie, *Trans. A.S.M.*, **42**, 785–843 (1950)
Bismuth	99.99+	<0.0002 Cu 0.0001 Fe 0.0001 Ag (No other elements detected)	Cast cake	8	
	99.9	None cited	Ingot	3	
Boron	99.50	0.16 C 0.28 Fe	Powder	5	
	98.60	0.32 C 0.80 Fe	Powder	5	
Cadmium	99.99	0.0009 Pb 0.0015 Cu (No other elements detected)	Cast cake	8	(Maximum order 1 lb)
	99.92	0.0128 Cu 0.0595 Pb 0.0048 Fe 0.0028 Zn	Cast cake	9	
	99.86	0 Cu 0.02 Pb 0.10 Fe 0.02 Zn	Cast cake	10	
Calcium	99.7	0.02 C 0.15 Al 0.10 Mg 0.03 N 0.001 Fe	Crystalline mass ¼ to 14 in.	11	Distilled calcium
	99.7	0.02 N 0.15 Mg 0.021 Fe 0.0015 Mn 0.001 Cu 0.0005 Ni 0.001 Cr	Crystal distillate, 4-in. rod	12	Distilled calcium

TABLE 1 *(Continued)*

COMMERCIALLY AVAILABLE PURE METALS

Metal	Purity	Principal Impurities (Weight Per Cent)	Form	Suppliers	Remarks
Calcium (*Cont.*)	99	0.12 N 0.4 Mg 0.006 Fe 0.003 Mn 0.001 Cu 0.005 Ni 0.001 Cr	100-lb billets, extruded rod	12	Distilled calcium
Cerium	98.5	None cited	Ingot	3	
Cesium	99.9	None cited	In glass in vacuo	3	
Chromium	99.0	0.04 Fe 0.01 Cu 0.01 Pb 0.01 C 0.02 S 0.02 H 0.01 N 0.45 O	Small plates, granules, powder	11	
	99.3	0.4 Fe 0.01 S 0.03 H 0.17 O			Lit. ref. "Pilot Plant Production of Electrolytic Chromium," R. R. Lloyd, J. B. Rosenbaum, V. E. Homm, L. P. Davis, *Trans. Electrochem. Soc.*, **94,** 122 (1948) (Note. O_2 content lower than in above grade)
	99.85	None cited	Granules	4	Spectrographic standard
Cobalt	99.99	None cited	Sponge	4	Spectrographic standard
	99.9	0.05 Fe tr Mn 0.02 Si nil C 0.04 Ni 0.01 Cu 0.003 S	Electrolytic plate		Lit. ref. "Thermal Expansion Properties of Iron-Cobalt Alloys," M. E. Fine, W. C. Ellis, *Trans. A.I.M.E., Inst. Metals Div.*, **175**, 742 (1948)
	99.5	<0.0001 N_2 <0.01 O_2 <0.0001 H_2 tr Ca <0.01 C 0.15 Fe tr Mg 0.3 Ni 0.05 Si	Vacuum-melted ingot	13	
	98.5–99.0	0.02–0.06 Cu 0.01–0.04 S 0.06–0.16 Fe 0.15–0.40 Ni 0.04–0.06 Mn 0.10–0.40 CaO <0.10 C		14	

TABLE 1 *(Continued)*

COMMERCIALLY AVAILABLE PURE METALS

Metal	Purity	Principal Impurities (Weight Per Cent)	Form	Suppliers	Remarks
Cobalt (Cont.)	99.0	0.40 Ni 0.047 Fe 0.002 Cu 0.05 C 0.018 CaO 0.03 Mn 0.019 S 0.043 Si	Rondelles	15	
Columbium (Niobium)	99.9?	0.01 C tr Fe tr Ti tr Ta tr Sn tr Zr	Powder sheet wire	16	
	99.99	None cited	Powder 50-mesh	4	Spectrographic standard
	99.5	None cited	Ingot	3	
Copper	99.999	<0.00007 Fe <0.0001 Sb <0.0001 Pb <0.0001 Sn <0.0001 Ni <0.00001 Bi <0.00003 Ag <0.0002 As <0.00005 Cr <0.00001 Si <0.0002 Te <0.0001 Se <0.0001 S	Continuous cast rod	8	Purest copper available
	99.99+	<0.0001 N_2 <0.0001 O_2 <0.0001 H_2 <0.001 As tr Bi <0.002 Fe <0.0001 Pb <0.0005 Ni <0.003 Ag <0.0001 S tr Sn tr Zn	Vacuum-melted ingot	13	
	99.99+	0.0001 Ag 0.0000 O_2 0.0032 S 0.001 Fe 0.0002 As 0.0005 Sb 0.0000 Bi 0.0003 Pb 0.0013 Ni 0.0000 Se + Te nil P nil Si	Cathode squares	42	Cathode copper—contains some hydrogen

TABLE 1 (*Continued*)

COMMERCIALLY AVAILABLE PURE METALS

Metal	Purity	Principal Impurities (Weight Per Cent)	Form	Suppliers	Remarks
Copper (*Cont.*)	99.98+	0.002 Ag 0.0000 O$_2$ 0.0025 S 0.0015 Fe 0.0008 As 0.0028 Sb 0.0000 Bi 0.0004 Pb 0.0016 Ni 0.0031 Se + Te 0.0000 P 0.0015 Si	Usually rods and rounds	42	O.F.H.C. (Oxygen-free high-conductivity) copper
Gallium	99.99	0.0001 Si 0.00005 Mg 0.00025 Ca 0.0060 Cu 0.0005 Fe 0.0050 Pb 0.0004 Sn (No other elements detected spectrographically)	Lump	17	Usually sold in glass or rubber containers as metal melts at ∼30°C
	99.9	None cited	Lump	3	
Germanium	99.999	0.00025 Si 0.00005 Mg 0.0001 Ca 0.0003 Cu 0.0001 Fe 0.0002 Pb (No other elements detected spectrographically)	Lump	17	
Gold	99.995	<0.001 Ag <0.001 Pd <0.005 Cu	40-mesh powder	18	High fineness gold
	99.96	<0.03 Ag <0.01 Pd <0.005 Cu	Sheet rod wire	18	Commercial fine gold
Hafnium	99.0	0.15-0.084 Si 0.018-0.074 Al <0.003 Ti <0.003-0.006 Fe 0.70-0.89 Zr 0.037-0.043 O$_2$ 0.003-0.004 N$_2$	Crystal bar	19	Probably not a regular commercial product See "Physical, Thermal, and Electrical Properties of Hafnium and High Purity Zirconium," H. K. Adenstedt, A.S.M. Preprint IW, 1951
	99.3	None cited		3	
Indium	99.99+	0.0003 Fe 0.00025 Al 0.002 Pb (No other elements detected)	Extruded stick	8	

TABLE 1 (*Continued*)

COMMERCIALLY AVAILABLE PURE METALS

Metal	Purity	Principal Impurities (*Weight Per Cent*)	Form	Suppliers	Remarks
Indium	99.9	None cited	Ingot	3	
(*Cont.*)	99.999?	0.0005 Mg		20	See "Constitution of the System Gallium-Indium," J. P. Denny, J. H. Hamilton, J. R. Lewis, *J. Metals*, **4**, 39 (1952)
	99.95	0.007 Cu tr Pb 0.01 Zn 0.01 Sn		20	
Iridium	99.995	None cited	Sponge	4	Spectrographic standard
	99.99	None cited	(Wire 1.6 mm diam.)	4	Spectrographic standard
	99.9	Traces of other platinum metals, plus iron, nickel, copper, lead, cadmium and silicon	Sheet, foil, strip, and wire	40	
Iron	99.95	<0.001 N$_2$ <0.02 O$_2$ <0.005 H$_2$ <0.001 Al <0.001 Cr <0.001 Co <0.001 W <0.001 Cu <0.001 Mn <0.001 Mo <0.001 Ni <0.001 Sn <0.001 Ti <0.005 C <0.01 Si	Vacuum-cast ingot	13	
	99.9	0.001 metallic impurities 0.08 O$_2$ 0.01 C nil S nil P nil N		21	"Puron"
	99.8	0.005–0.03 C 0.1–0.2 O$_2$ 0.005–0.05 N$_2$	Powder	22	Carbonyl iron
	99.9+	0.03 C tr Si nil Mn 0.011 S	Electrolytic plates	23	Electrolytic iron
Lanthanum	98.0	Balance largely thorium, 1.35 Fe		5	
	99.0	None cited	Ingot	3	
Lead	99.999+	<0.0001 Bi 0.0001 Cu 0.0002 Fe	Cast stick	8	

TABLE 1 (*Continued*)

COMMERCIALLY AVAILABLE PURE METALS

Metal	Purity	Principal Impurities (Weight Per Cent)	Form	Suppliers	Remarks
Lead (*Cont.*)	99.99+	0.0004 Ag 0.0003 Cu 0.005 Bi 0.0002 Zn 0.0001 Cd 0.0002 Fe 0.0001 As + Sb-Sn 0.0001 Ca + Ni		2	"Doe Run" grade
	99.99+	0.0004 Ag 0.0005 Cu 0.001 Bi 0.0002 Zn 0.0002 Fe 0.0001 As 0.0015 Sb 0.0001 Cd tr Ca + Ni		2	"U.S.S. Electrolytic" grade
Lithium	99.6	0.009 Si 0.03 Fe + Al 0.09 Ca 0.02 Na 0.07 heavy metals 0.02 N_2	Lump	25	Low sodium grade (other grade contains about 0.65 Na)
	99.6	0.005 Na 0.02 Ca 0.005 K 0.06 N_2 0.001 Fe	Lump	26	Low sodium grade (other grade contains about 0.6 Na)
Magnesium	99.98	0.005 Al 0.004 Ca 0.0006 Cu 0.003 Fe 0.005 Mn 0.0005 Ni 0.001 Pb 0.004 Si 0.001 Zn 0.005 Ag 0.001 Na	Round bar, notched ingot, cast slabs	12	High-purity magnesium (99.95 Mg guaranteed) Fe + Ni + Cu not to exceed 0.005%
	99.97	0.009–0.024 Al <0.001 Cu 0.001 Fe 0.003 Mn 0.0005 Ni <0.02 Zn <0.01 Si <0.003–0.005 B <0.0002 Be <0.015 Ca 0.002 Pb	Round bars	27	"Special purity" grade (Mn + Fe + B <0.006, all else <0.02)

TABLE 1 (*Continued*)

COMMERCIALLY AVAILABLE PURE METALS

Metal	Purity	Principal Impurities (Weight Per Cent)	Form	Suppliers	Remarks
Magnesium (*Cont.*)	99.9+	0.0005 Al 0.0013 Cu 0.030 Fe 0.0048 Mn <0.001 Ni <0.005 Si <0.00005 B	Round bars	27	Commercial electrolytic grade
Manganese	99.97	0.004 C 0.0135 S <0.001 Ca <0.001 Cu <0.001 Fe <0.001 Mg <0.001 Ag Absent specrographically: Al, Sb, As, Cd, Cr, Co, Pb, Mo, Ni, K, Si, Sn, Ti, W, V, Zn	Electrolytic flakes	28	See "Commercial Production of Electrolytic Manganese," C. L. Mantell, *Trans. Electrochem. Soc.*, **94,** 232–243 (1948)
	99.99	None cited	Broken pieces	4	Spectrographic standard
Mercury	99.9999	Residue max. 0.0001	Liquid	29	Redistilled mercury
Molybdenum	99.9	0.005 Fe 0.003 C	Rod and sheet	16	Type 124 powder
	99.9	0.015 C 0.10 O_2 0.02 Ni	Powder		
	99.9	None cited	Sheet, wire, powder	30	
	99.9	None cited	Powder	21	Detailed analytical data are very sparse on molybdenum
Nickel	99.9+	<0.001 N_2 <0.005 O_2 <0.0001 H_2 <0.001 Al <0.001 Ca 0.02 Co <0.001 Mg <0.001 Mn <0.001 Si <0.001 Sn <0.005 C 0.01 Cu 0.04 Fe	Vacuum-melted ingot	13	
	99.99	None cited	Sponge	4	Spectrographic standard
	99.9	None cited	Powder	3	Carbonyl nickel
	99.85	0.1 Co 0.01–0.03 Cu 0.01–0.04 Fe tr C tr S	Cathode squares	41	Electrolytic nickel

TABLE 1 (Continued)

COMMERCIALLY AVAILABLE PURE METALS

Metal	Purity	Principal Impurities (Weight Per Cent)	Form	Suppliers	Remarks
Nickel (Cont.)	~99.6	0.1 Fe 0.037 C 0.019 S 0.006 Si 0.013 Cu (~0.1 Co)	Pellets		Lit. ref. Mond nickel (see *J. Inst. Met.*, A. Taylor, **77**, 585 (1950)
Osmium	99.995	None cited	Sponge	4	Spectrographic standard
	?	None cited	Powder	3	
Palladium	99.995	None cited	Sponge, wire	4	Spectrographic standard
	99.9	None cited	Powder or solid	3	
	99.99	Traces of other platinum metals, plus iron, nickel, copper, lead, cadmium, and silicon	Sheet, foil, strip, and wire	40	
Platinum	99.999	None cited	Sponge, wire	4	Spectrographic standard
	99.99	Traces of other platinum metals, plus iron, nickel, copper, lead, cadmium, and silicon	Sheet, foil, strip, and wire	40	
	99.9	None cited	Powder or solid	3	
Potassium	99.0	None cited	Rods	3	
Praseodymium	?	None cited	Ingot	3	
Rhenium	99.9	None cited		31	
	99.99	None cited	Powder	4	Spectrographic standard
Rhodium	99.995	None cited	Sponge, wire	4	Spectrographic standard
	99.9	Traces of other platinum metals, plus iron, nickel, copper, lead, cadmium, and silicon	Sheet, foil, strip, and wire	40	
	?	None cited	Rod, sheet, wire, powder	3	
Rubidium	99.9	None cited	In glass in vacuo	3	
Ruthenium	99.995	None cited	Sponge	4	Spectrographic standard
	99.9	Traces of other platinum metals, plus iron, nickel, copper, lead, cadmium, and silicon	Sponge or powder	40	

TABLE 1 (*Continued*)

COMMERCIALLY AVAILABLE PURE METALS

Metal	Purity	Principal Impurities (Weight Per Cent)	Form	Suppliers	Remarks
Selenium	99.99+	<0.001 Te present Si tr As V. faint tr Cu V. faint tr Fe (No other elements detected)	Pellets	8	
	99.99	None cited	Shot	4	Spectrographic standard
	99.95	None cited	Pellets	3	
	99.85	0.08 Te 0.015 Fe 0.002 Cu 0.006 Pb			Lit. ref. "Recovery of Precious Metals and Production of Selenium and Tellurium at Montreal East," C. W. Clark, J. H. Schloen (Canadian Copper Refinery, Ltd.), *Metals Technol.*, **5**, T.P. 982 (October, 1938)
	99.70	0.12 Te 0.13 Ash 0.001 Cu 0.01 Fe	Powder		Lit. ref. "Recovery of Selenium and Tellurium at Copper Cliff, Ont.," F. Bernard (Ontario Refining Co.), *Metals Technol.*, **5**, T.P. 908 (February, 1938)
Silicon	99.8+	0.005–0.015 Fe 0.02–0.03 Al 0.0005–0.0015 Mn tr–0.01 Ca tr–0.004 Cr 0.02–0.04 C 0.005–0.01 P tr–0.004 Ca + Ni 0.002–0.005 Ti + Zr 0.03–0.08 O_2 0.004–0.0022 H_2 0.004–0.013 N_2	Powder 30-mesh or finer	11	
	99.99	None cited	Crystals	4	Spectrographic standard
Silver	99.99+	0.0001 Pb 0.0001 Cu 0.0003 Fe (No other elements detected)	Crystals	8	
	99.99	<0.005 Cu <0.001 Pb <0.001 Fe tr Mg	Sheet, rod, wire	18	High fineness silver
	99.97	0.02 Cu 0.002 Pb 0.001 Fe tr Mg	Sheet, rod, wire	18	High fineness silver

TABLE 1 (*Continued*)

COMMERCIALLY AVAILABLE PURE METALS

Metal	Purity	Principal Impurities (Weight Per Cent)	Form	Suppliers	Remarks
Sodium	99.9+	<0.0001 Cr 0.00005 Fe 0.0002 Hg 0.0150 K 0.0067 Li 0.0035 S 0.0021 Si 0.0002 Ba <0.0001 Ni <0.0001 Pb <0.0001 Cu <0.0001 Mn <0.0001 Cl <0.0001 Cd 0.0002 Cs <0.0001 Co 0.035 Ca 0.00017 Al 0.0002 B 0.004 C 0.0011 P rare earths <0.00005	Brick	32	
	99.9	None cited	Rod	3	
Strontium	99.0	None cited	Rod	3	
	98.0+	0.06 Al 0.25 Ca 0.55 Ba 0.25 Mg	Billets, extruded rod	12	
	99?	0.20 Ba 0.05 N_2 0.25 Mg 0.50 Ca	Billets, rods	5	
Tantalum	99.9	0.03 max. Fe 0.03 max. C	Rod, sheet	16	
	99.7	0.03 max. Fe 0.05 max. C 0.05 max. W 0.15 max. Cb	Powder	16	Type 268 powder
Tellurium	99.9+	None cited	Powder	8	
	99.99	None cited	Powder	4	Spectrographic standard
	99.5	None cited	Sticks, powder	3	
	99.7	0.07 Se 0.03 Cu			Lit. ref. (See paper by C. W. Clark and J. H. Schloen, under "Selenium")
Thallium	99.99+	0.001 Cu 0.002 Pb Bi <0.0001 Sb, As, Fe nil	Cast stick	8	
	99.9+	None cited	Rods	3	

TABLE 1 (*Continued*)

COMMERCIALLY AVAILABLE PURE METALS

Metal	Purity	Principal Impurities (Weight Per Cent)	Form	Suppliers	Remarks
Thorium	99.5	None cited	Rods, powder	3	
	98–99	None cited	Powder	5	
Tin	99.997	0.0005 Pb 0.0005 Cu 0.0015 Fe 0.0001 As <0.0001 Sb 0.0001 Bi + Ag + In <0.0001 Bi <0.0001 Ag nil In 0.0025 Pb + Cu + Fe 0.0001 As + Sb	Small bars	34	High-purity tin for spectrographic standard
	99.99+	0.0018 Fe 0.0005 Pb tr Cu tr Sb 0.0003 Ni	2 in. diam. balls	34	High-grade commercial tin
	99.99	0.004 Sb 0.031 As 0.029 Pb 0.007 Bi 0.025 Cu 0.009 Fe nil Ag nil S tr Ca + Ni nil Cd		2	Straits trading brand
Titanium	99.9+	0.03 C 0.02 Si 0.02 Fe 0.03 Al 0.01 N_2 0.04 Mn (Cu, Cr, Pb, Mo, Mg, Ni, V, W, Sn and others not over 0.01 each)	Crystal bar	35	
	99.3+	0.08 W 0.05 C 0.08 N_2 0.12 Fe 0.15 O_2	Ingot, sheet, plate, rod, wire	36, 37	Grade No. 1 (Tentative A.S.T.M. Specification)
Tungsten	99.9+	0.03 max. KCl 0.02 max. SiO_2 0.02 max. R_2O_3 0.02 max. CaO 0.052 O_2	Powder, −200 mesh	16	Type 425 powder
	99.9+	None cited	Wire	30, 21	

TABLE 1 (*Continued*)

COMMERCIALLY AVAILABLE PURE METALS

Metal	Purity	Principal Impurities (Weight Per Cent)	Form	Suppliers	Remarks
Uranium	99.9	None cited	Rod or turnings	3	
Vanadium	99.8	0.05 C 0.07 O_2 0.003 H_2 0.08 N_2	Chips, ingot, forged or rolled bar, plate, sheet	11	
	99.7	0.05 Si 0.05 Fe <0.05 Al <0.001 N_2 <0.001 Cr Balance O_2	Lump, pellets	38	
Zinc	99.999	<0.0002 Pb 0.0005 Fe 0.000052 Cd	Cast slab	35	Chemically pure grade ‡
	99.999	<0.0002 Pb <0.00005 Cd	Cast slab	35	Spectrographically pure ‡
	99.99	0.007 max. Pb 0.005 max. Fe 0.005 max. Cd	Cast slab	35	Special high grade ‡ ‡ See "Pure Zinc—Its Preparation and Some Examples of Influence of Minor Constituents," E. C. Truesdale and Gerald Edmunds, *Trans. A.I.M.E., Inst. Metals Div.*, **133**, 267–277 (1939)
	99.99+	0.0006 Cd 0.0007 Pb 0.0003 Cu 0.0002 Fe 0.0004 Ag (No other elements detected spectrographically or chemically)	Cast cake	8	
	99.99+	0.0026 Pb 0.0012 Cd 0.0009 Fe 0.0003 Cu	Plate	39	Electrolytic zinc See "New Electrolytic Zinc Plant of the American Zinc Co. of Illinois," L. P. Davidson, *Trans. A.I.M.E., Inst. Metals Div.*, **152**, 298–302 (1934)
Zirconium	99.9+	<0.005–0.06 Si <0.003–0.021 Al <0.003–0.007 Ti <0.003–0.020 Fe 0.004–0.12 Hf 0.005–0.054 O_2 0.005–0.034 N_2	Crystal bar	19	See "Physical, Thermal and Electrical Properties of Hafnium, and High Purity Zirconium," H. K. Adenstedt, A.S.M. Preprint 1W, 1951.
	98.5	1.9 Hf 0.15 C 0.10 N_2 0.07 O_2 0.75 Fe 0.04 Cr 0.01 Ni 0.015 Si	Sponge, ingot	24	

TABLE NOTES (SUPPLIERS)

1. Aluminum Company of America,
   Pittsburgh 19, Pa.
2. National Lead Co.,
   Research Laboratories,
   105 York St.,
   Brooklyn 1, N. Y.
3. A. D. Mackay, Inc.,
   198 Broadway,
   New York 7, N. Y.
*4. Jarrell-Ash Co.,
   167 Newbury St.,
   Boston 16, Mass.
5. Cooper Metallurgical Associates,
   Box 1791,
   Cleveland 5, Ohio
6. Brush Beryllium Co.,
   Cleveland, Ohio.
7. The Beryllium Corp.,
   Reading, Pa.
8. American Smelting & Refining Co.,
   19 Nassau St.,
   New York, N. Y.
9. United States Smelting, Refining &
   Mining Co.,
   75 Federal St.,
   Boston, Mass.
10. St. Joseph Lead Co.,
   250 Park Ave.,
   New York, N. Y.
11. Electro Metallurgical Co.,
   Div. of Union Carbide & Carbon
   Corp.,
   30 East 42 St.,
   New York 17, N. Y.
12. Dominion Magnesium Ltd.,
   320 Bay St.,
   Toronto, Canada.
13. National Research Corp.,
   70 Memorial Drive,
   Cambridge, Mass.
14. The Pyrites Co., Inc.,
   Wilmington, Del.

15 African Metals Corp.,
   25 Broad St.,
   New York, N. Y.
16. Fansteel Metallurgical Corp.,
   North Chicago, Ill.
17. Eagle-Picher Co.,
   Research Dept.,
   Post Office Box 290,
   Joplin, Mo.
18. Handy & Harman,
   82 Fulton St.,
   New York 7, N. Y
19. Foote Mineral Co.,
   410 Eighteen West,
   Chelton Building,
   Philadelphia 44, Pa.
20. Indium Corporation of America,
   1557 Lincoln Building,
   60 East 42 St.,
   New York, N. Y.
21. Westinghouse Electric Co.,
   Bloomfield, N. J.
22. Antara Products Division,
   General Aniline & Film Corp.,
   230 Park Ave.,
   New York, N. Y.
23. National Radiator Co.,
   223 Central Ave.,
   Johnstown, Pa.
24. Titanium Alloy Mfg. Co.,
   National Lead Co.,
   111 Broadway,
   New York 6, N. Y.
25. Maywood Chemical Works,
   111 West Hunter Ave.,
   Maywood, N. J.
26. Metalloy Corp.,
   527 Marquette Ave.,
   Minneapolis, Minn.
27. Dow Chemical Co.,
   1000 Main St.,
   Midland, Mich.

28. Electro Manganese Corp.,
   Knoxville, Tenn.
29. F. W. Berk and Co., Inc.,
   420 Lexington Ave.,
   New York, N. Y.
30. General Electric Co.,
   Cleveland Wire Works,
   Cleveland 14, Ohio.
31. A. D. Melanen,
   University of Tennessee,
   Knoxville, Tenn.
32. E. I. du Pont de Nemours & Co., Inc.,
   Wilmington 98, Del.
33. Eimer & Amend,
   635 Greenwich St.,
   New York, N, Y.
34. Vulcan Detinning Co.,
   Sewaren, N. J.
35. New Jersey Zinc Sales Co.,
   Front and Fletcher Streets,
   New York 7, N. Y.
36. Titanium Metals Corp.,
   60 E. 42nd St.,
   New York, N. Y.
37. Rem-Cru Titanium, Inc.,
   Midland, Pa.
38. Vanadium Corporation of America,
   420 Lexington Ave.,
   New York, N. Y.
39. American Zinc Company of Illinois,
   S. of American Zinc, Lead & Smelting Co.,
   1602 Paul Brown Bldg.,
   St. Louis, Mo.
40. Baker & Co., Inc.,
   113 Astor St.,
   Newark 5, N. J.
41. International Nickel Co.,
   67 Wall St.,
   New York, N. Y.
42. Any supplier of commercial copper.

* American Agents for Johnson, Matthey & Co., Ltd., London, England.

permissible moisture content of the hydrogen used to effect reduction is critical, and depends upon the value of the equilibrium constant P_{H_2O}/P_{H_2} in the typical reaction

$$MO + H_2 = M + H_2O \qquad (1)$$

This ratio is that of the partial pressures of water vapor and hydrogen respectively. If the reduction is carried out in a tube furnace with hydrogen flowing through the tube at essentially atmospheric pressure, the sum of the partial pressure of hydrogen and water vapor equals atmospheric pressure.

In the example cited, reduction will only occur if the value of P_{H_2O}/P_{H_2} is maintained below the equilibrium value which may usually be found in the literature. Obviously, one wants to maintain a high hydrogen pressure relative to water-vapor pressure, and this is readily done experimentally by maintaining a constant flow of dry hydrogen over the compound to be reduced, thus sweeping out the moisture produced.

The equilibrium constant varies with temperature and is usually larger at higher temperatures, thus making reduction easier, and, in addition, reactions go much more rapidly at higher temperatures. Thermodynamic data give some indication of an appropriate temperature level and hydrogen dew point to use, but do not predict actual rates of reduction, which must usually be found by actual experiment.

Metals which may be reduced from their oxides include chromium, cobalt, copper, iron, nickel, molybdenum, tungsten, tin, zinc, and lead. The last three comparatively low-melting metals, however, must be reduced at temperatures above their melting points for practical reduction rates. Dushman [1] discusses the thermodynamics of the hydrogen reduction of oxides of iron, nickel, cobalt, chromium, molybdenum, and tungsten.

Electrodeposition from Aqueous Solutions

The electrowinning of metals from aqueous solutions is an important commercial method for the production of many metals, including copper, zinc, chromium, and nickel, to mention just a few. However, the procedures for the electrodeposition of the various metals are so numerous, and so many variables must be under control, that much more space would have to be allotted to this subject than is warranted by its importance as a metals laboratory technique. Handbooks on this subject are available,[2,3] and should be consulted for the detailed procedures required for specific cases.

Electrodeposition from Non-aqueous Solutions

The outstanding example of electrowinning of a pure metal from non-aqueous solutions is aluminum, which is commercially electrodeposited from a solution of Al_2O_3 in molten cryolite. Other metals which are regularly reduced in an analogous manner are calcium, columbium, tantalum, lithium, magnesium, sodium, and potassium. In general, the reduction of metals from fused salts by electrolysis is difficult and requires considerable experience and study of specific cases. Metals other than those already mentioned could be, and in some cases have been, prepared by this method. The reduction of metals in this manner is ordinarily a research project in itself, and hence cannot be recommended as a general technique for the preparation of metals for experimental use.

Thermal Decomposition

There are certain compounds which decompose on heating to give the pure metal directly. One class of such compounds is the carbonyls such as $Fe(CO)_5$, $Ni(CO)_4$, $Co(CO)_4$, $Cr(CO)_6$, $Mo(CO)_6$, and $W(CO)_6$. The first two of these are volatile liquids at ordinary temperatures, but the others are solids which decompose at temperatures in the range of 50 to 150°C. Some metals of the platinum group also form carbonyls. When the carbonyls decompose on heating, they break down into the metal and CO, the latter tending itself to decompose at elevated temperatures, thus contaminating the metal with carbon. However, the amount of carbon contamination is usually rather small, and otherwise the metal produced is generally of high purity.

The only metal of significant industrial importance prepared by the carbonyl process is a certain grade of nickel made by the so-called Mond process. Mond nickel, which is about as pure as any commercial grade of nickel, is characterized by a low cobalt content (<0.1%) whereas electrolytic nickel, of comparable purity otherwise, is somewhat higher in cobalt. However, Mond nickel has a comparatively high carbon content. A small amount of carbonyl iron powder is made for powder-metallurgy applications.

There is no real incentive for the preparation of massive carbonyl-reduced metals in the laboratory since the metals which form carbonyls can be obtained commercially in equivalent or better purity. There is some application, however, for carbonyls in the laboratory as a means of coating (plating) articles with the metal thus reduced.[4, 5]

The best-known procedure for the preparation of pure metals by the thermal decomposition of a relatively unstable compound is the so-called hot-wire or iodide method (Figure 1). In this technique, a volatile halide, usually the iodide, is thermally decomposed upon an incandescent wire of tungsten or of the metal being reduced. This ingenious method was originated by Van Arkel and DeBoer,[6] who used it to prepare pure zirconium, titanium, hafnium, and thorium. These investigators used a heat-resisting glass envelope through which was strung a thin tungsten wire, subsequently heated to 2000°C. Within the glass bulb was placed a small quantity of zirconium iodide. Upon evacuation and subsequent sealing off, the glass bulb was heated to 650°C, thus filling it with zirconium iodide vapor. On contacting the hot wire, the iodide vapor was thermally decomposed to very pure metal and iodine, the zirconium remaining on the hot wire. In a few hours the thickness of deposited zirconium metal built up to a few millimeters' thickness.

A little later, DeBoer and Fast [7] improved upon the first technique, and arranged the apparatus for the production of somewhat larger quantities of metal. Instead of first making ZrI_4 and then placing it

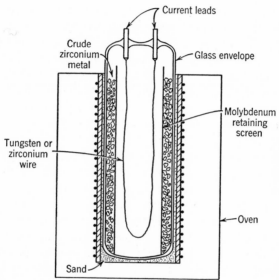

Figure 1. Hot Wire Deposition Apparatus for Zirconium. (Van Arkel–DeBoer Process.)

inside the reaction vessel, DeBoer and Fast used crude zirconium metal and iodine. The iodine vapor reacts with the crude zirconium, forming zirconium iodide, which upon contacting the hot wire breaks down as indicated above. Since zirconium is the only constituent in the crude zirconium which forms an appreciable amount of volatile iodide, the increase in purity during this process is very great, the zirconium metal deposited being nearly 99.99% pure. Some contaminants are carried along presumably by a very small amount of iodide formation, or possibly by mechanical entrapment. As the process proceeds, the wire grows larger and hence requires a larger current to maintain the temperature. Because the growing zirconium bar started from comparatively few crystal nuclei, the crystal grains grown are very large and generally extend entirely across the bar. Since there is no interference externally to the development of crystal habit, the bar is usually composed of a series of idiomorphic crystals showing cubic symmetry as the crystal form of the beta phase is body-centered cubic. Because of this appearance, it has been customary to refer to products prepared in this way as "crystal bar."

Van Arkel [8] describes the application of this method to vanadium, but this was not very successful because of the high temperature required for vaporizing vanadium iodide. The number of metals to which this technique may be applied is limited. This is understandable when considering the factors upon which the method depends for its success. In the first place, most halides are too stable or too non-volatile, so that the concentration of halide near the hot wire is low, and what concentration is present fails readily to decompose upon the hot wire. In addition, the yield of the desired high-valence halide may be considerably reduced by the formation of more stable, less volatile lower halides as in $MI_4 = MI_2 + I_2$. Still another difficulty is the extremely corrosive nature of some iodides which react with practically any known substance, including glass and fused silica. Finally, the temperature required for volatilization may be so close to that required for decomposition that the process breaks down, and it is possible that in some cases the temperature for rapid decomposition of the iodide is above the melting point of the metal.

In spite of the difficulties that can attend the functioning of the hot-wire method, it has proved to be the best method yet devised for the preparation of high-purity zirconium and titanium, and it may prove valuable for some other metals which have not yet been investigated by this method. It would seem feasible to use high-frequency induction heating of a rod or hollow cylinder instead of resistance-heating a wire, thus obviating the awkward power source difficulty and at the same time presenting a large surface for decomposition of the iodide.

Hydrogen Reduction on a Hot Wire

A method which is a modification of the hot-wire method was developed for the production of small amounts of quite pure boron, and is described here in some detail because it may be of potential value for the preparation of other metals. In essence, the method is the hot-wire method but instead of the thermal decomposition of a halide being relied upon solely, as in the preparation of zirconium, a hydrogen atmosphere is used to effect reduction.

For the preparation of boron by this method, Laubengayer, Hurd, Newkirk, and Hoard [9] prepared some pure BBr_3, which was placed in a glass bulb C in an all-glass system indicated in Figure 2. Hydrogen was passed into the system at D at a rate of 150 to 450 cc per minute. The boron bromide was maintained at 0°C or 42°C; at 0°C the vapor pressure of the bromide was 18 mm, whereas at 42°C it was 150 mm. A tantalum or tungsten wire 0.01 inch in diameter at B was heated to various temperatures up to 1600°C. The hydrogen gas carried the BBr_3 vapor into the reaction vessel at B, where it was reduced to metallic boron on the hot wire; the total pressure in the apparatus was one atmosphere. Excess bromide and bromine were condensed out in vessel A, which was connected to a vacuum pump.

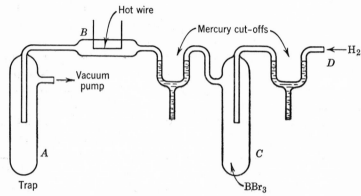

Figure 2. Apparatus for Hot Wire–Hydrogen Reduction of BBr_3. (Laubengayer, et al.[9])

It was found that a more crystalline deposit was obtained when the bromide container was maintained at 0°C rather than at the higher temperature. Also, hot-wire temperatures in the vicinity of 1000 to 1300°C gave better results than lower temperatures; at 800°C the deposit was an amorphous powder. The authors estimated that the purity of the boron obtained was well over 99.5%.

The Goldschmidt Process

Goldschmidt [10, 11] showed that many relatively pure metals could be obtained by heating suitable compounds with more electropositive metals such as aluminum, calcium, or magnesium.

Usually the compound to be reduced is either an oxide or a halide. A large amount of heat generated during the reaction is desirable from the standpoint of securing massive metal rather than powder. If the metal is reduced to a massive form or *regulus* it is less likely to pick up impurities such as gases from the environment than if it is in powder form, with a much larger surface area.

General Procedure. The compound to be reduced is in powder form, and is mixed with more than a stoichiometric amount of reductant (electropositive metal), also in powder or in granular form. Since very high temperatures are attained in such reactions, the charge is usually placed in a high-melting, non-reactive container which is ordinarily steel or a ceramic crucible contained in a steel container (bomb). If the reaction is allowed to proceed with the charge open to the air or at atmospheric pressure with a neutral gas atmosphere, a strong steel container may not be necessary; but a steel container must be used if a tight-fitting lid is placed over the top as is usually done in order to contain the reactants. In very vigorous reactions, the use of an open container will certainly lead to the charge's "exploding" out of the container. Also, unless the open vessel is surrounded by a completely inert atmosphere at all times, there is danger of contaminating the reduced metal and reductant with gases of the atmosphere.

When the well-mixed charge has been placed inside the bomb, and the cover secured in place (Figure 3), the bomb may be heated in any convenient manner to the ignition temperature, which is usually between 400 and 700°C. Open charges may be ignited by burning a piece of magnesium wire or ribbon sticking into the charge by some convenient remote method such as an electric spark. Occasionally, closed bombs have been set off by a high-melting fuse wire, which is heated to a high temperature by the passage of an electric current. Satisfactory firing, however, may most simply be accomplished by merely heating the bomb. High-frequency heating is particularly convenient as it is fast, and allows the condition of the bomb to be seen at all times. When the bomb fires, the temperature inside immediately rises to some very high value, sometimes well over 2000°C. The course of the reaction may be observed qualitatively by the rise in temperature of the bomb walls, which generally become suddenly much hotter than before. The onset of the reduction reaction can conveniently be followed by plotting a curve of bomb wall temperature versus time with the aid of a thermocouple attached to the wall. In a matter of a minute or so, the temperature will level off and commence falling, indicating that the reaction is over. If the temperature was sufficiently high with respect to the melting point of the slag and metal being reduced, a nugget or regulus of reduced metal will be obtained after cooling, at the bottom of the bomb. Lower temperatures tend to produce powder or pellets; some investigators have deliberately added inert materials to the charge in order to obtain a powder rather than massive metal.

The authors prefer the type of container shown in Figure 3a which is fitted with a ceramic crucible. The crucible prevents the reduced metal from alloying with the steel and also provides some thermal insulation which prevents too rapid chilling of the reduced metal, and thus allows better collection of the metal in the form of a regulus or *button* at the bottom. It is not necessary to use extremely thick steel bombs; ordinarily for bomb diameters up to 4 inches a wall thickness of about ⅜ inch appears to be sufficient. This is, of course, only

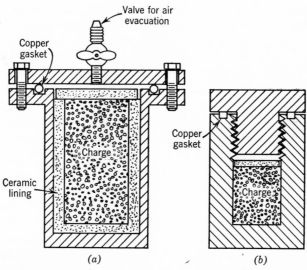

Figure 3. Two Types of Bomb for Reduction of Metals.

approximate as the internal pressure of a bomb of given diameter depends mainly upon the temperature achieved during reduction. In any case the extremely thick (1 to 2 inches) walls used by some investigators are unnecessary. The cover and bomb bottom should be somewhat thicker than the cylindrical wall as they are subject to maximum stress.

Both reactants should be in powder form to secure intimate mixing, although the reductant may consist of rather coarse particles of the order of $\frac{1}{16}$ inch in diameter or even somewhat larger without affecting the efficiency of reduction appreciably. More than a stoichiometric quantity of reductant must be used in order to drive the reaction to completion, although the amount of excess must be determined by trial. It is not unusual to have about 50% excess. A small amount of a "booster" such as iodine is frequently helpful, particularly in calcium reductions, as the reaction $Ca + I_2 = CaI_2$ starts at a compara-

tively low temperature and acts to "trigger" the main reaction.[12]   If
iodine is used, excess calcium must be provided for the booster reaction, and approximately 20% of the calcium used may be allotted for
this purpose.

The bomb cover may be fitted with a valve or opening for evacuation of the air, which is replaced by argon so that no reductant is used
up by reaction with the air.   After the argon is introduced the opening is closed off so that no reactants escape.   The replacement of air
by argon is probably not a very important procedure in most cases,
and perhaps may be found to be an unnecessary precaution in some
reductions.

Safety Precautions.   Bomb reductions sometimes live up to their
name and cause explosions which can be very damaging to both per-
sonnel and property.   What usually happens is that the cover is ripped
off or a hole is burned through the bomb wall, and the bomb becomes
jet-propelled.   The most frequent cause of explosions is the presence
of water in the compound to be reduced; more than 1% moisture can
be very dangerous.   Preferably the water content should be only a
few tenths of a per cent.   The reaction of molten alkali or alkaline
earth metals with water causes a detonation or shock wave propagation.

Small bombs holding only about 100 grams of reactants can be more
readily safeguarded by placing sandbags around the sides and on
top.   Larger reactions should preferably be located in a vacated area
with a reinforced concrete wall between the bomb and the operator.

Metal Reductants.   Aluminum has been much used in the past for
Goldschmidt reactions, but it is a poor choice on two counts: (1)
aluminum forms alloys with practically every metal and (2) it is not as
powerful a reductant as magnesium or calcium.   At 1000°C the free
energy of formation of the oxides of these metals *per gram atom of
oxygen* is as follows: aluminum, 99 kcal; magnesium, 114 kcal; calcium, 121 kcal.   Unlike aluminum, magnesium and calcium do not as
readily form alloys with most high-melting metals, and hence the
reduced metal is not so likely to be contaminated or embrittled by
intermetallic phases.

Calcium turnings can be purchased from chemical-supply houses,
or one can make them by turning down calcium ingots on a lathe (see
also Table 1 of this chapter).   As long as it is kept dry, calcium is
readily handled in air; it does not tarnish rapidly, but in finely divided
form should be stored in a dry noble gas to avoid gradual air contamination.   Calcium has a lower vapor pressure than magnesium and
hence generates less pressure inside the reduction containers (bombs)

for the same temperature level. Magnesium, on the other hand, is cheaper, more readily available in finely divided form, more stable in air, and is available in higher purity than calcium.

Thermochemistry of Bomb Reductions. It was stated earlier that one can use either oxides or halides in the Goldschmidt process. Conceivably other compounds such as sulphides might be considered, but since metals which can be reduced by this method are more readily available as either oxides or halides there is ordinarily no reason to use other compounds. Compounds for bomb reduction should be sufficiently stable so that they may be heated to the ignition temperature of the reaction without appreciable decomposition.

It is clear that to secure maximum temperature and hence maximum consolidation of the metal during reduction many moles of reductant compound should be formed relative to moles of starting material. This is illustrated below for the reduction of vanadium oxides by calcium.

Consider the reduction of V_2O_5:

$$5Ca + V_2O_5 \rightarrow 5CaO + 2V \tag{2}$$

Because of the high valence of vanadium $(+5)$ in V_2O_5, 5 moles of CaO are formed for every mole of V_2O_5 used. This results in a large free energy of reaction, $\Delta F = -340$ kcal in the range of 450 to 600°C.[12] On the other hand, in the reaction

$$3Ca + V_2O_3 = 3CaO + 2V \tag{3}$$

only 3 moles of CaO are required for every mole of V_2O_3, and here

$$\Delta F = -126 \text{ kcal at } 500°C$$

During reduction, reaction 2 develops enough heat to melt the vanadium into a massive regulus; whereas, if V_2O_3 is used according to equation 3, generally only powdered vanadium results.

The actual efficiency of the reduction depends mainly upon the heat losses, and hence upon such factors as size of reduction and amount of thermal insulation. One of the authors obtained about 75% recovery, using equation 2 when a charge of about 300 grams of V_2O_5 and 552 grams of calcium was used. This amount of calcium was 60% more than required stoichiometrically and was found to be necessary in order to provide a sufficiently high calcium atmosphere to prevent excessive oxygen absorption (and hence embrittlement) of the hot vanadium. The above charge also includes enough calcium to combine with 150 grams of iodine used as a booster.

Halides in some respects are preferable to oxides since the halide products formed, MgF_2, $CaCl_2$, etc., are generally much lower melting than the corresponding oxides. This characteristic results in better collection of the reduced metal in the bottom of the bomb since the dense liquid metal readily separates from the comparatively light liquid halide. However, when an oxide like CaO is formed, the reduced liquid metal must penetrate the solid spongy or viscous liquid mass of the oxide in order to collect as a regulus at the bottom.

Ordinarily, only chlorides and fluorides are sufficiently stable for satisfactory bomb reduction. As pointed out above, compounds of the highest feasible valence produce the greatest amount of heat upon reduction, but unfortunately halides of high valences are frequently too unstable or too hygroscopic to be used successfully. A disadvantage of halides is the difficulty of preparing them in very dry form. It is not hard to obtain halides containing about 5% moisture but to achieve less than 1% moisture is often very difficult. In this respect oxides offer less trouble as they are usually readily prepared in very dry form.

Reduction of Volatile Metals

The reduction of metals of high vapor pressure from their compounds (often oxides) usually allows easy preparation in high purity. Examples are zinc, magnesium, and barium. A commercial method for the production of zinc is the reaction

$$ZnO + C \rightarrow Zn + CO \tag{4}$$

Because zinc has a high vapor pressure, the zinc produced by this reaction at temperatures considerably in excess of its melting point is largely vapor, and hence readily escapes from the reaction chamber and is condensed in an adjoining condenser as quite high purity zinc. Reaction 4 goes very readily towards the right since both products are gases and quickly escape from the reaction chamber, thus continually upsetting the equilibrium toward the right. Since most of the impurities present have a much lower vapor pressure than zinc, the zinc is condensed out in very pure form.

Magnesium reduction by the well-known Pidgeon [13] process is somewhat similar to the process just described for zinc. In this method dolomite, a MgO-CaO mineral containing a large amount of MgO, is reduced by ferro-silicon according to the reaction

$$2MgO + Si = 2Mg + SiO_2 \tag{5}$$

This reaction is carried out in evacuated alloy steel retorts heated to about 1150°C. The pressure inside the retort is less than 1 mm Hg to allow maximum volatilization of the magnesium. Ferro-silicon is an iron-silicon alloy containing in this case about 75% silicon and is used rather than pure silicon because it is less expensive; the iron takes no significant part in the reaction. The CaO contained in the dolomite is tied up by the SiO_2 formed, thus removing SiO_2 from the reaction, and with it any tendency for a reverse reaction, hence aiding in driving the reaction 5 to the right. The volatilized magnesium is condensed in the cold end of the retort and is scraped off after the reaction is over as crystalline nodules of very high purity (about 99.98).

Kroll [14] describes a very similar process for the reduction of barium, which is reduced from BaO by aluminum or silicon.

Liquid Halide–Magnesium Reduction

In the Goldschmidt process discussed above, the reactants were used in solid form and heated to the reaction temperature to initiate the reaction. Beryllium is produced commercially [15] by holding BeF_2 in the molten condition at 900°C in a graphite vessel and adding solid magnesium metal a little at a time to reduce the beryllium. Since the BeF_2 is held below the melting point of beryllium (1285°C), the latter is formed in the solid condition and floats to the top of the graphite reaction vessel. An excess of BeF_2 is used to reduce the violence of the exothermic reaction. The excess BeF_2, together with the reaction product MgF_2, produces a slag of lower melting point than beryllium and aids in coalescence of beryllium particles during subsequent melting. After the magnesium is added, the pot temperature is raised to 1300°C by high-frequency induction; at this temperature the beryllium is quite fluid and floats on top of the molten salt. After freezing, the salt is washed away from the frozen pancake of beryllium, which is then broken up into pieces for vacuum melting. This technique is probably not applicable to other metals since it requires the use of a halide of extraordinary stability. It is also a technique of considerable potential hazard because of the possibility of splashing hot salt.

Kroll [16] used a modification of this technique in the reduction of titanium, but, instead of adding solid magnesium to liquid titanium chloride, he slowly dripped liquid titanium chloride on liquid magnesium from a vessel above. The magnesium reduced the $TiCl_4$ to metal, forming titanium metal and $MgCl_2$. The reduction operation was conducted inside a steel shell containing dry noble gas. These products were formed in a molybdenum crucible and were recovered by machining away the molybdenum and extracting the chloride with water. The resulting titanium sponge was then compacted and sintered, using the methods of powder metallurgy.

Gaseous Halide–Magnesium Reduction

Kroll [17] later modified his titanium reduction process to utilize $ZrCl_4$ gas instead of liquid $TiCl_4$. The gas formed in a separate gas generator was led to the reduction chamber containing liquid magnesium in a steel crucible. The reduction occurred at the magnesium surface with provision made to continuously drain off the liquid $MgCl_2$ formed as a by-product. This is the Bureau of Mines process developed by Kroll, and has been used to make many tons of zirconium metal of approximately 99.9% purity.

This method, in principle, could probably be used for several other metals which are difficult to prepare in pure form, provided a fairly stable gaseous halide can be made.

METHODS OF INCREASING PURITY

Hydrogen Treatment

The use of dry hydrogen to reduce the surface oxide of metal powders and to reduce the dissolved oxygen content of solid metals like iron has been described in the chapter on powder metallurgy and in the chapter on controlled atmospheres (Chapters 10 and 5).

The wet hydrogen treatment for removal of carbon in iron has also been discussed in Chapter 5. This technique should be applicable to other metals such as nickel and cobalt. It is feasible to reduce the oxygen content of many metals by the introduction of a hydrogen atmosphere during the latter stages of the melting operation, and it is preferable to carry out this operation in a vacuum melting furnace so that, upon completion of the hydrogen reduction step, the dissolved hydrogen may be pumped out of the melt; otherwise gas unsoundness in the casting is likely.

Oxidation

Purification by oxidation is generally restricted to melting operations where readily oxidizable impurities are preferentially oxidized and slagged off to the top of the melt. This technique in the laboratory is usually restricted to the removal of impurities which form gaseous oxidation products, like carbon. Carbon may be removed from pure iron or pure nickel, for example, by adding an excess of Fe_2O_3 or NiO to form CO. After carbon removal the oxygen may be removed by hydrogen treatment and evacuation as just mentioned above. Pyrometallurgical refining of gold is an ancient art, and in principle consists of oxidizing away the base metal impurities. Smart, Smith, and Phillips [18] describe a controlled oxidation of high-purity copper to remove the sulphur impurity by "blowing" the molten copper with oxygen until the oxygen content reaches 1.5%. Subsequently, the copper is cast and purified further by electrolysis, which eliminates the oxygen.

Vacuum Treatment

Vacuum annealing and melting are techniques which primarily prevent metals from becoming impure by reaction with the air. However, as mentioned in Chapter 7, certain volatile impurities, notably Ca, Mg, Mn, Zn, and H_2, may be removed in this way. Hydrogen is readily removed from all metals by vacuum annealing.

Distillation

Very pure zinc has been prepared commercially for many years by distillation because of its high vapor pressure at moderate temperatures; spectrographically pure zinc is made by distillation [19] (see Figure 4). Other metals which have been similarly purified are cadmium, calcium,[20] magnesium, manganese, mercury, and sodium. Magnesium and manganese are available today in quite high purity in the form of electrolytic metals, and it is much easier to make pure manganese metal by electrolysis than by distillation.

The metals just mentioned are all available commercially in a fairly satisfactory state of purity; hence there is not much need to purify them further by distillation.

However, there are other metals which offer some possibility of purity improvement by distillation. A partial list is beryllium, chromium, lithium, selenium, germanium, silicon, sodium, strontium, and tellurium. The rate of distillation is increased by:

1. Higher temperature of evaporation.

2. Absence of gas in the atmosphere other than the metal vapor itself (high vacuum).

3. Large surface area of evaporating metal.

4. Rapid condensation to provide maximum concentration gradient.

These conditions indicate that the distillation should be conducted at the highest feasible temperature consistent with a rapid but controlled rate of evaporation. However, if the temperature is too high, impurities of somewhat lower vapor pressure will be deposited on the condensing surface.

The distillation should be conducted in a vacuum to prevent impingement of metal vapor upon gas molecules, thus slowing down the rate of evaporation. This effect is very marked; an atmosphere of gas can reduce distillation rates manyfold. St. Clair and Spendlove [21]

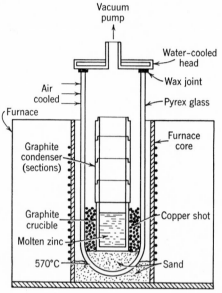

Figure 4.   Zinc Condensation Apparatus.   (Truesdale and Edmonds.[19])

found that for the evaporation of zinc at pressures of 50 to 100 microns the rate of evaporation was 60 to 80% of the theoretical rate, but at 2000 microns of residual air pressure the rate was only 7% of the theoretical rate.

Since metal atoms are removed from the surface of the molten metal, it is obvious that the rate of evaporation will be proportional to the surface exposed to the vacuum.

Finally, a steep concentration gradient in evaporated atoms between the evaporation surface and the condensing surface is required for efficient mass transfer. Hence the condensing surface should be cold, preferably water-cooled to quickly remove evaporated atoms from the immediate neighborhood of the condenser.

Evaporation is a slow process for preparing metals of moderate vapor pressure.

The rate of evaporation of a metal in a high vacuum is given by

$$G = \frac{P}{17.14\sqrt{T/M}} \tag{6}$$

where G is the amount of metal evaporated in grams/cm^2/sec,
$\quad$ M is the atomic weight of the metal,
$\quad$ P is the vapor pressure of the metal in millimeters,
$\quad$ T is the absolute temperature in °K.

This subject is treated more fully in connection with vacuum melting in Chapter 7.

Some additional data on the subject of laboratory metal evaporation techniques are given by Kroll.[22]

Liquation

It is sometimes possible to purify a liquid metal by holding it in a temperature region in which the liquid is in equilibrium with a solid, or which merely contains a solid, of considerably greater density. The heavy solid sinks to the bottom, thus making it possible to decant off the purified liquid at the top. This is the basis of the Pattinson process of removing lead from silver.

This method, depending upon differences in gravity, is not always successful, however, if the particles to be removed are exceedingly small, when they tend to remain suspended in the metal, possibly because of thermal currents or slight agitation in a melt. Oxides like MgO formed during deoxidation of a melt would probably float to the top if the melt were sufficiently quiet and if held for a long period of time.

However, to take advantage of a gain in purity achieved in this way, the melt should be frozen in place and cropped at the top because, during pouring, even bottom pouring, there would be enough agitation to again mix the insoluble constituent with the melt.

Purification by Crystallization

Progressive slow freezing of an ingot or rod starting from one end may be used for reducing the concentration of solid solution impurities since the higher melting constituent freezes out first, causing a segregation of the alloying metal in the frozen ingot. Hence, by cropping the ingot and discarding the portion somewhat enriched in the unwanted impurity, a gain in purity is realized.

Pfann[23] has described the principles of what he calls "zone-melting," in which a small increment of length of a long alloy bar or rod is successively melted and frozen by passing a hot zone along the length of the bar. By this technique, a rod can either be made more homogeneous or more segregated, depending upon whether the hot zone is passed back and forth over the rod or is passed in one direction. For best purification results, the ratio of the solute concentration in the solid to that in the liquid during the freezing process should be small, and the rate of solid diffusion should be low. Repeated zone melting can result in reductions in impurity concentration by several orders of magnitude without the necessity of intermediate cropping. The solute is essentially picked up and carried the length of the bar and dumped there, requiring only final cropping of a comparatively short rod length.

REFERENCES

1. Saul Dushman, *Scientific Foundations of Vacuum Technique,* John Wiley and Sons, New York, 1949.
2. *Metal Finishing Guidebook-Directory,* Finishing Publications, Inc., New York 18, N. Y., 1949.
3. *Modern Electroplating,* The Electrochemical Society, New York, N. Y., 1942.
4. J. J. Lander and L. H. Germer, "Plating Molybdenum, Tungsten and Chromium by Thermal Decomposition of Their Carbonyls," *Trans. Am. Inst. Mining Met. Engrs., Inst. Metals Div.,* **175,** 648–689 (1948).
5. B. B. Owen and R. T. Webber, "Plating Chromium by Thermal Decomposition of Chromium Hexacarbonyl," *Trans. Am. Inst. Mining Met. Engrs., Inst. Metals Div.,* **175,** 693–698 (1948).
6. A. E. Van Arkel and J. H. DeBoer, "Preparation of Pure Titanium, Zirconium, Hafnium, and Thorium Metal," *Z. anorg. u. allgem. Chem.,* **148,** 345–350 (1925).
7. J. H. DeBoer and J. D. Fast, "Preparation of Pure Metals of the Titanium Group by Thermal Decomposition of the Iodides: I. Zirconium," *Z. anorg. u. allgem. Chem.,* **153,** 1–8 (1926).
8. A. E. Van Arkel, *Reine Metalle,* J. Springer, Berlin, 1933.
9. A. W. Laubengayer, D. T. Hurd, A. E. Newkirk, J. L. Hoard, "Boron 1. Preparation and Properties of Pure Crystalline Boron," *J. Am. Chem. Soc.,* **65,** 1924–1931 (1943).
10. Hans Goldschmidt and Claude Vautin, "Aluminum as a Heating and Reducing Agent," *J. Soc. Chem. Ind.,* **19,** 543–544 (1898).
11. Hans Goldschmidt, "On a New Method for the Production of High Temperatures and the Reduction of Refractory Carbon-Free Metals," *Z. Elektrochemie,* **4,** 494–499 (1898).
12. R. K. McKechnie and A. U. Seybolt, "The Preparation of Ductile Vanadium by Calcium Reduction," *J. Electrochem. Soc.,* **97,** 311–315 (1950).
13. D. H. Killeffer, "Magnesium from Dolomite by Ferro-Silicon Reduction," *Chem. Eng. News,* **20,** 369 (1942).
14. W. J. Kroll, "Processes for Making Barium and Its Alloys," *Bureau of Mines Information Circular* IC 7327 (August, 1945).

15. Bengt R. F. Kjellgren, "The Production of Beryllium," *Trans. Electrochem. Soc.*, **93**, 122–128 (1948).
16. W. J. Kroll, "The Production of Ductile Titanium," *Trans. Electrochem. Soc.*, **78**, 35–47 (1940).
17. W. J. Kroll, W. W. Stephens, and H. P. Holmes, "Production of Malleable Zirconium on a Pilot-Plant Scale," *J. Metals*, **188**, 1445–1453 (1950).
18. J. S. Smart, A. A. Smith, Jr., and A. J. Phillips, "Preparation and Some Properties of High Purity Copper," *Trans. Am. Inst. Mining Met. Engrs., Inst. Metals Div.*, **143**, 272–286 (1941).
19. E. C. Truesdale and Gerald Edmonds, "Pure Zinc—Its Preparation and Some Examples of Influence of Minor Constituents," *Trans. Am. Inst. Mining Met. Engrs., Inst. Metals Div.*, **133**, 267–277 (1939).
20. A. H. Everts and G. D. Bagley, "Physical and Electrical Properties of Calcium," *Trans. Electrochem. Soc.*, **93**, 265–271 (1948).
21. H. W. St. Clair and M. J. Spendlove, "Rate of Evaporation of Zinc at Low Pressures," *J. Metals*, **3**, 1192–1197 (1951).
22. W. J. Kroll, "Melting and Evaporating Metals in a Vacuum," *Trans. Electrochem. Soc.*, **87**, 571–583 (1945).
23. W. G. Pfann, "Principles of Zone—Melting," *J. Metals*, **4**, 747 (July, 1952).

CHAPTER TWELVE

Preparation of Metal Single Crystals

Single-crystal specimens are becoming more and more commonly used in metallurgical investigations, so much so that single crystals of a few metals can now be obtained commercially in simple shapes.[1] In most cases, however, the investigator has special requirements of shape, size, purity, or identity of the metal and finds it convenient to make the single crystal himself. With techniques that are now available, single crystals of many metals can be readily made in the form of sheet, wire, or rod.

The literature on the preparation of single crystals is voluminous, and no attempt will be made to refer to original sources in this chapter. An extensively documented summary of methods has been published by Holden [2] and may be consulted for references to the original literature.

Although the general principles involved in growing single crystals are relatively simple, the detailed mechanisms of crystal growth are still not completely understood. Thus art as well as science is needed to grow satisfactory metal single crystals. The conditions for some metals such as lead and copper are not critical, but a considerable amount of experimentation may be required to find the best conditions for other metals and alloys.

Single crystals are commonly grown in the laboratory either by the controlled solidification of a metal from the liquid phase, or by utilizing the crystal growth that occurs when a deformed metal is heated to a suitable temperature. In either case conditions are arranged so that the first crystal to form grows without interference from other crystals until it is as large as the specimen. Other methods such as electrolytic deposition and growth from the vapor phase are occasionally used, but it is rare that crystals of suitable size, shape, or perfection can be produced in these ways. In this chapter the general principles used to prepare single crystals by solidification and by crystal growth in the solid state will be outlined, the kinds of equipment used will be described, and finally some special techniques used to grow multiple crystals and crystals having predetermined orientations will be presented.

GROWTH OF SINGLE CRYSTALS FROM THE LIQUID PHASE

Single crystals are grown from the liquid phase by passing the molten metal through a temperature gradient to initiate solidification at one point and proceed throughout the melt. Many techniques for accomplishing this have been described, and it has become customary to apply to the technique the name of one of the early workers to describe the method. This system is somewhat confusing because European metallurgists and American metallurgists apply different names to the methods, and the processes are known by yet different names when used for nonmetallic crystals. We shall use the names commonly used by American metallurgists.

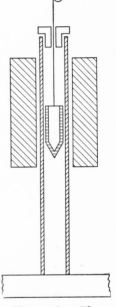

The Bridgman Method

The *Bridgman* method, shown schematically in Figure 1, illustrates most of the principles involved in growing single crystals by solidification. The metal is contained in a cylindrical crucible with a point at the bottom and is melted by suspending the crucible from a wire in a vertical tube furnace. By slowly lowering the crucible with a suitable mechanism through the furnace into a cool zone, a nucleus crystal can be formed at the point and caused to grow until all the liquid solidifies on it. If the conditions are proper, a single crystal the shape of the crucible will be obtained.

Figure 1. The Bridgman Method. Molten metal contained in a crucible is slowly lowered through a tube furnace.

The difficulty most frequently encountered is the formation of several crystals in the useful volume. They may results from the appearance of several nuclei when the melt starts to solidify. The object of making a point at the bottom of the crucible is to decrease the volume in which the first crystal nucleus forms and thus decrease the probability of multiple nucleation. Some workers have used one or more additional constrictions above the initial point to filter out unwanted crystals, as shown in Figure 2. Actually, the usefulness of these constrictions is doubtful. If the temperature gradient is proper, and conditions are otherwise correct, points having an included angle of well over 90 degrees can be used, and only one crystal will form. If conditions are not proper, additional crystals nucleate readily, and a single crystal cannot be grown even with multiple constrictions in the tube.

Only one crystal can form if the temperature of the liquid above the single crystal is always kept above the freezing point of the metal. This means that the major part of the heat must be abstracted through the already solidified single crystal. This is relatively easy to do if the metal has a high thermal conductivity like aluminum or copper, and it is probably for this reason that it is easy to grow single crystals of these metals. If the metal has a low thermal conductivity compared to that of the crucible material, an appreciable part of the heat will flow out through the crucible walls. Under these conditions it is possible to cool below the freezing point portions of the liquid which lie ahead of the growing single crystal and unwanted crystals will form at these points. The cure for this condition is to maintain the temperature gradient in the desired pattern by artificially cooling the initial end of the single crystal, or by lowering the crucible through the furnace more slowly so that heat can flow out naturally from the bottom. Particular care must be taken if the crucible is of irregular shape, because the temperature gradient is disturbed around these points, and extra crystals may form.

Figure 2. The Bridgman Method. An additional constriction in the tube may help to "filter" out unwanted grains.

It is frequently observed that the crystals produced are rather imperfect. This is particularly true when attempts are made to grow very large single crystals. There is no simple way of overcoming the difficulty. Slower speeds of growth help to some extent, as does the use of new or carefully cleaned crucibles. In addition, the orientation of the single crystal with respect to the thermal gradient is of some importance. Crystals have preferred directions of growth, and it is observed that crystals oriented so that the most rapid growth direction is parallel to the thermal gradient are usually more nearly perfect than those that are constrained to grow in other growth directions by artificial seeding.

It is usually desirable to superheat the liquid as much as possible without unduly contaminating it. If the metal is heated to just above the melting point, many impurities remain crystalline and act as nuclei for grains upon resolidification. Superheating eliminates many of these impurity nuclei.

The growth rates used vary widely. The commonly reported rates are in the neighborhood of one to several centimeters an hour. They are imposed largely by the necessity of maintaining a proper temperature gradient and have little to do with any intrinsic growth velocity of the metal grains. The crystals will grow as fast as the latent heat solidification can be removed. If artificial cooling is used to remove heat from the bottom of the crucible, so that the temperature gradient can be controlled independently of the lowering rate, growth rates as great as 100 cm an hour can be used.

Other Methods

Although the Bridgman method, or minor variations of it, is most commonly used for the preparation of metal single crystals, a wide variety of other methods have been used to solidify the melt progressively. They are useful mostly for low-melting metals such as lead, zinc, cadmium, and tin.

In the *Czochralski* method (Figure 3) no container is used for the solidified metal. A cold seed crystal is touched to the surface of the liquid metal and then slowly raised. Often a mica disk with a circular hole the size of the desired single crystal is held close to or floated on the surface of the liquid to aid in shaping the crystal. The rate of raising is controlled by the rate at which heat can be withdrawn from the solidified crystal. Usually a gas blast is directed at the crystal just above the mica disk to aid in cooling. This permits growth rates as great as several millimeters a minute. Crystals grown by this method are frequently quite irregular in shape.

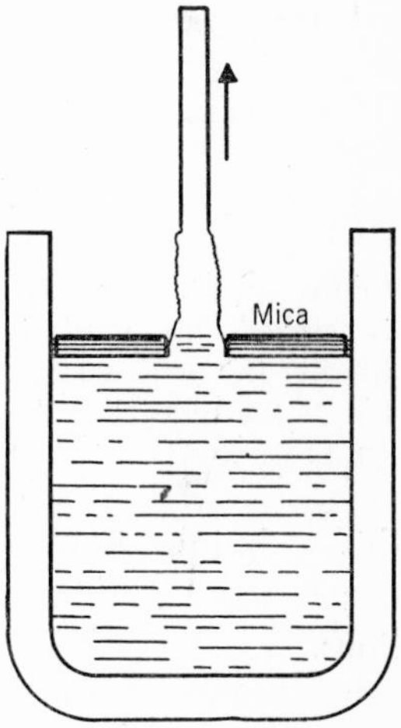

Mica

Figure 3.   The Czochralski Method. The seed crystal is slowly drawn out of the melt through a hole in a mica plate floated on the surface.

Another method that is occasionally used to obtain the desirable steep temperature gradient and a well-formed crystal is illustrated in Figure 4. A glass or fused quartz tube with a constriction is lowered into a crucible of the molten metal superheated to an appropriate temperature. By applying slight suction the metal is drawn up into the constriction of the tube just above the surface of the melt where it solidifies and forms a seed crystal. The tube is then slowly raised out of the liquid so that the molten metal in the tube solidifies progressively.

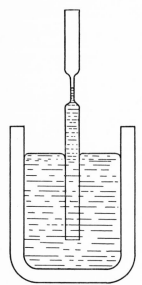

Figure 4. Method of Obtaining a Steep Temperature Gradient. The metal is sucked up until it freezes in the constriction in the tube, then the tube is slowly raised.

Occasionally it is desirable to grow the crystals in a horizontal position; this makes it particularly easy to seed the melt to produce a crystal of predetermined orientation.

Kapitza used the exceedingly simple technique of melting bismuth on a glass slide on a hot plate, and causing progressive solidification by moving the glass slide slowly off to a cooler surface. The oxide skin on the bismuth holds it in approximately cylindrical shape. Somewhat larger diameter crystals can be grown by containing a bismuth metal bar in a horizontal glass tube of about 25% greater inside diameter. Both these methods are very useful for bismuth since it expands on freezing and will be deformed if constrained by a crucible of ordinary shape.

A method frequently used by *Chalmers* is to contain the metal in a horizontal boat of the type shown in Figure 5. The boat can be drawn out of a tube furnace onto a water-cooled copper block; or, if it is desired to keep the crucible still, a hot coil of wire or a small furnace may be moved along the boat to permit it to freeze gradually. By this technique it is easy to seed the specimen in complicated ways to produce single or multiple crystals having predetermined orientations.

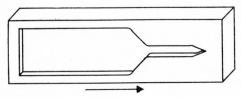

Figure 5. Chalmers Method. The single crystal is grown in a horizontal graphite boat. This is particularly convenient for seeding.

A final method that is occasionally useful with low melting metals that are not attacked by hydrofluoric acid is to melt the metal in a glass tube and then continue heating until the glass itself softens.

If a fine capillary is made by drawing out the glass tube it will contain a fine wire of the metal and this will be a single crystal over rather large distances. The glass may be removed by dissolving it in a dilute solution of hydrofluoric acid, or for some purposes such as electrical resistance measurements it may be left in place to protect the crystal.

Special Conditions

Alloy single crystals are difficult to make because the difference between the composition of the solid and the liquid with which it is in equilibrium produces a composition gradient along the crystal bar. This can be overcome to a great extent by growing the crystal in a narrow tube to prevent convection currents. Then a steady-state condition is reached, and over a great part of its length the composition of the crystal is identical with the average composition. This state is illustrated schematically in Figure 6. If the interfacial liquid has a density greater than that of the average liquid, the crystal should be grown from the bottom to the top; if it is less, the crystal should be grown from the top to the bottom to prevent mixing by convection.

Some alloys, such as brass, contain a volatile constituent, and additional difficulty is encountered in obtaining a uniform composition. In fact no completely satisfactory solution to the problem is available, but high rates of growth,

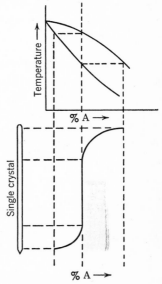

Figure 6. Variation in Composition of a Single Crystal of an Alloy with Distance. The upper diagram shows the phase diagram of the alloy. The lower one the variation in composition along the crystal that started to freeze at the bottom. If the crystal is grown in a slender tube where no convection occurs, the central portion will have the nominal composition.

and the lowest possible temperature, and a tight-fitting cover used to prevent volatilization, will usually lead to reasonably satisfactory results.

Crucible Materials and Design

Almost any compatible refractory may be used to make the crucible in which a single crystal is grown. However, the special shapes needed frequently require that the crucible be made in the laboratory. For this reason pyrex glass is quite regularly used for the lower melting metals, and graphite for those of higher melting point, since both these materials can be readily fabricated with commonly available equipment. Where other crucible materials must be used the methods described in the chapter on refractories may be used to make crucibles.

Simple crucibles for making cylindrical single crystals of low-melting metal such as lead, tin, zinc, and cadmium may be made by drawing pyrex tubing of a suitable size to a point. The metal can be prevented from sticking to the crucible walls by coating the inside of the tube with a thin film of colloidal graphite. Another method is to rinse the tube with a dilute solution of mineral oil dissolved in an organic solvent, and then bake it to carbonize the residual mineral oil. For higher melting alloys fused quartz may be substituted for pyrex.

When completely non-porous refractories are used bubbles may be trapped at the metal-crucible interface, and they give an irregularly shaped crystal. These are particularly troublesome if an attempt is made to evacuate and seal off the tube above the metal. If an evacuated tube is desired, it is usually necessary to melt the metal and pour it back and forth in the tube several times to permit the bubbles to rise to the top before the crystal is grown, or to suck the molten metal from an evacuated container up into a glass tube and then constrict the tube.

Since glass tubes rarely have parallel sides, it may be difficult to remove the final crystal from its container. It will usually be found that commercial glass tubing is slightly tapered. By measuring it first, the appropriate end can be cut off with an abrasive cut-off wheel to withdraw the crystal. If this cannot be done, the glass can be shattered by heating the tube and quenching it in cold water. Precision ground-glass tubing can be procured but it is rather expensive.

Graphite is the most useful crucible material for the many metals with which it does not react. Since it is always slightly porous no difficulties are encountered with surface bubbles. Sticking to the crucible walls is rarely encountered, and of course crucibles or boats of almost any desired shape are quite readily prepared in the machine shop. Graphite has a very low coefficient of expansion so that the solid single crystal can be withdrawn without danger of distortion. Graphite crucibles can be used repeatedly although there is some evidence that later crystals grown in a given crucible are less perfect than earlier ones because preferred nucleation occurs from small fragments of crystalline metal embedded in the walls of the crucible. The difficulty can be overcome by reaming the crucible out after each use, by leeching it with an appropriate solvent and then baking it out to remove moisture, or by highly superheating the liquid. In many cases no such difficulty is encountered.

For much work it is convenient to use a single-cavity crucible, but if a number of crystals are required it is desirable to grow more than one at a time. Excellent results are obtained by drilling a number of holes in a graphite bar, or by lowering a bundle of glass tubes through a furnace at the same time. When this is done, it is frequently time-saving to produce mechanically rods of approximately the final dimensions of the desired piece and drop them into the crucible, then melt and freeze to grow the single crystal. Larger bars can be used readily in graphite crucibles by counterboring the crucible cavity at the top to take a short length of the large rod. Upon melting it will run down and fill the crucible cavity.

SOLID-STATE METHODS

It is frequently advantageous to grow single crystals entirely in the solid state. In some metals it is impossible to grow crystals by solidification because there is a phase change between the melting point and room temperature. Sometimes the desired shapes are more readily obtained in the solid state, particularly if sheet-like specimens are needed.

As is well known, there are several mechanisms by which the crystals can be caused to grow in a solid specimen. A cold-worked metal will recrystallize upon heating. During this process new grains appear and consume the surrounding matrix. Under certain conditions grain growth will occur in a strain-free metal, the process frequently called "secondary recrystallization." Finally a metal which exists in two allotropic modifications can be passed through a temperature gradient so that the first grain of the new phase to form is forced to consume the other phase, a process analogous to the liquid solid-phase change employed in the Bridgman method. All these methods have been used to grow satisfactory single crystals. It does not seem to be desirable to describe in detail all the procedures that have been used in specific cases; rather the general principles involved will be considered.

The "Strain-Anneal" Method

The number of nuclei that appear in a deformed metal upon annealing depends upon the amount of strain and the initial grain size. Below some reasonably well-defined critical strain (corresponding to elongations of 1 to 3%) no new nuclei appear at all. At larger strains the number that appears increases rapidly with increasing strain. In the strain-anneal method, the object is to strain the specimen by the smallest amount necessary to produce recrystallization.

For many purposes, satisfactorily large grains can be obtained by merely stretching a strip or bar of the fine-grained metal by 1 to 3% and then recrystallizing it by slowly heating to temperature well above that necessary to cause recrystallization. With certain metals, such as commercially pure aluminum, this produces a single crystal in a very large proportion of specimens, and the remainder will have very large grains after this treatment.

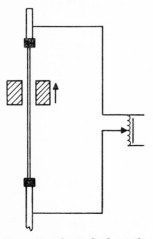

Very frequently it is observed that the surface layer of grains is not consumed during recrystallization so that superficial etching reveals only a fine-grained specimen. Heavier etching will remove this surface layer of grains and expose the single crystal underneath. Small grains are frequently found to be included in the single crystals. In some experiments they cause no difficulty. Often they can be eliminated by long annealing at elevated temperature or prevented by altering the amount of the initial strain.

Figure 7. The Andrade Method. A moving furnace or radiation shield progressively heats parts of a wire above the recrystallization temperature. The whole wire is heated to a low temperature by passing a current from a transformer through it.

The simple method just described depends largely upon chance to produce a single grain. A superior method is to pass the specimen through a temperature gradient so that recrystallization starts at one end and proceeds throughout the specimen. In the recrystallization process there is an incubation period or nucleation period before recrystallization starts; the specimen must be held at the recrystallization temperature for a finite time before any new grains appear. On the other hand, there is no incubation period for the grain-growth part of the process. Thus if a single grain is nucleated at the end of a specimen and it is then passed through a temperature gradient, that grain can grow and consume the deformed matrix before any other new grains appear.

The equipment used for growing single crystals in this way can be very similar to that used for growing single crystals from the liquid.

If oxidation is not a serious problem, the deformed specimen can be slowly lowered past a baffle or through a hole into a heated tube furnace. If oxidation is important it may be first sealed into a glass or fused quartz tube. This makes it somewhat more difficult to achieve the necessary large temperature gradient, but usually it is satisfactory to use a close-fitting tube.

Andrade has used the ingenious technique illustrated in Figure 7 to cause a high-temperature zone to pass along the wire and produce progressive recrystallization. He heated the wire electrically to a temperature somewhat below that necessary to cause rapid recrystallization by passing a current through it and then added local heating by moving a small radiation shield along the wire. Alternatively, a small electric furnace can be substituted for the radiation shield, and, of course, if suitable temperature can be attained, the primary electrical heating of the wire is unnecessary. In the *Pinsch* process for the production of long tungsten single crystals, the wire is passed between two contacts so that it is progressively heated to the desired temperature. This method is objectionable for laboratory use because the contacts may distort the final crystal.

It is also possible to heat the specimen progressively by lowering it slowly into a fused salt or fused

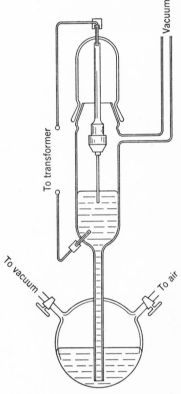

Figure 8. Method of Progressively Heating a Wire. One end of the wire is held in a chuck in a vacuum system. The other end dips in mercury. A current is passed through the wire and the mercury is raised or lowered by adding air to or removing it from the lower flask.

metal bath. An advantage of this method is that a very high temperature gradient is produced. A similar method is illustrated in Figure 8. Here the specimen is heated electrically, and the heated zone is increased in length by slowly lowering the mercury level. The current can be held essentially constant by connecting a resistance in series with the wire. By using a resistor having several times the resistance of the wire itself, the change of resistance of the circuit from changing the length of the wire can be made negligible. The vacuum setup of Figure 8 can be used if the specimen material oxidizes severely at the recrystallization temperature. Otherwise, the recrystallization can be conducted in air.

Effect of Variables

There is a wide variation in the ease with which single crystals can be grown by the strain-anneal method. With the exception of aluminum, all face-centered-cubic metals develop a large number of annealing twins during recrystallization and subsequent grain growth. Thus, except for certain special cases described below, it is hopeless to attempt to grow untwinned single crystals by this method. The common metals such as copper and its alloys, lead, gamma iron, nickel, silver, gold, etc., are thus eliminated.

The method is useful for aluminum (although it is face-centered-cubic, it does not form many annealing twins) and for the body-centered-cubic metals alpha iron and its alloys, tungsten, and molybdenum, and should be considered as a possibility for other high-melting metals which are not face-centered-cubic. It is rarely used for very low-melting metals such as zinc, cadmium, tin, and indium because single crystals of these materials are so readily grown from the melt, and because they recrystallize at relatively low temperatures and thus would have to be strained at subatmospheric temperatures. If circumstances warrant it, single crystals of these metals could undoubtedly be grown by the strain-anneal method.

The exaggerated grain growth necessary to produce single crystals is favored both by a fine grain size and a highly preferred orientation in the starting material; thus it is customary to deform the starting material as heavily as possible, and to recrystallize at the lowest possible temperature before proceeding with the final treatment. For most metals a prior reduction of at least 75% in thickness is desirable. The proper annealing temperature can be best determined by annealing several specimens at different temperatures to find the lowest one at which recrystallization will occur.

In certain special face-centered-cubic metals, particularly pure copper and austenitic iron-nickel alloys, it is possible to produce quite large single crystals by secondary recrystallization of the cube texture. Here the specimen must first be reduced drastically, at least 90% and preferably more in thickness, and the initial grain size must be small— less than 0.1 mm. Upon heating, these materials recrystallize to give a cube texture, a highly preferred orientation in which every grain has a cube face nearly parallel to the sheet surface, and another cube face parallel to the rolling direction. Further heating, at about 1000°C for copper, causes the appearance of very large grains, sometimes several centimeters in diameter. If the heating is carried out in a gradient, a single grain can be grown along the sheet. The crystals resulting from this treatment are usually somewhat twinned, but, by using larger initial reductions and by annealing the cube texture sheet at about 600°C for several hours, twins can be largely prevented. This method is the best one for obtaining very thin copper single crystals of large area and reasonable perfection. The method does not work for copper alloys.

Another requirement for growing single crystals by the strain-anneal method, which follows from a peculiar consequence of the geometry of grain growth, is a proper dispersion of second-phase inclusions. Thus it is quite easy to grow single crystals by strain anneal in aluminum of commercial purity. On the other hand, it is virtually impossible to get exaggerated growth in aluminum of the highest available purity (99.99+%). Instead, the grain size increases uniformly upon annealing, and growth stops when the grain size approximates the thickness of the sheet. Thus, in quite pure metals, the initial reduction must be very heavy, and the final strain must be carefully controlled if large grains are to be produced. Conditions become less critical as the amount of impurity increases, until finally so much second phase is present that no grain growth occurs at all, and again single crystals cannot be grown by the technique. Similar considerations apply to iron. Single crystals can be grown readily by strain anneal in decarburized aluminum-killed steel, armco iron, ingot iron, and silicon-killed steel but are more difficult to produce in decarburized steel.

Phase Transformations

Another method for growing single crystals is to pass a wire or rod progressively through a phase transformation. This would appear to be a readily controlled method, but it has been repeatedly attempted with iron, and the stresses associated with the transformation invariably distort the newly formed crystal so that it consists of a range of orientations rather than a single one. It has been possible to grow single crystals of beta uranium,[3] by using the gamma-to-beta-phase transformation. This method appears to work because the gamma phase is exceedingly soft, and the new beta-phase single crystals are not distorted. In a few cases of diffusionless transformation, an already existing crystal has been transformed to a single crystal of the new phase.

Furnaces and Equipment for Growing Single Crystals

The equipment needed for growing single crystals is usually quite simple, and the same equipment can usually be used either for growing single crystals from the melt or by a solid-state transformation or gradient growth. Tube furnaces of the type described in Chapter 1, wound with 80 Cr–20 Ni wire can be used for many metals. It is usually desirable to insert a long tube through the furnace and seal its ends to aid in maintaining a suitable temperature gradient (Figure 1). For higher temperature molybdenum-wound furnaces or even induction heating can be used.

The temperature gradient in the metal is partly controlled by the gradient in the furnace and partly by the rate of lowering the crucible through the furnace. Since the crucible passes through a temperature gradient, accurate control of the temperature is less important than constancy. If the temperature in the furnace cycles over a period short compared to the rate of travel of the crucible through the furnace, the result as far as the temperature gradient in the metal is concerned is equivalent to moving the crucible through the furnace in a jerky fashion. For this reason it is better to control the furnace temperature with a rheostat or autotransformer than with an on-off temperature controller of short period, since long-time variations in furnace temperature from line voltage fluctuations are unimportant. Instead of moving the crucible, it may be rigidly supported and a small furnace pulled along the crucible, or raised over it to progressively melt and solidify or recrystallize the specimen.

Another method that is particularly useful in vacuum systems is to use a gradient-wound furnace, with the windings more closely spaced at one end than at the other. By heating the furnace so that the cooler end is above the melting point and then gradually reducing the temperature, the liquid metal may be frozen progressively from one end. Such furnaces usually superheat the liquid a great deal in the hot end, but this fault can be overcome by using a large number of individual windings on the furnace tube, and turning them off progressively to pass a gradient along the tube.

Methods for growing single crystals in a vacuum can be devised by using equipment described in Chapter 6. A simple method is to use a large evacuated tube, in which a molybdenum-wound furnace core with radiation shield is inserted. The crucible can be lowered with a molybdenum wire, using any one of several methods for introducing the motion into a vacuum. Another method is to use a movable induction coil, and abstract heat through a water-cooled copper stool as shown in Figure 9. The drawing shows the method for seeding a single crystal with another one of the desired orientation. The crucible cavity extends through to the bottom of the crucible, and the seed crystal rests directly on the copper stool. The graphite crucible has a large diameter at the top so that coupling to the induction coil is good, and only the upper part of the seed crystal is heated to the melting point.

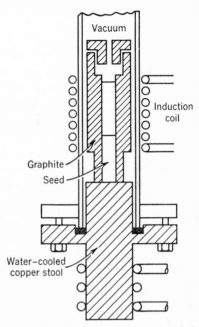

A simple crucible lowering device can be made by attaching a spool to the winding key of a cheap alarm clock. For small crystals, synchronous clock motors with gear boxes are useful, and for larger crucibles fractional horsepower motors may be used. In most cases it is necessary to provide an assortment of spool sizes so that variable lowering rates can be obtained. Miniature variable ratio gear boxes are available for more permanent setups. Toy construction sets provide a cheap source of a multitude of parts that are useful for building lowering devices, or small cars and tracks on which to move crucibles or furnaces.

Figure 9. Method of Growing Seeded Single Crystal with Induction Furnace. All the metal above the seed and part of the seed are melted, and then the induction coil is slowly raised, or the power slowly reduced.

The growth rates used vary widely, depending upon the mechanical setup and the metal. Except in special cases, lowering rates less than about 2 cm per hour are not needed. Rates as high as several centimeters per minute can be used if heat is removed with a cooling device.

Control of Orientation

Single crystals solidified from the liquid frequently have a fairly definite orientation with respect to the thermal gradient, and the effect is usually more pronounced in alloys than in pure metals. For example, in hexagonal and tetragonal metals the unique axis usually aligns itself perpendicular to the thermal gradient. Although this effect may be pronounced, the scatter in orientations is large, and it would be difficult to prepare several single crystals having the same orientation within a few degrees. When single crystals are grown by recrystallization from highly textured starting material, the orientation may be reproducible within a few degrees.

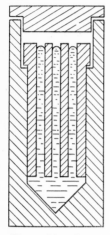

Figure 10. Crucible Design for Growing Several Single Crystals of the Same Orientation.

When it is necessary to obtain a series of single crystals of a single orientation, or to obtain single crystals in orientations different from those that normally appear, it is necessary to resort to a seeding technique. One has already been described for copper crystals using induction heating. In principle all the other methods of growing seeded crystals from the liquid are the same. Figure 10 shows a method of growing a number of single crystals from a common seed. Bicrystals or tricrystals can be grown in a similar fashion by inverting the device so that several seed crystals feed into a single block. Chalmers introduced the technique of growing single crystals in a horizontal boat since this is so advantageous for seeding. Several designs for growing single and bicrystals of predetermined orientations are shown in Figure 11.

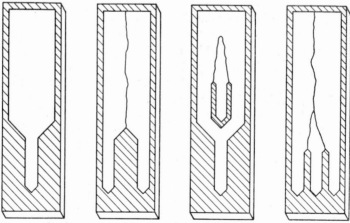

Figure 11.   Crucible Designs for Growing Several Kinds of Bicrystals and Tricrystals by Seeding.

Another solution to the problem of obtaining several identical crystals is simply to grow a very long crystal rod by one of the gradient methods and cut off several pieces.

A considerably different technique must be used if it is desired to grow single crystals of predetermined orientation by a seeding technique. Dunn [4] has developed this to a high degree of perfection for silicon ferrite. To grow a single crystal of a wire in a desired orientation, the end of the wire is transformed to a single crystal by lowering it into a furnace. The orientation of this crystal is then determined, and the wire is bent in the unrecrystallized portion so that further growth will impose the proper orientation upon the recrystallized part. Dunn applied the method to sheet by arranging one or more tabs on the end of the specimen (Figure 12) and heating so that recrystallization caused the growth of a single crystal in part of the tabs. The orientation in all the tabs is determined and all but the one having nearly the desired orientation are cut off. This one is bent in the unrecrystallized neck so that further growth will yield a crystal having the final desired orientation.

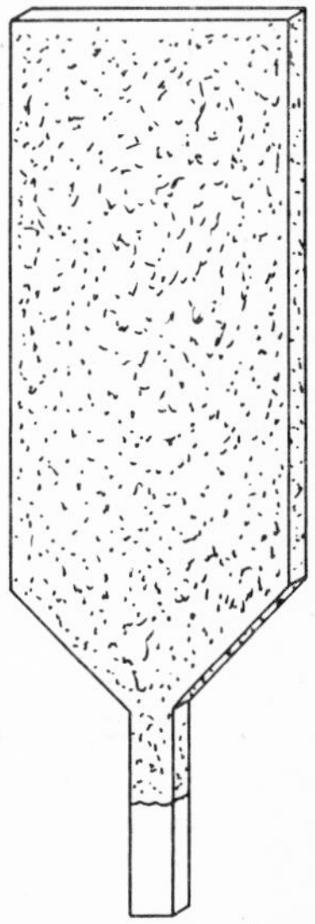

Figure 12. Dunn's Method of Growing Oriented Crystals by the Strain Anneal Method. The single crystal on the tab is bent in the unrecrystallized part to the desired orientation, and the piece is then recrystallized completely by passing through a temperature gradient.

Inspection of Single Crystals

It is usually necessary to determine whether the product of an attempt to prepare a single crystal is indeed a single crystal. The most satisfactory method is to etch the bar with a suitable reagent to produce an oriented luster, so that the orientations can be distinguished. A number of solutions suitable for this purpose along with the conditions for their use are listed in Table 1. Other etchants may, of course, also be used, but it is necessary to select ones which produce sharp etch facets if minor imperfections are to be detected.

Standard crystallographic goniometric techniques may be used to determine the orientation of crystals if they are first etched with suitable reagents. Barrett [5] has described a simple two-circle goniometer for this purpose. It is usually necessary to use a microscope to examine the surface rather than the telescope used by crystallographers for more perfectly reflecting surfaces, but otherwise the technique is iden-

TABLE 1

REAGENTS TO DEVELOP ORIENTED LUSTER FOR SINGLE-CRYSTAL EXAMINATION

Metal	Reagent	Planes Developed	Remarks
Aluminum	9 parts HCl 3 parts HNO_3 2 parts HF 5 parts H_2O	{100}	Keep etchant cool
Iron	1 part HNO_3 4 parts H_2O	{100}	Wipe during etching
Copper	1 part HCl 1 part saturated solution of $FeCl_3$ in water	{100}	
Brass	1 part copper solution 1 part water	{100} {110}	
Lead	3 parts 3% H_2O_2 2 parts glacial acetic acid 2 parts H_2O 1 part 30% H_2O 1 part glacial acetic acid	{100}	Wash in cold running water and dry with air blast Chemical polish to prepare crystal
Tin	Same as brass	{100} {110}	
Zinc	1 part concentrated HCl 1-2 parts H_2O		

tical. Barrett[5] has also described the standard methods of plotting orientations with the aid of a stereographic projection.

Another method that is very commonly used for determining crystal orientations is by Laue back-reflection X-ray diffraction patterns, using the reading net devised by Greninger.[6] This method has the great advantage that it is not necessary to discover a suitable etching reagent, but on the other hand it is difficult to determine the orientation of a slightly distorted or of a very small crystal.

Cutting Single Crystals

For most purposes, some shaping of single crystals is necessary. This is a difficult operation to perform satisfactorily without seriously distorting the specimen, because single crystals are so weak. It is, however, possible to machine single crystals by most of the common methods if very light cuts are taken, preferably with a single-point tool that is carefully sharpened. It is usually imperative to use a suitable cutting oil and to support the crystal fully so that no bending stresses are applied.

Similarly, the crystal can be supported in a form and cut with a jeweler's hack saw or even with a fine-toothed ordinary hack saw. After any of these machining operations it is desirable to etch the cut surface heavily or remove it by electrolytic polishing. The distortion produced in a single crystal extends many times deeper than it does in a polycrystalline metal subjected to similar cutting operations.

Where no distortion may be permitted the crystal can be cut by an etching technique. This may be as simple as dissolving the excess material away by immersing it in a solvent, or the surface may be protected with a suitable stop-off lacquer. These methods are rarely very satisfactory because they do not produce well-defined edges. Maddin[7] has used a more precise method of etching out specimens of a predetermined shape and orientation. The specimen is supported in a suitable goniometer head, and the etchant is carried to the surface on a nylon thread. The operation is slow, but can be set up to operate almost without attention and gives a surface that is free from distortion.

REFERENCES

1. Single crystals of some metals may be purchased, for example, from Horizons Incorporated.
2. A. N. Holden, *Trans. Am. Soc. Metals*, **41**, 319 (1949).
3. A. N. Holden, *Acta Crystallographica*, **5**, 182 (1952).
4. C. C. Dunn, *Trans. Am. Inst. Mining Met. Engrs.*, **185**, 72 (1949).
5. C. S. Barrett, *The Structure of Metals*, McGraw-Hill Book Co., New York, 1943.
6. A. B. Greninger, *Trans. Am. Inst. Mining Met. Engrs.*, **117**, 75 (1935).
7. Robert Maddin and W. R. Ashor, *Rev. Sci. Instruments*, **21**, 881 (1950).

INDEX